ADAM'S ANCESTORS

hARPER ✦ TORCHBOOKS

A reference-list of Harper Torchbooks, classified
by subjects, is printed at the end of this volume.

FOURTH EDITION

THE EVOLUTION

HARPER TORCHBOOKS ❦ THE ACADEMY LIBRARY

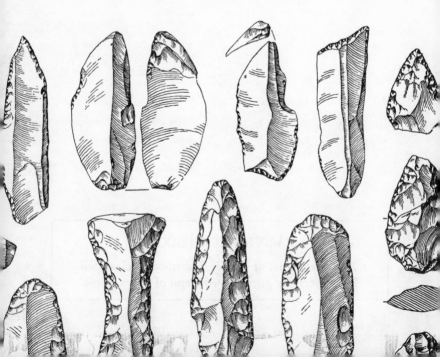

ADAM'S ANCESTORS

OF MAN AND HIS CULTURE

ARPER & ROW, PUBLISHERS **L. S. B. LEAKEY**

New York

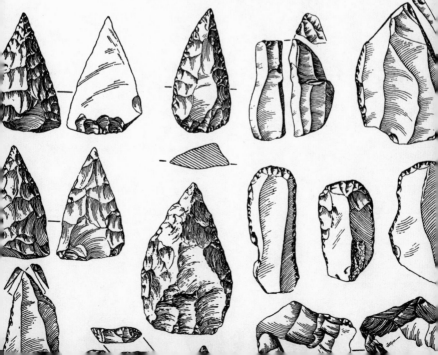

ADAM'S ANCESTORS

Printed in the United States of America
This book was originally published in 1934 by Methuen &
Co., Ltd., London; a fourth edition, completely rewritten
and reset, was published in 1953 and is here reprinted
by arrangement.

First HARPER TORCHBOOK edition published 1960

PROLOGUE TO THE TORCHBOOK EDITION

Since I wrote this book, there have been a number of most important developments in the field of human fossil studies; and it is necessary now to comment on these, and summarise their effect on the conclusions set out in Chapters XI and XII.

Piltdown. First and foremost, there has been the exposure of the Piltdown fraud. In my Chapter in which I discussed the Piltdown skull, I indicated that there were some among us who preferred (page 189) to believe that a million to one chance had led to the jaw of an ape and the skull of a man being fossilised and embedded within a few feet of each other, rather than accept the idea of the ultra ape-like jaw with a simian shelf belonging with a skull that showed such modern man types of morphological characters. Now, thanks to the magnificent work of Weiner, Oakley and Le Gros Clark, it is known, once and for all, that Piltdown was a hoax, that the jaw was that of a modern ape, while the skull was that of a modern type of man (perhaps Neolithic), and that the supposedly associated fossil fauna had been brought to the spot from distant lands.

It is a very good thing for the study of human evolution that Piltdown has been exposed, for the belief in Piltdown did more than anything else to distort our theories of human evolution, and make people reject evidence that showed, more and more, that man was very far removed from the over-specialised modern apes, like Gorilla and Chimpanzee, (who are only very, very remote cousins). It has become increasingly clear that our pre-human ancestors must not be expected to exhibit some of the modern ape characters that have in the past been wrongly labelled "primitive," when in fact they are highly specialised.

I first of all contemplated removing the pages that dealt with Piltdown from this book and substituting others, but I think it is better to write this Prologue and leave the Piltdown discussion as it is in the body of the book as a warning against too easy acceptance of evidence which, in itself, is contrary to all that we know of biology.

The Piltdown fraud also provides a stern warning against

v

the practise of keeping a scientific specimen under such conditions that it cannot be fully and critically examined by those qualified to do so.

On several occasions in the past, I tried to get permission to make a detailed study of the original Piltdown fossils, but on each occasion was only shown them for a few brief moments and not allowed to examine them properly, and was then given a cast to work on.

It was only when Weiner was allowed to make a critical check upon the surface of the original teeth and only when he saw what appeared to be file marks, (which do not show in the casts of the teeth), that he began to suspect fraud, and intensified his check-up.

Atlanthropus. In North Africa, Professor Arambourg has made some most important finds of fossil human remains in association with hand-axes, at Ternifine in Algeria.

The Ternifine remains have been given the rank of a new genus under the name of *Atlanthropus.* They consist of large parts of one jaw and two nearly complete jaws, and also a parietal. There are no frontal bones, no occipital bones, and no temporal bones, so far.

Arambourg considers that *Atlanthropus* is allied to *Pithecanthropus,* and more particularly to the Chinese species of that genus, from Pekin. He compares the jaws from Ternifine with some of those from Chou Kou Tien, and comes to the conclusion that they are very similar.

This view has been widely quoted by many people who have not seen the original material, nor examined the position sufficiently critically, and who speak of it as belonging to a "Pithecanthropine stage" of human evolution.

Moreover, many quote Arambourg's original claim that the Ternifine Stone Age culture material belongs to the Chellean culture, but it is clearly not so, it is Acheulean. The assemblage includes a few specimens which, taken out of their context, could be classified as Chellean, but as there are also many specimens which exhibit clear evidence of Acheulean workmanship, it is these latter which must be used to date the find.

The culture of Ternifine is clearly Acheulean, and is comparable to that of Bed IV at Olduvai, and is *not* Chellean comparable to that of Bed IV at Olduvai, as was first suggested.

Atlanthropus belongs, therefore, to the closing stages of the Middle Pleistocene.

In the genus *Pithecanthropus*, (and I include, of course, *Sinanthropus*, as a synonym of this genus), the most diagnostic parts of the skull are the frontal bone, the occipital bone, and the temporal bone, *all of which are so far missing*, from the Ternifine assemblage of the *Atlanthropus* specimens. It is, at least, just as likely that *Atlanthropus* represents a local, North African variant of the type of human represented by the Steinheim and Swanscombe specimens, which are emphatically *not* Pithecanthropines, as that it belongs with the Far Eastern extinct human group.

Arambourg has advanced the view that the discovery of *Atlanthropus* in association with *hand-axes* at Ternifine *"proves"* that it was the Pithecanthropine kind of man who was responsible for making the hand-axe cultures wherever they are found. This statement is so much at variance with the available evidence that it must be carefully examined, since it is a view which has been widely quoted by others, who have not stopped to consider whether it is well founded. In the first place, the fragmentary nature of the human remains at Ternifine, found as they were all mixed up with animal bones similarly broken up and incomplete leaves open the strong possibility that they represent the remains of a meal, just as the other animal bones do. This could mean one of two things, either that they represent the type of man who *made* the associated hand-axes, but that he was a cannibal and ate members of his own race, or it could mean that another race of men was responsible for making the hand-axes, and that both the human and other animal remains left at the site represent the relics of his meals.

Since both alternatives are possible, the association of such fragmentary bones with the hand-axe culture cannot possibly be said to "prove" anything about what type of man made the hand-axe culture. Moreover, we know that at Chou Kou Tien, the tools made by the Pekin variant of *Pithecanthropus* were not hand-axes, and we also know that at Swanscombe, the human skull fragments which are in close association with hand-axes, are of *Homo sapiens* appearance, and not Pithecanthropine. All we can therefore safely say about the *Atlanthropus* remains at present is:

   i). They include specimens in which the jaws and teeth *re-semble* to some extent those of the Pekin variant of *Pithecanthropus*.

  ii). That those parts of the skull which might be sufficiently diagnostic to determine whether *Atlanthropus* was a Pithecanthropine or not have not yet been found.

 iii). That the *Atlanthropus* specimens are associated with Acheulean hand-axes and may perhaps represent the the makers of that culture in North Africa, but that this is not yet conclusively proved.

Saldahna. The Saldahna skull from the extreme south of South Africa has revealed, once again, a man of the so-called "Rhodesian" type, showing that the skull from Broken Hill was not an isolated freak. The new skull is probably relatively late in the geological time scale, either at the very end of the Middle Pleistocene, or at the start of the Upper Pleistocene. The Saldahna skull was not, however, *in situ*, and its exact association with the stone tools also found at the site, on the surface, is not known.

It is, I think, possible in the light of the new evidence that the Eyassi skull fragments of the Upper Pleistocene age in Tanganyika (see page 194) represent a female of the Rhodesian type of humanity.

Oreopithecus. In recent years, there have been some very important discoveries in Italy of remains of *Oreopithecus* in deposits of Pontian (lowest Pleistocene) age. The new finds include many teeth, a number of crushed jaws, a number of individual bones and a nearly complete, but crushed, skeleton. The detailed report of this discovery will be awaited with great interest.

There is no doubt that *Oreopithecus* belongs to the super family Hominoidea, rather than to the Cercopithecoidea, but there is considerable difference of opinion as to its exact status at the "family" level. The problem derives from the fact that most zoologists and anthropologists, at present, recognise only two families within the super family, namely Hominidae and Pongidae.

I agree with those who maintain that *Oreopithecus* exhibits characters which clearly exclude it from the Pongidae, but I cannot agree when they, therefore, argue that it must rank with the Hominidae. What seems to be required is to recognise a third aberrant family of Hominoidea, under the name of Oreopithecoidea, as was suggested many years ago.

Oreopithecus has certain pelvic characters which suggest parallel evolution to the Hominoidea and, in origin, it may stand rather closer to the root stock of the Hominidae than to the root stock of the Pongidae. Those who see in *Oreopithecus* a possible direct ancestor of the Australopithecinae are, I think, unaware of the many morphological characters in *Oreopithecus* which will not justify such a conclusion as, for example, the very peculiar pre-molars and the very specialised calcanium.

Telanthropus. Telanthropus is the name given by Broom and Robinson to some fossils from the Swartkrans site near Pretoria, in the same deposits as *Paranthropus*. The new genus *Telanthropus* was, in the first instance, based upon a mandible much smaller than the average *Paranthropus*, and with smaller teeth, but in which the *corpus mandibularis* or ramus of the jaw containing the teeth did not greatly differ *morphologically* from *Paranthropus*, though much smaller. The teeth, however, showed considerable differences, as Broom and Robinson pointed out.

Many anatomists inclined to the view that the jaw only represents an unusually small and aberrant *Paranthropus*.

Since the first find, another mandible fragment and a maxilla fragment have been found at Swartkrans. These cannot possibly be regarded as falling within the range of variation of *Paranthropus* and, having examined the material in person, at Pretoria, I am satisfied that they represent something quite distinct, and much closer (morphologically) to man as we know him today, to *Homo* in fact.

Zinjanthropus. In July, 1959, my wife discovered a new fossil human skull at Olduvai Gorge. It was found upon a living floor of the Oldowan culture, with the bones of animals upon which the individual fed, and many waste flakes struck off in the making of stone tools, as well as some well-made Oldowan stone tools—even the most delicate nasal bones and the ethmoid region of the skull are present, (but badly cracked by the expansion and contraction of the underlying bentonitic clay). Since they are not smashed up, while the bones of the other animals are all broken, it may be reasonably assumed that the skull represents the maker of the culture who lived upon the floor. In view of our accepted definition, therefore, of man as a "primate who makes tools to a set and regular pattern," or "Man—the Tool Maker," we must accept *Zinjanthropus* as a true "man." Morphologically, *Zinjanthropus* has many characters which are reminiscent of the Australopithecine group, and I have assigned him to the sub-family Australopithecinae, while setting up a new genus *Zinjanthropus* to accommodate him.

There are those who decry the setting up of this new genus and who believe that the new skull is simply a variant of *Paranthropus*, or even of *Australopithecus* However such a view is not, in my opinion, tenable. While clearly, I think, within the sub-family of Australopithecinae, the new find exhibits more than twenty anatomical characteristics (as well as many minor ones) which distinguish it from those members of the sub-family which are at present on record from South Africa.

The most important of these characters are (i) the facial architecture in the region of the malar-maxillary angle, (ii) the mastoid process, (iii) the shape of the nasal bones, (iv) the much more straight (orthognathous) face. Details of the preliminary diagnosis have been published in "Nature" of August 15, 1959.

Earlier, we had regarded Bed I at Olduvai, with its Oldowan culture, as belonging to the early part of the Middle Pleistocene, and not clearly separable from Bed II. More critical examination of the faunal and geological evidence has led, however, to the necessity of separating Bed I from Bed II, and treating Bed I as the equivalent in geological age of Omo in Abyssinia, Taung and Sterkfontein (lowest beds) in South Africa, that is to say, belonging to the upper half of the Lower Pleistocene, (or upper half of the Villafranchian).

Bed I, Olduvai, would thus be older than the Djetis Beds in Java, and much older than the Trinil Beds in the same area, both of which are now regarded by nearly all geologists and palaeontologists as of Middle Pleistocene age.

Zinjanthropus is, therefore, not only a "true" man, but the earliest known stone-tool making man.

In this connection, it is necessary to comment upon the claim of *Australopithecus teeth* in association with Oldowan culture from an upper level at Sterkfontein in the Transvaal. This claim was put forward in 1956, but since then the number of stone tools from the site has been increased, and the culture includes early *Chellean type* hand-axes, like those from Bed II at Olduvai. It is therefore not Oldowan but early Chellean.

The associated teeth, which I have examined, are certainly hominid, and *possibly* Australopithecine, (in the widest sub-family sense), although I am not wholly sure of this. These teeth are certainly not sufficiently diagnostic to be able to say what genus they belong to.

On the other hand, the so-called stone tools with *Australopithecus* from the Makapaan site occur in a thick gravel bed, and are none of them capable of being treated as unequivocal stone tools, nor can it be said that they are associated with *Australopithecus*, since the fragment of fossil hominid is also, I think, not really diagnostic.

Swanscombe. Since the writing of this book, a further part of the Swanscombe skull has been found by associates of the late Mr. Wymer, whose patience in watching and working at the site has been most valuable. The most diagnostic parts, such as the frontal and temporal bone and the face, still elude us. It seems possible, however, that the Swanscombe skull may closely approximate to the Steinheim skull, and that both are early members of *Homo sapiens*. As I have indicated above, it is not impossible that *Atlanthropus* also falls into this group, rather than with *Pithecanthropus*. This, however, remains to be seen, when more material comes to light.

The Kanam Mandible. The discovery of *Zinjanthropus* in association with the Oldowan culture at FLK I at Olduvai makes it necessary to re-examine the evidence relating to the Kanam mandible.

The Kanam mandible was discovered in 1931–32 at a time when scientific opinion was obscured by the Piltdown hoax: nearly everyone believed that an early man must have a simian shelf and large canine teeth and, of course, no chin. The Kanam mandible came from deposits of Lower Pleistocene age, and in the same deposits there were a few Oldowan-type tools. On describing this specimen in detail, I stressed the very small canines and incisors and the very large pre-molars, the massiveness of the jaw and the presence of a small chin, and I ascribed the specimen to a new species of *Homo*. Now that we know that occasionally members of the Australopithecinae have a small chin eminence (as, for example, several specimens of *Paranthropus* from Swartkrans), and as we know that the combination of heavy mandible, very small canines and incisors and large pre-molars are characteristic of the Australopithecinae, it becomes highly probable that the Kanam mandible represents, in fact, a female of *Zinjanthropus*.

The Hominid milk teeth from Site BK Olduvai Bed II. In 1958, a note was published by me on two hominid milk teeth found on the living floor of Chellean Stage I at Olduvai. The milk molar is exceedingly large, and the milk canine relatively small. A considerable amount of argument has taken place as to whether the milk molar is an upper or a lower tooth, because it has, on the one hand, three roots, (suggestive of an upper tooth, but by no means definitely so,) and a cusp pattern, which some regard as belonging to a lower dentition, and others an upper. There are even those who believe the molar to be a permanent one. I think it is relatively certain that this tooth represents a descendant of *Zinjanthropus* stock, with the same dental proportions, but sufficiently further evolved to be a maker of a Chellean Stage I culture. The very large size of the molar suggests the possibility that the cheek teeth of Chellean man may prove to be even larger than those of *Zinjanthropus*.

Living Sites of Early Chellean Stages of the Hand-Axe Culture. Excavations at the lower levels of Bed II at Olduvai published in a preliminary note in "Nature" in 1958 show that in the earlier stages of the hand-axe culture, man was still mainly using Oldowan type tools, and had only just begun to make simple hand-axes. The discoveries of the very greatest interest were found with these Chellean living sites. At the Chellean I living site evidence was found of the use of red ochre, while at the Chellean II site a very simple but well made ivory chopping tool was found.

The Kafuan Culture. (page 66). Since the writing of the present edition of *Adam's Ancestors*, I have been more and more forced to the conclusion that most of the material attributed to the Kafuan culture is not certainly of human origin. In nearly every case, the material is found under conditions where Nature could have played a part, and it is better, therefore, to discard the term "Kafuan" for the time being, and regard the few fairly certain signs of human tool-making in the Lower Pleistocene (the later Kafuan) in East Africa as early Oldowan, as, for example, the specimens from Kanam.

January 1960

PREFACE TO THE 1953 EDITION

WHEN I prepared the first edition of *Adam's Ancestors* in 1933–4 it was far from easy to compress the story of what was then known about Palaeolithic man into one small book intended for laymen interested in the story of man's past and for students entering on the study of Prehistory.

In subsequent editions a few important finds, that had been made since the first publication of the book, were noted in an additional preface, but no revision was carried out.

The writing of the present edition has been a very difficult task indeed, for the number of important discoveries that have been made since 1934 is very great, and many of them have necessitated a revision of earlier theories. Instead, therefore, of revising the earlier edition I have in fact completely rewritten the whole book. Most of the chapter headings remain the same, but three new chapters have been added.

One of these became necessary as it was no longer possible to describe the Palaeolithic cultures—even in general terms—within the space of two chapters. I also felt that a chapter on Palaeolithic art was necessary (however inadequate): while the discoveries in South Africa of many fossil 'near-men' by Dart, Broom, and Robinson, and in Kenya of numerous Lower Miocene apes, made it necessary to include a chapter on fossil apes and 'near-men'.

I am deeply conscious of the fact that I have had to leave out a very great deal (that I would have liked to include) in writing the present edition. This is due to the fact that the size of the book must be limited to some extent if it is to serve the purpose for which it is intended. It would be very easy indeed to extend the contents of almost every chapter into a full volume and still leave the story incomplete, so greatly has our knowledge of Palaeolithic man and his ancestors increased during recent years.

To those of my many colleagues all over the world who find that I have omitted reference to some discovery that they consider should have been discussed, while including facts about some other discovery that they consider less important, I tender my deepest apologies. It is inevitable that much has had to be left out in trying to present a general picture as an introduction to an immense subject.

I also apologize to the authors whose books and papers do not appear in the very short bibliography that I have provided at the end of the book. This is not due to any lack of appreciation, but because the choice lay between a comprehensive bibliography, which might have run to more than a thousand references, or else a brief bibliography which had, perforce, to be highly selective. Readers who consult the references I have given will find in most of them much more extensive bibliographies of which they can make good use.

In my final chapter I have indicated a few problems connected with man's past which I believe are in very great need of further research work. Naturally, there are many other problems besides these which must also be investigated, and which, I feel sure, will be investigated in the next ten years or so.

Finally, I want to record my deepest gratitude to my wife for her help in the preparation of this new version of *Adam's Ancestors*. I want, too, to thank my many colleagues, whom I have consulted by letter while preparing the text, for their willing help in clearing up a number of points.

L. S. B. LEAKEY

Nairobi
   March 1953

CONTENTS

TEXT ILLUSTRATIONS

PLATES

CHAPTER I

The Search for Man's Ancestors

IT is not so very long ago—a matter of about a hundred years only—that most people still accepted the opinion of Bishop Usher that man was created in 4004 B.C., and that Adam was the first representative of humanity on earth.

Today the position has changed to such an extent that the discovery of any new piece of evidence relating to human evolution is considered important news by the Press and is also often discussed at length in the wireless programmes of most countries.

Most educated people believe in evolution in the animal and plant kingdoms, and consequently are more than usually interested in any light that can be thrown on the stages of evolution of man himself.

The first discovery to be made of an authenticated fossil human skull was that of the Gibraltar skull, found in 1848, but its significance was not realized until some twenty years later, by which time its pride of place had been taken by the discovery of the famous Neanderthal skull in 1856, which has given its name to a whole race of extinct humanity which, until relatively recently, was regarded as being in the direct line of ancestry leading to man as we know him today.

Since these early discoveries, finds of fossil human and sub-human remains have been made in ever-increasing numbers, and whereas most of the early discoveries were to a great extent accidental, and incidental to a search for other things, today the search for the ancestors and cousins of *Homo sapiens* is being conducted increasingly by trained scientists in a determined effort to clear up the story of man's early history.

The study of Prehistory is a complicated subject and is not only confined to the search for and interpretation of fossil human remains. This aspect of the subject is in fact only one very small part, although it is the central figure of the picture, so to speak, but the background is made up of studies of the climate, geography, cultures, and associated fauna and flora of the periods in the past history of the earth when man was gradually and slowly evolving into the creature we call *Homo sapiens* today. But before we pass on, in the succeeding chapters of this book, to discuss the many different component parts of the picture of Adam's ancestors, let us briefly consider some of the ways in which the evidence is found.

It has to be admitted that even today, when the search for Stone Age cultures and fossil humans is more scientifically organized than ever before, luck still plays a very major part in most discoveries of importance.

After all, the surface of the earth is immense, and a very large part of the earth's crust is covered up by vegetation and by surface deposits of humus and hillwash and other superficial deposits, so that, to a considerable extent, the search for evidence of man's past in geological deposits is governed by chance. Rivers and other forces of nature cut through geological deposits containing the evidence which we seek, and it is a matter of luck whether this erosion takes place at a time when some trained scientist is on the spot to recognize the hidden treasures so exposed.

Similarly, commercial undertakings carried out for the exploitation of river gravels and brick earths, or alluvial deposits containing gold or diamonds or tin are often the means by which deposits containing missing parts of the giant jigsaw puzzle are revealed. Here again it is a matter of pure luck whether a person qualified to recognize the stone tools and fossils is present before they are destroyed.

The old terraces of the Thames valley at Swanscombe have for a long time been exploited commercially for gravel and sand, and for years it has been known that they contained many Stone Age tools, washed into them when the geography of England was very different from today. The workmen soon learnt from visiting prehistorians how to recognize the commoner types of stone tool and most of these were preserved as the work progressed, and found their way to museums and private collections. It was, however, definitely a matter of luck that one of Dr. Marston's periodic visits to Swanscombe should have coincided with the uncovering of part of a fossil human skull—a piece of bone which many other visitors to the site might have failed to recognize—and thus lead to the preservation and study of the oldest human fossil so far discovered on English soil.

The Companhia Diamentes de Angola, in the course of their exploitation of old alluvial gravels containing a great wealth of diamonds, had to remove an immense overlying deposit of red wind-blown sand, and it was a matter of luck that the chief geologist to the company, in the person of Mr. J. Janmart, was interested in Prehistory and able to recognize stone tools when he saw them, thus leading to the discovery of a most important chapter in the story of the Stone Age cultures of the African continent, in a place where, but for this commercial exploitation of diamonds, little if any evidence would have been found.

It was a matter of considerable luck, too, that in 1926, the steamer in which I was crossing Lake Victoria from Kisumu to Entebbe had to change its sailing schedule and pass Rusinga Island in daylight instead of in darkness. This enabled me to examine the stratified deposits of rock on the island with field-glasses and make a note that the island looked a very promising place to search for fossils. This little incident led to my making my first visit to the island in 1931 and discovering, on my very first day there, some fragmentary fossil fragments of an ape jaw; a discovery which led up to the finding of the famous *Proconsul* skull by my wife on 2 October, 1948.

These three typical examples of the part which luck has played and must continue to play in the search for the evidence of the story of man's past, must suffice to make us remember always that the element of chance is very great and that we owe most of our knowledge of our past to this cause.

But it would be wrong to let you think that everything is a matter of luck, for it is not. No amount of luck, in the way in which nature or man exposes the deposits containing the evidence of man's past, would be of any use if there were not people with sufficient knowledge and training to recognize the finds. Moreover, it is not only in geological deposits that the evidence is to be found; many discoveries of fossil human skulls and stone implements are made in the accumulated debris in caves and rock-shelters and at such sites only excavation by persons who have been very carefully trained for the work can result in a proper interpretation of the story that is revealed by the digging of the deposits.

This fact is being more and more impressed upon us as we reconsider some of the work upon which the foundations of Pre-history were laid. A great deal of the early work on the Stone Age cultures to be found in caves was carried out in France, in the Dordogne, by people who inevitably—since they were pioneers in Prehistory—were not really trained to the work. The results of their work were magnificent, but the interpretation was over-simplified, so that for years it was believed that the sequence of evolution of Stone Age cultures was a simple series of successive stages, whereas, in fact, the story is far from simple, as we shall see in later chapters.

If we want to make a proper study of man's past in any particular area, one of the first things that has to be done is to study the evidence of what we may call Prehistoric Geography and Prehistoric Climate. This can only be done by the aid of geological studies.

Climate and geographical position have always played a most important part in determining where man made his home, where he hunted, and where he lived, just as they do today, and since neither the climate nor yet the geography of the world has remained the same over the long period of time since man first became man, and the still longer period when man's ape-like ancestors were slowly evolving to a human status, we must study the world changes of climate and geography before we can appreciate details of the story of man's past history.

As we shall see when we discuss early man's environment in more detail in the next chapter, there have been a number of major fluctuations in the climate of the world as a whole since the earth was formed, but it is the changes during the last million years or so that are the most important to us, for it was during this period that man was gradually making himself dominant over the rest of the animal kingdom.

Since these changes of world climate manifested themselves in the temperate zones by advances and retreats of the ice-sheets and in tropical and subtropical countries by alternating very much wetter and much drier periods than today, we clearly cannot study man's past without knowing something about the climate of the times. It would be useless to look for living-sites of prehistoric man at a place which—at the particular point of time in which you were interested—was covered by vast glaciers. Nor would it be any better to search in a place which, at the relevant time, was covered by the deep waters of a lake, or was so dry as to be completely waterless.

But equally, a locality which might have been quite uninhabitable at a certain point in the time-scale may have had a really suitable climate for human occupation at a later or an earlier date. Let me illustrate this point by reference to the prehistoric site known as Olorgesailie in Kenya Colony.

Today, the Olorgesailie area is practically a desert, and for the greater part of the year is uninhabited by man, for that reason. But when you begin studying the geological deposits of the area you can see that they are composed in large part of clays and sands and silts and gravels laid down in a lake.

Clearly, if there was ever a big lake in an area that is now desert this must have been at a time when the climate was much wetter than today, so it is first of all necessary to start to make a more detailed study of these old lake deposits, to see what story they have to tell.

Part of the deposits are very fine-grained silts, obviously laid down in calm and fairly deep water; it would be useless to look for Stone Age man's living-sites in these beds for they were formed under water. But at the top of the silts there is an irregular line separating them from the sands above. What does this mean? The lake must have dwindled so that the silts, laid down in the deep water, were exposed to the sun and wind, and a land surface formed; but probably the lake did not dry up completely, so that this would have been a land surface reasonably near to the waters of the lake while it receded. Such a land surface would have been an excellent place for Stone Age hunters to camp on, near to water for their own needs and with the likelihood that the wild animals of the time would be plentiful near the lake shore, as they are today in Africa by the shores of lakes, where man has not yet destroyed them. This old land surface, then, is worth exploring in more detail, and so you start your search, and if you are lucky—for clearly you cannot excavate the whole land surface—you find, as we did, the clear evidence of a camp site with hundreds of discarded stone implements and the fossilized bones of the animals which Stone Age man killed and ate.

Over this ancient land surface, with its Stone Age camp site, lies a thick layer of water-deposited sand, laid down in shallow water as the level of the lake responded to a fresh oscillation in the climate and started to rise again. The sandy nature of the deposit gradually changes to clay, betokening the presence of deep water again in the area. Above this clay is another irregular line separating it from another series of water-laid deposits. This is another land surface and, as before, it is worth investigating for possible human occupation sites. Actually, at Olorgesailie we found ten different old land surfaces, and on each, in due course, we located one or more camp sites of Stone Age man. Thus, the study of the geological deposits revealed the story of climatic changes in the area, as well as evidence of some of the stages of development of the Stone Age culture of that particular part of the world at the period corresponding to the formation of the series of deposits.

I mentioned that the sites of the old camps were marked by 'hundreds of discarded stone implements and the fossilized bones of the animals which Stone Age man killed and ate'. In finding these fossil bones we were particularly fortunate, for by no means all geological deposits are suitable for the preservation of bones and teeth as fossils, and they are one of the things we need most for the dating of any given geological deposit in order to be able to assign it to its correct position in the time-scale.

In working out the story of the earth's history geologists are dependent to a very considerable extent on the fossil remains of animal and plant life. Such fossil remains do not of course give an absolute date in terms of years, but they do provide an excellent clue to the relative date of one deposit compared with another. I shall discuss this a little more fully in the next chapter, but I will indicate here very briefly the methods that are used.

We know that evolution has not only taken place in the past but is still taking place, as you can see for yourself if you consider for a moment the history of the dog. The numerous races of present-day dogs, ranging from St. Bernards to Dachshunds, have all been evolved in the last few thousand years from one, or possibly a few, very generalized kinds of dog which were domesticated by man towards the end of the Stone Age. Of course, this very rapid evolution is unusual and has been greatly accelerated by man's careful selection of breeding stock. If thousands of years hence scientists find deposits containing fossil bones of Dachshunds and Pekingese and, shall we say, merino sheep, in the same deposit as the bones of the otter, rabbit, and fox, they will date the deposit by the creatures which are obviously *new* to the geological sequence and not by the fox or the otter whose bones will also be known as fossils in somewhat older deposits.

So, in studying the past, we can examine the fossil bones of animals which we find in deposits that we wish to date, and can say 'here is a fossil representing the straight-tusked elephant', or 'this is the tooth of some particular stage in the evolution of the horse', and by this means arrive at a backward limit of dating in the time-scale.

The estimation of the forward limit is not quite so easy, since it must be based upon negative evidence to a considerable extent; except when there is a good stratification and where the overlying deposits can also be dated.

It must also be remembered that in any area where the Stone Age culture sequence has been fairly fully worked out on a stratigraphical basis, it is sometimes possible to use the actual stone implements found at a site as evidence for dating a deposit.

Here I must digress for a moment to stress one very important point. Any conclusions which are based upon one or two specimens only, whether they are fossil bones or Stone Age tools, must be regarded with the gravest doubts, and it is essential to have a large assemblage of specimens—the larger the better—from any geological horizon or level in a cave deposit before drawing conclusions. And the conclusions must be based upon a study of the total assemblage and not by reference only to selected specimens.

This would seem to be such an obvious matter of common sense that it should be unnecessary to state it categorically in a book of this kind. But even today, when the study of Prehistory has had more than a hundred years in which to develop a code of procedure, it is unfortunately still easy to find examples of single selected specimens being used as a basis for dating purposes and causing erroneous conclusions to be drawn.

Just pause for a moment to consider the contents of the room or the house in which you are reading these words. In all probability there will be some objects such as candlesticks, for instance, which could as well belong to 300 years ago as to the present day. There will also be many objects whose first appearance in our culture can be dated to the present century—wireless, perhaps, or plastic cups, or stainless steel furnishings. There are also likely to be one or two objects in the house which, in their form and material, are genuine antiques that are not made at all today.

Now clearly, should all this material be buried and preserved, it would be most misleading to use either the antiques or the objects with a wide range of use in time, like the candlesticks, for dating purposes, and it would be upon a consideration of the whole assemblage, including the wireless set and other objects of the present century, that the scientist of the future would be justified in saying 'this level dates to about the twentieth century, although it contains several elements from an earlier period'.

Whereas the first discovery of an authenticated skull of fossil man was, as we have seen, made a little over a hundred years ago, the story of the discovery of the stone tools which represent part of his material culture dates back to a much earlier period.

So far as we know, the first person who found a Palaeolithic stone implement and actually recognized it as a relic of some culture long antedating the historical period, was John Frere, F.R.S., who in

1791 found a number of hand-axes of the culture which we now call the Acheulean, at Hoxne in Suffolk, and described them as 'belonging to a very remote period indeed, even beyond that of the present world'.

Prior to this, a pear-shaped stone implement had been found at what was then Gray's Inn Lane in London during 1690, in close association with the tooth of an extinct elephant, but the full significance of this discovery had not been appreciated.

The next important milestone was the demonstration, by Tournal in 1828, that man had been the contemporary of an extinct fauna of the Pleistocene Age in the deposits found in a cave at Bize. A few years later Schmerling confirmed this as a result of his excavations near Liège. But it was not until 1858 and 1859, after the discovery and study of the Neanderthal skull found in 1856 had caused such a sensation, that British scientists began to give serious considera-tion to the question of the great antiquity of the Stone Age.

It was in these years that a number of leading British scientists visited Abbeville and Amiens to examine for themselves the dis-coveries made by Boucher de Perthes, who, as early as 1847, had published his first account of the finding of unquestionable stone implements in ancient river gravels and other similar deposits in association with bones of extinct animals. As a result of this visit the British scientists became convinced of the claims that were being made for the antiquity of man, and a paper was read before the Royal Society in 1859, while in 1863 the first monograph on the subject appeared. This was the famous book by Charles Lyell, the geologist, entitled *Geological Evidence of the Antiquity of Man*.

The publication of this book marked a very important step forward in the study of Prehistory. From that date onwards new discoveries were made in quick succession, and the study of the Stone Age cultures, based upon an examination of the strati-graphical evidence, began to be seriously undertaken.

By the end of the century a vast amount of material had been accumulated and published, not only in Europe, but also to some extent in other countries such as South Africa and even Java.

During the fifty years of the present century (in spite of the interruption of two world wars) the study of the story of man's past before the dawn of history has advanced so rapidly that there is now practically no country in the world which has not yielded some evidence to help fill in parts of the picture. Naturally, one of the results of this mass of work is that we find that the story is a much more complex one than the earlier workers supposed. Many of the earlier conclusions, based mainly on work in South-west Europe, have got to be reconsidered and the evidence re-interpreted in the light of discoveries made in other countries and even other continents.

The picture, therefore, as it will be presented in the chapters that follow, differs in a great many respects from that which I gave in the edition of this book written in 1933. It is equally certain that some of the conclusions presented here will have to be revised within the next few years, as further work continues.

To conclude this chapter I want to try to answer a question which I am very frequently asked. How do remains of Stone Age cultures, and sometimes of the men who made them, come to be preserved in caves and in geological deposits? It is of the greatest importance to understand the answer to this question, for unless we do, we cannot hope to interpret correctly the results obtained by excavation.

Let us for a moment imagine that we can stand back and observe the sequence of events at a rock-shelter some twenty or thirty thousand years ago.

A Stone Age hunter is wandering down the valley in search of game when he espies a rock-shelter in the side of the rocky cliff above him. Carefully, and with the utmost caution, he climbs up to it, fearful lest he may find that it is occupied by the members of some other Stone Age family who will resent his intrusion, or possibly even that it is the lair of a lion or a cave bear. At last he is close enough, and he sees that it is quite unoccupied, and so he enters and makes a thorough examination. He decides that it is a much more suitable habitation than the little shelter where he and his family are living at present, and he goes off to fetch them.

Next we see the family arriving and settling into their new home. A fire is lit either from some embers carefully nursed and brought from the old home, or else by means of a simple, wooden fire drill. (We cannot say for certain what methods Stone Age man used for obtaining fire, but we do know that from a very early period he did make use of fire, for hearths are a common feature in almost any occupation level in caves and rock-shelters.)

Probably some of the family then go off to collect grass or bracken to make rough beds upon which they will sleep, while others break branches from bushes and trees in the near-by thicket and construct a rude wall across the front of the shelter. The skins of various wild animals are then unrolled and deposited in the new home, together with such household goods as they possess.

And now the family is fully settled in, and the day-to-day routine is resumed once more. The men hunt and trap animals for food, the women probably help in this and also collect edible fruits and nuts and roots. Gradually, rubbish starts to accumulate on the floor; decaying vegetation mingles with wood ash scraped from the hearth, and mixed with all this are the bones and teeth of the animals that have served as food. The stone and bone tools, which comprise the weapons and domestic implements of the family, break or become blunt through use, and they are discarded and new ones made. Blocks of suitable material collected during hunting expeditions have been brought to the new home, and from these flakes are knocked off to make new tools. This process involves the scattering of many waste flakes and chips over the floor, and these soon become incorporated in the debris in the same way as the tools that have become too blunt for further use. When the weather is fine a great deal of the work is done on the platform outside the shelter, so that deposits accumulate there too.

Years pass, the older members of the family die and—according to custom—are buried in the floor of the shelter; the younger members of the family grow up and marry, and all the time the home continues to be used, so that more and more debris accumulates on the floor. A large part of this debris is perishable material which by the process of decay turns into soil, throughout which imperishable objects of stone and bone are scattered.

Naturally enough, the deposits so formed do not accumulate evenly over the whole floor, and although the floor may have been level to start with (and even this is seldom the case) it very soon ceases to be so.

And so generations pass and a considerable depth of deposit is formed representing an occupation level, and then something happens which results in the shelter being vacated. When this occurs the shelter may perhaps be taken over almost immediately by some other Stone Age family—possibly of a different tribe and with a somewhat different culture—in which case we shall get a somewhat different occupation level superimposed upon the first one. On the other hand, the shelter may remain untenanted for a considerable period of time, in which case dust and leaves and other purely natural material will collect and gradually build up a sterile layer covering the occupation level, until the place is once more selected as a living site.

And so the story goes on; occupation levels alternate with sterile layers, blocks of rock fall from the roof, and slowly but surely the floor level rises.

If the shelter happens to be in a limestone cliff and the site is unoccupied during a period when the climate is very moist, a hard deposit of stalagmite may form over the floor and seal in the underlying deposits. On the other hand, if the shelter is not very high above the level of the river, a spell of heavy floods may result in the partial or complete scouring out of the unconsolidated deposits. Or, alternatively, a layer of water-laid sand may be formed.

Such occurrences and many other events will all leave their traces in the shelter, and if the eventual scientific excavation is carried out with patience and skill the evidence can be recognized and interpreted and the story worked out. If, however, the excavator is not well trained, or if he works too fast, part at least of the evidence will be lost. Above all, the excavator must be very critical, taking care not to confuse facts with his own theoretical interpretation of them, and seizing every opportunity to check and re-check each stage of his work.

Once the facts have been collected, it may be necessary to call in specialists in various branches of science before the data can be fully interpreted. The palaeontologist will have to help identify the various animal bones and teeth and state what conclusions as to geological age and climatic conditions may be drawn from them. The geologist and soil analyst may also be able to give aid in determining climatic conditions from soil samples of the deposits from different levels in the excavation, while the botanist may be able in some cases to identify certain trees and plants from well-preserved pieces of charcoal found in hearths. Even the physicist, by the latest methods of analysis of carbon 14, may be able to help to provide an approximate age from examination of the charcoal.

The stone and bone implements and even the waste flakes will also tell their own story, and so, when all the necessary collaboration has been achieved, the prehistorian will be able to present a reasonably accurate story of the sequence of events in the rock-shelter.

I have already indicated how Stone Age living sites may come to be sandwiched between geological deposits along the shores of a fluctuating lake, but many other types of geological deposit will also be found to contain stone implements. These, too, if properly studied and understood, will yield very valuable information about Stone Age man and his cultures.

Let us first consider the case of river deposits such as gravels, clays, and sands. These, if they were formed during the period when Stone Age man lived, will often be found to contain stone implements, sometimes in great quantity.

It is not difficult to understand how remains of Stone Age cultures came to be incorporated in river deposits if we think in terms of what is happening today. Who has not stood upon a bridge and, looking down into the water beneath, has seen lying on the gravel in the bed of the stream broken bottles, tin cans, bits of china, bones, and other relics of our present-day culture? All of these objects are now being slowly incorporated in the sands and gravels and clays of the river, and they have reached their present position either because they have been thrown in or else washed in by flood waters.

Stone Age man—especially at certain stages of his history—was particularly fond of living close to the banks of streams and rivers, probably because he had no vessels in which to store and carry water and therefore liked to live as close as possible to his water supply. Living thus—and by analogy with what happens today— it is quite natural that many of his cultural objects as well as the bones thrown away after his meals got washed into the rivers and incorporated in the deposits. Owing to changes of climate and topography, as we shall see in the next chapter, many of these old river deposits of Stone Age date lie, today, either on high-level terraces well above the present river levels, or in sunken channels; whole parts of these old deposits are sometimes washed into the present-day rivers, and in this way cultural material of a much earlier date, that was originally incorporated in the old gravels, gets re-deposited in younger gravels, bringing about a mixture of elements in the newly forming gravels.

Such a mixture of the remains of Stone Age cultures of several periods, in a single level of gravel or sand, is not an unusual phenomenon, and it is only by very careful examination of all the evidence that the story can be sorted out.

Another type of geological deposit which is often found to contain Stone Age man's tools, is that formed under glacial conditions. Considerable areas of the zones that at the present time have a temperate climate were, during the Stone Age, covered from time to time by ice-sheets. This was the result of world changes of climate which we shall discuss in the next chapter. Deposits formed under glacial conditions often consist of boulder clays and glacial outwash gravels. When an ice-sheet advances over the countryside it tends to plough up all the surface deposits that lie in its path and also to pick up most of this material and carry it forward. If the deposits so ploughed into and picked up already contained Stone Age tools of an earlier period, or if such implements were lying on the surface, they too were carried forward and churned up with the mass of other material. When further changes of climate resulted in the melting of the ice-sheets, all the mass of rubble and rock and earth that had been caught up in the ice was deposited in the form of boulder clays and outwash gravels. Thus it often happens that such glacial deposits contain Stone Age implements, but that does not mean that the men who made them were living in the area while the ice-sheets were there. It means rather that they had lived at some period before that particular advance of the ice.

From what I have said, it is clear that ordinary common sense is a very important factor in the interpretation of the past. To this must be added a great deal of scientific knowledge, if we are to obtain a proper picture of the climate, geography, and general environment which existed in the days when Stone Age man lived. In the next chapter we will consider some of the results of this study and try to see what the world was like when our prehistoric ancestors roamed over the land.

CHAPTER II

Early Man's Environment

AS a matter of convenience, geologists have divided up the long period of time through which the world has passed into a number of major divisions. These are the Archean, Primary, Secondary, Tertiary, and Quaternary (see table). There are a few who would add one more division under the heading of Holocene or Recent, but the majority view is that the Recent period is merely the last of the minor subdivisions of the Quaternary.

We shall not be concerned with the first three major divisions at all, except that we may note in passing that most of the great flint-bearing deposits, which later provided the material for so many of early man's tools and weapons—at least in Europe—were formed during the Secondary division.

The Tertiary is divided into four major subdivisions called, respectively, Eocene, Oligocene, Miocene, and Pliocene, each of which in turn has a number of lesser divisions with which we need not seriously concern ourselves for the purpose of our study. The Quaternary has as yet only the two main divisions, the Pleistocene and the Holocene (or Recent). Of these, the former has important subdivisions, as we shall see in the course of this chapter.

By analogy with the time-scales in use in everyday life, the reader might perhaps be tempted to think that the major divisions like the Archean, Primary, Secondary, etc., were all considered to be of approximately equal duration, in the same way that we divide a year into months, a month into weeks, and a week into days. But such an idea is quite contrary to the facts. In the geological time-scale the more remote the period, the longer is the duration likely to have been.

For example, the main division called the Primary represents a period of probably ten to fifteen times the length of the Tertiary, while the Miocene subdivision of the Tertiary was at least five times as long as the Pliocene subdivision of the same period, and the whole of the major division known as the Quaternary only equals in time about one twenty-fifth of the Miocene subdivision of the Tertiary.

It is most important to bear these facts in mind when looking at the following table of the geological time-scale, which does not in any way attempt to show the relative length of the periods.

TABLE TO ILLUSTRATE THE GEOLOGICAL TIME-SCALE

Main Divisions	*Subdivisions*	
Quaternary	Recent Pleistocene	Age of Mammals (Cenozoic)
Tertiary	Pliocene Miocene Oligocene Eocene	
Secondary	Cretaceous Jurassic Triassic	Age of Reptiles (Mesozoic)
Primary	Permian Devonian Silurian Ordovican Cambrian	Age of Invertebrate life (Palaeozoic)
Archaean	(The subdivisions need not concern us.)	(Archaeozoic)

As you see in the table, the 'age of mammals', or the Cenozoic starts at the beginning of the Tertiary division. When we come to consider the available evidence of the pre-human stages of man's evolution in a later chapter we shall have to discuss some of the discoveries made in deposits formed during the various subdivisions of the Tertiary.

In our study of Stone Age man himself and of his cultures, we shall only be dealing with the Quaternary period, and, so far as this book is concerned, only with the first part, the Pleistocene, and not at all with the Holocene.

Here we must consider for a moment what we mean by the word 'man'.

It is generally agreed that man has slowly and gradually evolved from earlier pre-human stages of the stock to which man, apes, and monkeys all belong, and in the appropriate chapter of this book we shall consider the available evidence concerning human evolution.

Naturally, during the slow course of physical evolution it would be impossible to say positively 'this is where the pre-human creature ceased to be sub-human and became a man', unless we have an agreed definition of what we mean by man.

There have been many attempts to arrive at a satisfactory definition, some based upon the absolute size of the brain, some upon the peculiarities of dentition, and some on a variety of other physical criteria which we need not discuss in detail.

Recently, however, there has been an increasing tendency to realize that none of these definitions is really satisfactory in practice, and in consequence most prehistorians now favour a definition which can be summed up in the phrase 'Man the Tool-maker', and this definition is the one we shall follow in this book. In other words, we only accept as 'man' a creature belonging to the primate stock which had reached a stage where it actually *made* tools, as distinct from merely using suitable natural objects as tools.

On the basis of this definition of man, we can say that as far as the available evidence shows, man first appeared during the Pleistocene subdivision of the Quaternary.

When I wrote the first edition of *Adam's Ancestors* I devoted several pages to a discussion of a definition of the word Pleistocene, for whereas it was generally agreed that the Pliocene represented the last subdivision of the Tertiary and the Pleistocene the first subdivision of the Quaternary, there was no general agreement among geologists and palaeontologists (let alone among pre-historians) as to the dividing line between the end of the Pliocene and the beginning of the Pleistocene. This lack of agreement on a definition of the word Pleistocene led to very serious confusion, for deposits of identical age were being described as Upper Pliocene by some workers and Lower Pleistocene by others, and so on.

Consequently, in 1934, I urged that a simple definition that was originally put forward by Haug in 1912 should be generally adopted by prehistorians; this was 'If members of one or more of the genera *Elephas, Equus,* or *Bos* (however primitive) occur in a deposit, that deposit is Pleistocene rather than Pliocene.'

Fortunately it is no longer necessary for me to urge the accep-tance of this definition, for at the International Geological Congress held in London in 1948, the geologists of the world decided upon a definition which has now been unanimously accepted; this reads as follows:

'The Commission considers that the Plio-Pleistocene boundary should be based upon changes in marine faunas, since this is the classic method of grouping fossiliferous strata. The classical area of marine sedimentation in Italy is regarded as the area where this principle can be implemented best. It is here, too, that terrestrial (continental) equivalents of the marine faunas under consideration can be determined.

'The Commission recommends that, in order to eliminate existing ambiguities, the Lower Pleistocene should include as its basal member in the type-area the Calabrian formation (marine) together with its terrestrial (continental) equivalent the Villafranchian.'

This definition is to all intents and purposes the same as Haug's definition which I so strongly supported, for it is in deposits of the Villafranchian (and in other deposits of comparable age elsewhere in the world) that the three genera which were the basis of his definition do in fact first appear.

An attempt was made in 1950 to persuade the prehistorians at the International Congress of Prehistoric and Proto-Historic Sciences held in Zürich to follow the lead given them by their colleagues, the geologists, and agree that they, too, would recommend to the prehistorians of the world that they would adhere to this definition. But the attempt unfortunately failed. However, it may be hoped that the majority of individual prehistorians who are concerned with the study of early Stone Age man will, of their own free will, accept the geologist's definition.

After all, words like Pliocene and Pleistocene are merely man-made labels, invented with the intention of helping us to be intelligible to each other and to do our work satisfactorily. It therefore matters little *where* we make the division between Pliocene and Pleistocene, provided that we make it at a point which is easily and quickly recognizable, *and provided we all use the words with the same meaning.*

For the purposes of this book, then, we shall follow the geologists and consider that the formation of the deposits called Villafranchian in Europe and in North Africa and deposits of comparable age elsewhere in the world mark the beginning of the Pleistocene. But in a sense this definition begs the question, for it may be argued that the words 'Villafranchian or deposits of comparable age elsewhere' are in themselves too vague.

That is only partly true. The Villafranchian can be recognized by the first appearance of certain marine mollusca in those places where deposits of the Villafranchian were formed under the sea, and by the appearance of certain types of mammal in the terrestrial deposits of the same period. The most important of these new mammal forms are in fact true elephants, true horses, and true bovids. But the early elephants of this period, although they were formerly included in the genus *Elephas*, have now been renamed archidiskodonts, although they are true elephants, all the same.

The two important facts that we must stress, however, which result from the adoption of the new definition are: (*a*) that on this basis we have, at present, no evidence whatever of the existence of 'man the toolmaker' in the Pliocene, and (*b*) that many of the deposits which are referred to in the literature of Prehistory as Upper Pliocene become Lower Pleistocene; similarly, deposits which have often been called Lower Pleistocene now rank as Middle Pleistocene.

Now, since we have seen that the criteria upon which the division between Pleistocene and Pliocene is made are based upon fossils, we must briefly discuss an important problem which arises from this fact. To what extent and under what circumstances can the fossil remains of animals be used for dating purposes?

If we look around the world today, what do we find? Various kinds of animals such as the lion, hyaena, hippopotamus, and elephant—to mention but a few—which have long since become extinct in Europe still roam at large in other parts of the world. On the other hand, many of the wild animals which still exist in Europe, such, for example, as the deer, wolf, bear, and wild boar, belong not only to the same genera as those which were hunted by Stone Age man during the Pleistocene in Europe, but even, in some cases, to the same or scarcely differentiated species. What does this mean? How does it affect our use of the fossil remains of animals as criteria for dating geological deposits?

The answer is that with fauna—as indeed with everything else— it is the appearance of new forms and not the persistence of old ones that is the significant factor and which must therefore be taken into account. This axiom is sometimes forgotten by pre-historians and others, not only in connexion with the study of fossil fauna, but also in the interpretation of Stone Age finds, and this occasionally leads to claims being made that are far from being warranted by the facts.

On the whole, the fossil remains of the larger mammals are more useful for dating purposes than invertebrate creatures such as molluscs, because the changes in their evolutionary status are more readily discernible and also because they are less limited in their geographical distribution than many other forms of life, making it possible, therefore, to correlate geological deposits over a wide area.

For example, there was a time when the definition of the Pleistocene period was based upon the presence or absence of certain types of *marine* mollusca in deposits laid down in the sea when the relative land and sea-levels were very different from what they are today.

Clearly this sort of definition could only have a very limited value for purposes of correlating geological deposits, since it could be used only in connexion with marine formations, while many of the Pleistocene deposits which prehistorians and geologists want to compare with each other are of terrestrial or fresh-water origin.

The new definition, which places the Villafranchian and deposits of comparable age as marking the beginning of the Pleistocene, has the great advantage that it includes both marine and terrestrial deposits, while the evolutionary stage of the various species in the fauna is fairly well known from a large quantity of specimens.

So far as the end of the Pleistocene and the dawn of the Holocene or Recent period is concerned, there is still no absolute agreement. Some scientists consider that the Pleistocene ends with the final retreat of the ice-sheets at the end of the Ice Age and with the comparable end of the pluvial periods in tropical areas, i.e. about 10,000 B.C.

Others, however, would prefer to use a definition based upon fossil faunas, and generally speaking we may say that on this basis the definition is linked with the appearance of domesticated animals or evidence of such domestication. This second definition of the end of the Pleistocene and the beginning of the Holocene would put the end of the Pleistocene at about 5000 B.C., a date somewhat more recent than that which would be given by the first definition, but in terms of geological time the period fixed by the two definitions would be synchronous *since a few thousand years in geological time are but 'a moment'.*

The geological period which we call the Pleistocene, with which we are mostly concerned in this book, since it is the period covering the Palaeolithic part of the Stone Age, was marked by a cycle of major climatic fluctuations which affected the whole world and which played a very important part indeed in determining the development of Stone Age cultures and their distribution, through the migrations and movements of both man and the animals which he hunted for food.

The study of these great fluctuations in climate, which took place during the Pleistocene period, provides yet another method of dating geological deposits and the Stone Age cultures contained in them and sometimes also of correlating deposits over a wide area.

Provided that they are severe enough and of sufficiently long duration, climatic changes inevitably leave their marks upon the surface of the earth and this evidence can be studied and interpreted by the geologists in comparison with what is known of the effects of present-day climate on the earth's surface.

The world today has, in its various zones, examples of all sorts of climatic conditions, from the extreme cold of the frozen ice-sheets of the polar regions to the deserts such as the Sahara, and the study of the climatic changes of the past is based upon the interpretation of deposits found in regions which today have a certain kind of climate, but which were clearly formed under quite different climatic conditions.

A general lowering of the mean temperature on the earth's surface, together with an increase in precipitation of moisture in the form of rain or snow, will result in the formation of great ice-sheets and snow-fields in suitable geographical zones, while in other parts of the world the effect of the same climatic change will result in rivers and lakes being greatly enlarged and new rivers and lakes forming where previously there were none; yet no snow-fields or ice-sheets will form, except, perhaps, in the mountains.

Similarly, if the cycle of climatic change swings towards increased temperature and decreased precipitation, the results will not be the same in different parts of the world, for in the regions where there have been huge ice-sheets and snow-fields the increased temperature will lead to the melting of the locked-up waters and, in consequence, a great increase in the size of rivers and streams fed by the waters of the melting ice and snow. In the zones where no major ice-sheets ever formed, the same climatic change will result in the gradual drying up of rivers and of the lakes which they fed and in increasingly arid conditions.

Then, again, even if a cycle of climatic change affects the whole world, numerous regional factors come into play to complicate the picture and make the interpretation of the evidence more difficult.

For example, quite apart from the primary effect of a general lowering of the surface temperature of the earth, combined with a general increase in precipitation, the positions of the ice-sheets and snow-fields that are formed by the world-wide climatic change will have a secondary effect upon the climate of zones elsewhere in the world through such metereological factors as depressions, wind movements, and changes in atmospheric pressure.

At the present time the study of the world changes of climate, which we know occurred during the Pleistocene period, is far from complete and there is still much more to be learned, but in general terms it seems fairly clear that there were seven major changes.

These started at the beginning of the Pleistocene with a period of increased precipitation and lowering of the surface temperature of the earth, resulting in what is called a glacial period in present-day temperate zones, such as North and Central Europe and a pluvial period in tropical and subtropical zones, such as the greater part of the African continent. This first climatic cycle is known as the Günz glaciation in Europe and as the Kageran pluvial in Africa.

The second major climatic change was a period of increased surface temperature, combined with a general decrease of precipitation, and this is known as the first interglacial in Europe and the first interpluvial in Africa. Then came another period such as the first, with a second glaciation in Europe and a second pluvial period in Africa. These are known respectively as the Mindel glaciation and the Kamasian pluvial.

The fourth climatic change was another interglacial and interpluvial period, known as the second interglacial and second interpluvial.

The fifth cycle was a return to lower temperature and increased precipitation resulting in a third glaciation and a third pluvial period which are known respectively as the Riss glaciation and the Kanjeran pluvial (sometimes called Upper Kamasian). This fifth cycle was again followed by conditions which led to a third interglacial and interpluvial. This was the sixth cyclic climatic change. Finally came another swing towards lower temperature and increased precipitation, leading to the fourth or Würm glaciation in Europe and to the Gamblian pluvial in Africa.

The end of this seventh cycle was marked by a gradual change, once more, to relatively warmer and drier conditions leading slowly to the present-day climate, which may be regarded as the early stages of a fourth interglacial and interpluvial.

The reader must not imagine that any of these major climatic changes happened suddenly; on the contrary, they took place as slow and gradual trends, spread over tens of thousands of years, just as the period in which we are now living is only the beginning of a fourth major interglacial and interpluvial, although it is now about 10,000 years since the swing in the climatic cycle started towards warmer and drier conditions.

Moreover, the change of climate that marks a new cycle is not constant, but consists rather of a series of minor fluctuations, although the general trend is evident. Thus the period of the fourth interglacial in which we are now living, and which started about 10,000 years ago, has seen several *minor* cold periods in Europe and several minor increases in pluvial conditions in Africa, but the general trend has been towards interglacial and interpluvial conditions. These minor oscillations within the major climatic trend are likely to continue—if we may judge by the past—until we finally reach the peak of an interglacial in Europe and an interpluvial in Africa, many thousands of years hence.

In the same way the change, for example, from the second glacial and second pluvial periods to the second interglacial and interpluvial periods respectively was certainly not sudden or catastrophic and must surely have been marked by a series of minor fluctuations as the cycle advanced. Unfortunately, however, the next major climatic change ultimately obliterated all, or nearly all, of the evidence of these minor fluctuations.

I have referred in the foregoing passages only to glacial and interglacial periods in Europe and pluvial and interpluvial in Africa. That was for convenience, for naturally world changes of climate did not only affect these two continents; they affected the whole world. Similar changes of climate have been noted and studied in Asia, North and South America, and to some extent in Australia. In America, especially in North America, the story is fairly clear, but in Asia, Australia, and South America a great deal more work remains to be done before even the general outline of the picture is clear.

What is perhaps still more interesting is that recent geological studies of the floor of the great oceans of the world indicate that evidence of the major climatic changes of the Pleistocene period can also be studied under the sea, and a vast new field for investigation is thus being opened up.

I have written of these major changes of climate as though it was wholly accepted by scientists that glacial periods in temperate zones and pluvial periods in tropical and subtropical areas were contemporary.

In fact, this is a matter which is still in dispute, and there are some scientists who believe that a glacial period in Europe was accompanied by an interpluvial or dry period in Africa, and therefore that an interglacial period in Europe should be equated with a pluvial (not an interpluvial) period in Africa.

The reason for this divergence of opinion is due to the fact that there is still so much more work to be done on these world changes of climate and also upon the study of the causes of climatic cycles.

There are numerous theories to account for the known world changes of climate, but having given careful consideration to most of them, I feel that the only one which satisfactorily fits all the facts is Simpson's theory,[1] or the 'theory of major cyclic changes of solar radiation'.

We known, of course, that solar radiation is not constant and that there are very minor cycles linked with what we term sun-spots. But Simpson's theory postulates that these minor cycles are but very small oscillations within immense major cyclic changes of solar radiation, and that it was these that were the primary cause of the world changes of climate during the Pleistocene.

The changes of intensity in solar radiation have effects that, at first sight, seem paradoxical, but which are really quite logical.

In broad outline, an increase in the amount of heat reaching the earth from the sun makes the climate colder and wetter, while a decrease makes for warmer and drier conditions.

Let us see how this happens. The total amount of moisture available in the earth and its atmosphere is a constant factor which we may call X. This total moisture X is made up of moisture in many forms, the chief of which are: (*a*) the seas and oceans; (*b*) the lakes and rivers and other fresh water on the surface of the earth; (*c*) underground water; (*d*) snow and ice locked up in the arctic and antarctic regions and the ice-caps and glaciers of the high mountains; (*e*) cloud and other moisture above the earth's surface. Now, while X remains constant, the proportions into which X is divided among (*a*), (*b*), (*c*), (*d*), and (*e*) are clearly variable, and an increase in any one or more of them must mean a decrease in one or more of the others.

---

[1] Simpson's theory was advanced some years ago, and while its general proposition still seems to provide the best explanation of the facts of world climatic change, I have modified some of his original conclusions, in the light of our increased knowledge.

When there is an increase in the amount of heat from the sun reaching the earth there is a greater evaporation from the seas, oceans, lakes, and rivers, etc., and this results in a greater amount of cloud and an increase in precipitation in the form of snow or rain, according to where it falls. Moreover, the increase in cloud-cover results in some decrease of temperature on the earth, and therefore to a decrease in the melting of snow and ice.

In consequence, there is a gradual advance of the polar ice-sheets, resulting in a glaciation in the affected areas, while there is also an increase in the glaciation of the high mountains of the world and an advance of the glaciers to lower levels. There is, as well, a general increase in precipitation, i.e. an advance to what we call a pluvial period in regions which are too warm—by reason of their geographical position—for snow and ice.

Naturally, this change in climate—owing to secondary conditions—is more intense in some regions than in others, while the annual seasonal variations of summer and winter, etc., continue. Taken on the whole, however, a long period of gradually increasing solar radiation causes glacial and pluvial conditions.

When the pendulum starts swinging the other way and solar radiation starts to decrease, there is a reversal of the processes described above, and with less evaporation there is less cloud-cover and thus higher actual temperatures on the earth's surface, resulting in the gradual melting of the ice-sheets and snow-fields and the retreat of the glaciation. There is also a lessening of precipitation in zones unaffected by ice and snow, leading to an interpluvial.

The gradual melting of the ice-sheets and snow-fields that accompanies the decrease in solar radiation and leads to generally warmer and drier conditions, also results in a considerable increase in the amount of water in rivers that have their source near the edge of the melting and retreating ice-sheets, so that in spite of a decrease in precipitation there is a tendency for the rivers and lakes in such regions to increase their size and volume.

Thus in England, for instance, during an interglacial period, or at least during the earlier stages of it, the rivers were carrying more water than usual.

Another matter that is very closely linked with these major changes of climate is a change in the relative land and sea-levels.

Marine beaches well above the present-day sea and ocean-level can be traced all round the continental masses of the world, while there is also evidence of submerged beach lines below the seas and oceans. In other words, there have been times when the general sea and ocean-level was higher in relation to the land masses than it is today, and, similarly, times when the level dropped considerably below its present-day position.

A very great deal more detailed study remains to be done on this subject all over the world, but it is generally accepted that as more and more of the total moisture X became locked up in the ice-sheets and snow-fields during a glaciation there was a corresponding decrease in the size of the seas and oceans, leading to a lowering of the beach lines. Similarly, as the ice-sheets retreated farther and farther there was a decrease in (d) and a corresponding increase in (a), resulting in high-level beaches being formed. Clearly, if this explanation is correct, we must assume that during the height of an interglacial the ice-sheets retreated far beyond the position they hold today in the arctic and antarctic, and it has been computed that almost the whole of the polar ice-sheets would have had to disappear in order to release enough water to raise the seas and oceans to the level of the highest Pleistocene terrace.

But it must not be imagined that the relative changes in land and sea-levels were solely caused by the effects of the climatic changes already described. Were that the case, then the old high-level marine beaches of the Pleistocene would be at exactly the same levels all over the world—*which they are not.* We know, however, that the earth's crust is not stable and is subject to all sorts of movements. It is distinctly possible that the weight of the ice-sheets advancing over a large part of North Europe may have depressed the land masses in that area—and this might, or might not, cause uplift in other areas. We also know that during the Middle Pleistocene period there were very severe earth movements, resulting in great deepening and widening of the cracks in the earth's crust that are known as the Great Rift Valley system —cracks which run from Palestine right down through Africa to the Rhodesias.

We also know that at about this time there were earth movements which resulted in an elevation of the mountain mass of the Himalayas. A variety of other movements of the earth's crust certainly took place about the same time, and some of these, in North Africa and in Java, have been studied.

While, therefore, we may accept the view that during interglacial and interpluvial periods there was a general rise in sea-level relative to the land masses, we must not forget that the story is a highly complicated one which is not yet fully understood and studied.

Among the results of these changes in relative land and sea-levels we may mention the formation of land bridges connecting parts of the world at present separated by sea-water. For example, we know for certain that there were times when England was not an island but was linked with the continent of Europe, so that man and wild animals could move freely backwards and forwards. Some scientists also believe that one or more land bridges were formed—at least once—across the Mediterranean, linking North Africa with South Europe and allowing free migration there too. Similarly, it seems likely that there was a land bridge across the southern end of the Red Sea at some time during the early Pleistocene period, and that Java and some of the other islands of the Malay Archipelago were linked by land bridges to the continent of Asia.

These matters are all of the highest importance to the student of the story of man during the Stone Age, for it is only by understanding these things that we can begin to appreciate the significance of the distribution of the different Stone Age cultures that we shall be studying in later chapters of this book.

The subjects I have referred to can really be studied by geographical exploration, and now that the present-day geography of the world is so well known, more and more 'explorers' are likely to turn their attention to the geography of the earlier stages of man's occupation of the world—to prehistoric geography, in fact.

Earlier in this chapter we have briefly discussed the subject of the use of fossil remains of animals and other forms of life for dating purposes, and we must conclude our study of early man's environment by a further reference to the fauna and flora of the Stone Age.

Naturally, the vast changes of climate and geography which took place during the Pleistocene period were reflected in the fauna and flora of the different parts of the world.

Unfortunately, remains of animal and plant life are only preserved by fossilization under somewhat rare conditions, so that very often we find sites with Stone Age man's tools preserved, but without any trace of the contemporary life.

But sites do occur where conditions for fossilization were good and where we can collect the remains of animal life—and also sometimes of plant life—in association with Stone Age tools. When this happens we can get a fairly clear idea of this aspect of Stone Age man's background.

By collecting the fossils associated with a culture at any site where bone is preserved, we can get a picture of the kind of animals that the men of the period hunted and against which they had to guard themselves. To some extent also, the study of such fossils will give an indication of the climate and general environmental conditions of the time.

As we have already seen, great caution has to be exercised in using the evidence from the fossilized remains of large land mammals as a guide to climatic conditions because many of these animals are very adaptable, and, generally speaking, a study of plant life gives a much more reliable indication of climate.

The conditions under which plant remains become fossilized are, however, even more rare than those under which animal remains are preserved, but research has shown that minute grains of pollen from flowering trees and plants were sometimes preserved under conditions where leaves and wood were not. This has opened up a big new field of study in 'pollen analysis' which has made it possible to get a very good idea of the flora of the time when certain types of geological deposits were formed.

Another new approach to more definite dating of prehistoric sites and cultures is that known as the C.14 or Radio-carbon Test, based upon studies of charcoal and other materials from pre- historic sites. This method was pioneered in America, and it looks as though very important results may be expected when the methods are more perfected.

These last two lines of approach, which are still in their infancy so far as the greater part of the world is concerned, offer scope for a large number of workers in the future and may be expected to give very important results concerning the story of man's past.

Early man's environment has of necessity been discussed very generally in this chapter since it is a subject to which it would be easy to devote a large number of chapters, but it is to be hoped that the reader has been given some idea of the climatic and geographical conditions which existed during the period of the earth's history with which we are concerned.

Looking back, as we can today, we see that the Pleistocene period, during which man gradually evolved and developed, was a period of almost unbelievable changes. Even though we still have so much to study and to learn about both the climate and the geography, we can now begin to see the general outline of the picture, and we cannot but be rather appalled and wonder that man survived at all. We must, therefore, remember that all the various changes of climate, geography, and fauna took place so gradually and slowly in relation to the lifetime of a single individual that it is doubtful if any of our Stone Age ancestors and cousins were ever really aware of what was happening.

Stone Age man lived and died in the world into which he was born and went about his occupations of making himself tools and weapons and providing himself and his family with food and clothing, knowing nothing of what had happened in the past nor what was going to happen in the future. We, at least, can now begin to understand something of the past, even of the remote past, and maybe, if we learn the lessons of the past aright, we can hope to foretell with some accuracy something of the future.

CHAPTER III

Interpreting Stone and Bone

STONE is the most imperishable of all the materials which were used by prehistoric man for the manufacture of his tools and weapons, and therefore it is the stone implements of the various cultures that are most commonly found and studied. To a very great extent, too, it is on the basis of the stone tools—rather than other cultural elements—that Stone Age cultures are classified, except in the very late stages of Prehistory.

It is therefore of the very greatest importance that the reader who is going to pass on to the later chapters of this book should understand the way in which stone implements were made.

The stone implements of the more advanced stages of culture are usually so obviously the result of human workmanship that nobody—no matter how untrained or sceptical—would doubt their authenticity.

But among the assemblages of tools of the earlier cultures there are always many specimens that require careful examination before they can be classified, and among which are many that the ordinary person, without special knowledge of the subject, would not regard as humanly made tools at all.

Many prehistorians, when displaying one of their most treasured implements belonging to some very early Stone Age culture, have been rebuffed by the comment, 'Do you mean to say that you seriously regard *that* as a humanly worked piece of stone? Why, I could show you hundreds like it on my garden path.'

On the other side of the picture, not a few people collect and retain as Stone Age specimens objects which are of purely natural origin, because the shape is suggestive, and are very surprised if the expert to whom they show the specimens tells them that they are not humanly made stone implements.

In this chapter, therefore, the methods by which human workmanship on stone can be distinguished from natural fractures will be carefully examined.

First of all let us consider what choice of material early man had for the making of his stone implements and to what extent—

if any—the nature of the available rock influenced the tools that were made.

Rocks of an infinite variety occur all over the world, and naturally some types of rock are more suitable than others for making stone implements. In many parts of Europe flint of one kind or another occurs, and owing to its homogeneous nature it is very much easier to flake than some of the other coarse-grained rocks. For the same reason, where obsidian—natural volcanic glass —occurs, it was a favourite choice of Stone Age man. Where, therefore, either of these two types of rock occurs, it is common to find that it was extensively used by Stone Age man. But all over the world, many other kinds of rock were also made use of. In some cases even such unpromising materials as quartz and granite were used, and, surprisingly enough, implements made from these materials were sometimes very perfectly finished.

This is a matter of importance, for there are some prehistorians who argue that the nature of the available material had a very great influence on the type of stone tool made—whereas in fact there is abundant evidence to the contrary.

One of the most astonishing things which is revealed by the study of Stone Age cultures from all over the world is the constancy of the tool types which characterize the different cultures, irrespective of the material that was used.

This is important, for otherwise one might be tempted to explain the very primitive nature of some Stone Age industry by arguing that the available material did not lend itself to the making of more evolved types of implements, when in reality the true explanation is more likely to be that the men who made that industry were too unskilled to make better tools, or else belonged to a culture group which had not evolved higher forms.

The only way in which Stone Age techniques of working stone can be fully appreciated and understood is by practical experiments, and not a little of the confusion that still exists about Stone Age techniques, as exemplified in varying Stone Age cultures, arises out of a failure to appreciate this fact.

I must confess that I myself was guilty of a failure to experiment sufficiently during the earlier years of my work, but for the last twenty-one years I have done a very great deal of study on the fracture of stone, and what follows in this chapter is based upon these experiments.

Even today there still seems to be a widely held view that the making of tools and implements out of stone was a slow, laborious process, and it is often suggested that this did not matter in Stone Age times since early man is commonly supposed to have had plenty of time on his hands, as he lived such a simple life.

This is probably far from true. Early Stone Age man was dependent for his livelihood on his success in hunting and trapping animals and birds, etc., and the collection of wild edible fruits, nuts, and berries. Anyone who knows about the way of life of primitive hunting tribes of the present day, such as the Bushmen or the Wanderobo, will realize that the provision of enough food is almost a whole-time job under such conditions, and will realize that, had the making of stone implements required many hours of work, early man would probably have starved.

Experiment shows that once the technique required for making a particular tool type has been fully mastered, the actual making of the implement is a very quick process indeed, while the discovery of new techniques is often wholly accidental and un-expected, as indeed it must also have been in the past.

Slight modification of basic techniques may be necessary, depending on whether the material being used is fine-grained and homogeneous like flint, or coarse-grained with relatively poor fracture, like some forms of quartzite or lava. It takes longer, too, to learn how to apply a given technique successfully to a bad material than to a good one.

Since this book is in the main intended for the British public, and since in Great Britain flint was more often used for making stone tools than any other form of rock, we will take flint as the material for our main study in this chapter, noting only that obsidian and chert, as well as a number of other fine-grained rocks, behave in exactly the same way as flint *and that the difference in respect of coarser-grained rocks is only a matter of degree and not of basic technique.*

Flint can be obtained from two different sources, and both were available to and used by Stone Age man. It can either be obtained direct from the deposits in which it was formed—usually chalk—or else from a gravel bed or other secondary deposit whither it had been brought by some natural agency from its original source.

Flint obtained from a secondary deposit such as a gravel bed is often found to have been subjected to so much battering and rolling by natural agencies that it has been reduced to a pebble and during the process incipient cracks will have formed so that when an attempt is made to flake it, it will fracture along these incipient cracks instead of in the direction intended by the worker.

Similarly, such flint from secondary sources is likely to have been exposed to extreme changes of temperature, which often render it brittle and very hard to work.

In spite of these facts, prehistoric man not infrequently did use material derived from such secondary deposits, but this usually meant that a far higher proportion of tools broke in the making and were discarded unfinished than when fresh material was utilized. The relative proportion of waste flakes and broken specimens to complete finished specimens, on sites where flint from secondary deposits has been used, is therefore usually much higher than on sites where Stone Age man was using good fresh flint.

Even when freshly mined flint is used, the number of waste flakes that result in the process of making one good stone implement is quite astonishing. For example, on those occasions when I have counted the waste flakes with a surface area of more than a square inch (that is to say, not counting the very small flakes) which resulted from making one large implement of hand-axe type, I have usually found that they numbered more than a hundred.

To understand the making of stone tools and to appreciate the differences between the various cultures, as well as those which distinguish the various techniques employed in making the tools, it is first necessary to know what happens when force is applied in different ways to a piece of flint or other stone.

The direction in which the force is applied, the way in which the force is applied, i.e. by a blow or by pressure, the nature of the actual 'hammer' used for the blow (whether stone, bone, or wood), even the shape of the 'hammer', and the nature of the blow itself, whether a sharp tap or a slow, follow-through shot, all these are controlling factors.

What follows on this subject is, as I have said, based on the results of my own long years of experiment, but I am only too well aware that I still have much to learn on this subject, to which far too little attention has been given by prehistorians. I am also fully aware of the inadequacy of the descriptions and diagrams in this account, for it is far easier to give a visual demonstration than to write a description of flint fracture and the control of force.

First of all, let us consider what is called 'quartering' a large block of flint—a subject which I did not deal with in the earlier editions of this book, as at that time I did not understand it, although I could achieve it.

Plate I

(a) The method of 'quartering' a block of flint

(b) The Acheulean method of flaking stone by means of a soft cylindrical hammer

Let us imagine that we have taken a large, irregular nodule of flint from the chalk in which it was formed and want to use it to make stone tools. The surface of the nodule is covered by a white chalky crust of dehydrated flint, and there are irregular projections and lumps due to the way the flint was formed. We want to break this nodule into two parts through the middle so as to expose the pure, unaltered flint and obtain a surface on which we can strike blows with a hammer in order to detach flakes.

What, in effect, we wish to do is to *pull the nodule in half,* just as a person with strong hands can take an apple and break it in half. But, since we cannot do it quite like this, we must produce the same effect by a different method. Fortunately, most nodules of flint are very irregular and have numerous projections, and we must take advantage of one of these to achieve our object.

We examine our nodule carefully, therefore, for a suitable projection, and then place the nodule (which may be a big one as large as a leg of mutton and weigh 12 lb. or more) on one knee so that the projection we have chosen is facing our right hand, while one end of the nodule is on the knee and the other end is held *loosely* in the left hand, just supporting the block, *but not pressing it down on to the knee.*

We must then take a large hammer-stone—preferably weighing 2 or 3 lb.—and with the right hand hit a blow on the projecting lump, as near to the main body of the nodule as possible, the direction of the blow being *at right angles* to the direction in which we want the large nodule to break in two. The effect of such a blow properly delivered is to pull the block in half, and the nodule will fall into two parts with surprising ease (see Plate I*a*).

This technique is entirely different from any that is used to remove flakes or blades from a block, and does not result in any bulb of percussion at the point where the fracture starts, for it does not start at the point where the projection from the nodule was struck, but rather on the main body of the nodule near the base of the projection.

The point of impact will, of course, have been on the dehydrated crust of flint on the projection, and this may crack up after being struck, or may remain intact with some incipient cracks.

In some cases the nodule of flint which it is desired to quarter may have no suitable projections which would enable the process just described to be carried out. If this is the case it will be necessary to try to 'snap' the nodule in two, much as one would break a biscuit.

Here again, however, the bare hands alone cannot be used. To break a biscuit, or a very thin flint flake or blade, all that is necessary is to hold it in the thumbs and fingers of the two hands and apply a 'bending' pressure, when it will snap in two parts since it is brittle and cannot bend.

In the case of a large flint nodule covered in crust and having no suitable projections which would allow the first and best method of quartering to be used, the nodule must be laid on the knee with the long axis across the knee and one end must be held with a *downward* pressure while a blow with a heavy hammer-stone is struck about half-way along the other (free) end of the nodule. If the blow is properly struck with a suitably heavy hammer-stone, the effect will be to snap the nodule in half. The fracture will take place not at the point of impact of the hammer-stone, but roughly at the point where the nodule ceases to be supported by the knee.

This method of quartering is far more difficult to carry out accurately than the first one described, and, moreover, has the added disadvantage that the part on which the blow was struck will become practically useless for subsequent flaking since the heavy blow will have caused lines of shatter and incipient cracks.

Having described briefly the two techniques of quartering, let us pass on to the problem of removing flakes from the lump of flint thus quartered.

First of all, we must discuss the use of hammer-stones for flaking purposes: to understand this properly we must consider the question of how force is distributed following the impact of a blow.

Let us imagine that we have quartered a large nodule of flint and now have one flat surface of the unaltered flint available to strike on.

If we take a hammer-stone—in the form of a natural water-worn pebble of some suitably hard stone—and if we were to strike a blow *vertically* on the middle of the flint surface—the effect of the blow would be for the end of the hammer-stone to crush a small area of the flint (see fig. 1B), and, unless the blow was struck with very great force, no other effect would be visible, although incipient cracks and lines of weakness would have been caused in the mass of flint.

Small and roughly circular crushed marks on the surface of flint can frequently be seen, not only on large lumps that man has tried to break up, but also on boulders in river gravels, where they have been caused by the impact of one boulder against another by natural agencies.

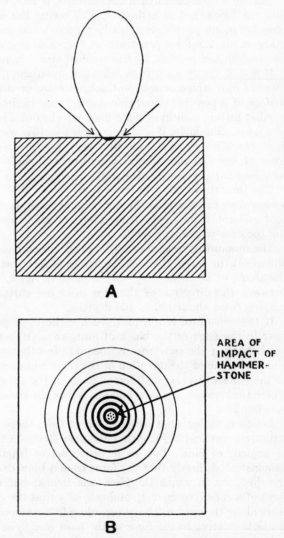

Fig. 1. Diagrammatic figure to illustrate the effect of striking a hammer-stone against a block of flint or other rock

In such a case, the force of the blow has, in fact, been distributed into the block, not in a single line following the direction of the blow (as many people erroneously suppose), but about a cone. In other words, the force penetrates in ever-widening circles from the point of impact marked by the crushed area (see fig. 2).

If a sufficiently hard blow is struck upon the flat surface of a piece of flint which is not too thick, directly perpendicular to the surface, it is possible to punch out a full cone in the same way that a bullet hitting a sheet of plate-glass knocks out a hole in the form of a cone. Similarly, if a blow is struck in this way on a piece of flint which is too thick, the flint may fracture with a complete cone at the top and irregular fractures along natural lines of weakness farther down (see fig. 3).

The important thing to learn from this is that the force from a blow does not travel in the direction of the blow but at an angle to it, and not in one single straight line, but along a curve representing the ever-widening circles.

The amount of resistance in the block which has been so struck will affect the speed at which the circles of force penetrate, so that the shape of the cone may vary as seen in fig. 2, with the angle between the direction of the blow and the surface of the cone ranging from about 120 to 160 degrees.

If the resistance is unequal because the blow has been struck near to the edge of the block of flint, an asymmetrical cone will result because the resistance is unequal. In other words, the angle which the line of the direction of the blow makes with the surface of the cone will vary at different parts of the cone, being greater where the resistance is less, and less where the resistance is greater (see fig. 2*C*).

Let us consider what we have learnt from these descriptions of striking a vertical blow with a hammer-stone on the flat surface of a piece of flint. Two basic principles of fracture have been demonstrated; firstly that the force from a blow does *not* travel in the direction in which the blow was struck, but radiates in the form of a cone (see fig. 3*A*), and secondly that the direction of the force along the cone will vary according to the amount of resistance it meets relative to the force of the blow (see fig. 2).

Let us now see how we can apply these basic principles to achieve the removal of flakes from a lump of flint.

In fig. 4 a diagrammatic outline of a block of flint is shown, from which it is desired to detach a flake along the dotted line *x–y*. Clearly, from what we have learnt, we must *not* strike a blow with

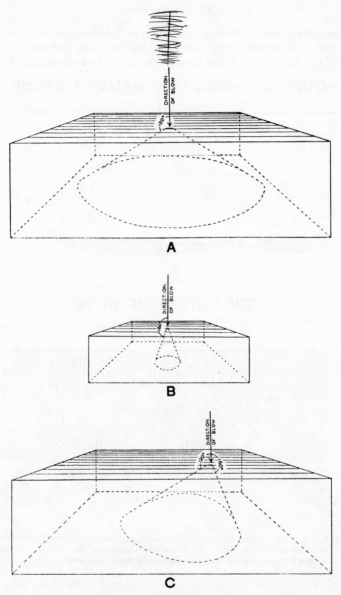

Fig. 2. Diagrams of cones of percussion

a hammer-stone in the same direction as the line x–y, for if we did so the force would travel not along the line x–y, but much more into the thickness of the block. We must instead calculate the

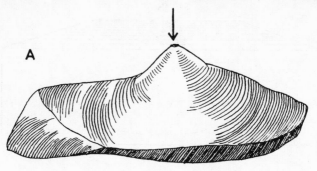

POINT OF IMPACT OF HAMMER-STONE

A

DIRECTION OF BLOW

B

DIRECTION OF FORCE   DIRECTION OF FORCE

Fig. 3.   *A.* Drawing of an actual cone of percussion resulting from a single blow on a block of flint.   *B.* Diagram to illustrate the direction in which a blow travels when a hammer-stone hits a piece of rock

angle of the blow in relation to the thickness of the flake we wish to knock off (see fig. 4), remembering that the force will enter the block about a variable cone.

But if we strike a blow in this manner, near the edge of a block of flint, it will be very difficult indeed to control the nature of the flake which we knock off and to prevent it from breaking up, unless we have some sort of *lesser resistance* against the face marked *a–b* in fig. 4*A* and 4*B*.

Therefore in practice we shall have to hold the block of flint on our knee (or against some other suitable substance such as the soft

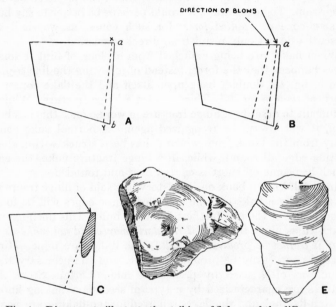

DIRECTION OF BLOWS

Fig. 4.—Diagrams to illustrate the striking of flakes and the differences between natural and artificial fractures

bark of a log of wood) in such a way that *a–b* is pressed against the knee or the bark. Thus, part of the cone of force resulting from the blow which is to be struck at an angle to the surface of the flint will be absorbed by the knee or the log of wood. By this method, although the force of the blow is distributed about a cone, in accordance with our first principle, only a small part of that cone affects the flint, and the rest is absorbed outside the flint. As a result, a flake is removed with a semi-cone or bulb of percussion at the point of impact of the hammer-stone (see fig. 4*E*).

Nothing but regular practice will serve to teach the person who wishes to experiment in flint flaking just how hard to press the block of flint against the knee in order to detach the required thickness of flake. Similarly, only practice and experience will teach one what size of hammer-stone to use to remove a particular type of flake from a particular block at any given point.

The semi-cone or bulb which results from the removal of a flake by a blow, at the point of impact of the hammer-stone on the block of flint, is called the bulb or cone of percussion, and the corresponding hollow on the block itself is called the negative bulb of percussion. To be accurate, it would perhaps be better to say bulb or semi-cone of *applied force*, for such cones, as we shall see presently, do not only result from direct percussion.

When flakes are being detached from a block of flint it sometimes happens that the force, instead of following the line *x–y*, as seen in fig. 4*B*, doubles back upon itself and the flake comes off short, as seen in fig. 4*C*. This is called a hinge fracture. While it is difficult to describe a hinge fracture in words, once this has been seen, it will always be recognized again. A normal flake comes away from the block from which it has been struck with a sharp cutting edge all round, while, in a hinge fracture flake, the edge which has come off short is curved over and rounded.

In a well-known book on Prehistory it is said of hinge fractures: 'Occasionally a flake may be observed whose edges will be found to curl over at the end farthest from the bulb. This phenomenon is known as hinge fracture. *Prehistoric man could not make use of it as it cannot be produced at will.*' The italics are mine. Hinge fractures can easily be produced at will, and the necessary technique was often used by prehistoric man. Certain Stone Age cultures are characterized by a type of secondary flaking known as 'step-flaking', and the flakes removed in step-flaking are nearly all small hinge fracture flakes. The removal of flakes with hinge fractures is entirely dependent on the relationship between the direction of the blow and the amount of resistance in the material, relative to the thickness of the flake removed.

We have so far discussed the removal of flakes by means of a hammer-stone, but there is a certain amount of evidence to suggest that, sometimes at least, Stone Age man preferred to use what is called the anvil technique rather than a hammer-stone. When a hammer-stone is used, the block of flint is hit with a hammer-stone in the appropriate direction; to use the anvil technique the block itself is hit against the projecting point of a large, fixed block of stone or anvil.

Flakes can certainly be struck from a block of flint or other stone in this way, but it is much more difficult to achieve accuracy of flaking, and I am more and more doubtful whether this technique was very widely used in the Stone Age. The Abbé Breuil, however, the leading French prehistorian, believes that a great deal of Stone Age flaking was done in this way and more particularly that this was the technique employed for the removal of really large flakes.

He postulates that the block of stone from which a really large flake was to be removed was tied to the end of a leather thong, the other end of which was fastened to a rough wooden tripod, and that the block was swung pendulum-fashion against the anvil. Personally, I find it hard to believe that sufficient accuracy could be achieved by this method, and I think that, if such a method was ever used, it must have been only on very rare occasions.

We have so far mainly been considering the removal of large flakes from a block of flint or other stone, but it is obvious that the same principles apply in a general way to the removal of smaller flakes, in the course of trimming a large flake, or a small block, into an actual implement.

The vast majority of Stone Age tools were made from primary flakes struck from a block or core in the way that we have already discussed. When such a flake is taken and made into an implement, it becomes, in one sense, a core, for small flakes have to be removed from it in order to shape it.

In some cases the technique for the removal of these smaller flakes in the process of making a stone implement exactly reproduces (but on a smaller scale) the methods already described; that is to say, the small flakes may be removed either by hitting with a hammer-stone in the appropriate direction and with the correct amount of force, or else the flake may be struck against a small, stationary stone anvil.

But whereas large flakes can only be obtained by man if he uses one or other of these two processes, the removal of smaller flakes can be achieved by a number of additional processes which must now be discussed.

As we have already seen, flaking by means of an ordinary hammer-stone—using the rounded or pointed end of a natural pebble—results in a semi-cone, or bulb of applied force, on the flake knocked off, and a negative semi-cone, or negative bulb, on the block of flint from which the flake was removed.

Now, when we come to examine the stone tools of certain cultures, such, for example, as the Acheulean stages of the Hand-axe culture, which we shall consider more fully in a later chapter, we find that many specimens show that very flat flakes have been removed and that the resulting flake scars on the implements exhibit a very flat bulb of applied force, quite unlike that which results from the use of the ordinary hammer-stone or anvil technique.

Many years ago the Abbé Breuil noticed this fact, and he encouraged a technician, M. Coutier, who was working with him, to carry out experiments in order to find out how such flakes could be removed.

M. Coutier discovered that if he struck blows on the side of a piece of flint with a rounded piece of wood he could achieve results exactly comparable to those seen on Acheulean hand-axes—he could remove thin, flat flakes with flat bulbs of applied force. This technique was therefore named the 'wooden hammer' technique.

The fact that flakes could be struck from such hard substances as flint and other rocks by means of a soft wooden hammer came as a great surprise to most students of Prehistory who, up till then, had always assumed that a hard hammer of stone was needed to remove flakes from other stones.

My own experiments with the so-called 'wooden hammer' technique show that it is not the use of wood in itself that is the significant factor in removing these flat flakes. It is rather that the type of wooden hammer used by M. Coutier in his experiments was cylindrical, and that he was striking his blows on the flint *with the side of a soft cylinder*: in other words, with a curved and relatively soft edge and *not* with a hard point.

My experiments have shown that exactly the same results in respect of flaking technique can be achieved by using the side of a more or less cylindrical pebble as a hammer, provided it is not too hard, and also by using fresh bone. In particular, the jawbones of large ungulates, the cannon-bones of bovids, and the metacarpals and metatarsals of equids make especially good hammers for the purpose (see Plate 1*b*).

When a cylinder hammer is used for flaking, whether of stone, bone, or wood, the specimen from which flakes are to be removed is held in one hand in such a way that the fingers support the surface from which flakes are to be struck, and very flat flaking is achieved, partly because the blow is struck with a soft curved edge and not with a point, and partly because when using such a hammer it is impossible to strike a blow except at the very edge of the block which is to be trimmed.

Another method of flaking by percussion that may have been used by Stone Age man is the indirect or punch technique.

Instead of blows being struck direct on the flint which is being flaked, a punch of wood or bone is held against the block so that the point of the punch is on the spot where the flake is to be struck off, and the long axis of the punch is in the correct position for the direction of blow relative to angle of fracture. The free end of the punch is then hit with a hammer-stone.

To achieve success with this method, the participation of two people is necessary, one to hold the block against his knee or on a log of wood, and the other to operate the punch and hammer.

Indirect percussion flaking of a different sort provides the surest technique of removing narrow, thin flakes from the side of a larger flake in order to make the type of tool which is known as a 'burin' or chisel.

In this method, the large flake from which a smaller flake is to be removed is held against an anvil so that the point from which a flake is to be removed is resting against the anvil at an angle of about 120 degrees. A sharp tap on the side of the flake is then struck downwards with a wooden or bone hammer. The effect of this is to force the main flake downwards so that pressure from the anvil is exerted at the tip where it rests on the anvil. This forces off a small, narrow flake along the edge of the large flake.

Next, we must consider another method of removing flakes from a piece of flint or other fine-grained rock; a method known as 'pressure flaking'.

Surprising as it may seem, it is perfectly possible to push off flakes from a piece of flint or other stone, and several pressure flaking processes were employed by prehistoric man during the later cultures.

The most commonly recognized form of pressure flaking is that which removes small, flat flakes from the surface of a larger flake in the making of certain very specialized types of Stone Age implements, such as, for example, Solutrean leaf-shaped points, and some Neolithic and Bronze Age arrow-heads, and, in particular, the Egyptian predynastic implements. Pressure flaking of this type is still carried out by some of the aboriginal tribes of Australia and by some tribes of American Indians.

A variety of objects, such as points of ivory, hardwood, bone, and even the teeth of some animals, can be used to push off flakes, and the pressure may be applied either by hand or by the weight of the whole body. We have no evidence to show which method was used by Stone Age man.

If hand pressure is to be applied, the long flake from which the small, flat flakes are to be removed is held in the hand and the tip of the flaking tool (whether of bone, ivory, or wood) is held against the edge, at the point where the flake is to be removed, *at the correct angle* and is then pushed firmly. The little flake which is thus pushed off has a flat bulb of applied pressure similar to that resulting from the cylinder-hammer technique.

Less commonly recognized, but widely used pressure-flaking techniques of the Stone Age, are those in which a special stone tool is used as a means of removing small, steep flakes.

The very fine trimming along the backs of some types of backed blades and microliths (see later chapters) can most easily be achieved by means of pressure applied with a 'fabricator' or with a *'lame écaillée'*.

Such a 'fabricator' consists of almost any irregular piece of flint or other stone which has a thick right-angle edge on it. This right-angle edge is held against the small flake which is to be trimmed, and pressure is applied. Minute flakes are then pushed off the edge of the large flake.

The right-angle edge of a flake used for this type of pressure flaking soon acquires a characteristic crushed appearance which shows that it has been used as a fabricator.

Pressure flaking by the *lame écaillée* technique is slightly different. A broken or snapped blade of flint or other stone is used to apply pressure along the flake to be trimmed by holding the latter down on a piece of bark or leather and pushing downwards with the broken edge of the *lame écaillée*. During the process very small, flat flakes are scaled off which give the *lame écaillée* its characteristic appearance.

In some of the very late Stone Age cultures small flakes and blades occur which have been made into saws by very fine denticulations along the edge. Experiment shows that the easiest way to make such a saw is to press out the little flakes with the fingernail, so that this may be regarded as yet another pressure-flaking technique.

One further highly specialized method of pressure flaking must be mentioned, and that is by means of a slit in a piece of dried raw hide.

During the closing stages of the Stone Age, small implements known as microliths are found in certain cultures. These tools could be made in a variety of ways, one of which is known as the 'micro-burin' technique. By this method a small, narrow blade-flake was notched in two places, on one side, and then the ends of the blade were broken off at the mid-points of the notches.

Although the removal of the end-pieces could be achieved by various methods, experiment suggests that one of the easiest and surest means of breaking them accurately is to pass the notched blade through a slit in a piece of hard raw hide until the centre point of the notch coincides with the slit. A slight half-turn of the flake will result in pressure being applied to the mid-point of the notch. This causes a pressure fracture with a minute bulb of applied pressure, and a curved or twisted flake scar.

We must now pass on to an examination of the ways in which Nature can simulate the types of human flaking which we have described, and consider what criteria, if any, can be used to distinguish human from natural flaking. Let me say at once that under certain very special conditions Nature can simulate human workmanship to an extraordinary degree.

In respect of the more advanced and highly specialized Stone Age cultures, there is no fear that confusion or mistakes will arise. In fact, this may be said of any stage of Stone Age cultures which have been found and studied in the occupation levels of cave deposits. For in such culture stages the various types of characteristic tools have been found under conditions where their connexion with man is beyond doubt, or where the natural conditions for their production by other than human agency is lacking. But, thus far, the majority of the earliest and most primitive of the Stone Age cultures have only been recovered from geological strata, and we must therefore examine carefully to make sure that the specimens attributed to them could not be due to natural, instead of human, agency.

There are not many natural conditions which give opportunity for the removal of flakes by the percussion method. Pieces of stone that are being carried down by the waters of a rapidly flowing stream may be hurled against other pieces that are firmly imbedded in the bottom of the river, or even against other pieces that are being carried down by the water. Pebbles on a sea-shore may be hurled by the waves against others that are lying on the beach. Both of these 'natural conditions' are often quoted as providing the possibility of flakes being produced by natural percussion. But in my opinion it is very rarely that flakes produced under these conditions could be mistaken for humanly made flakes. This is due to the fact that the production of a flake which will genuinely simulate a humanly produced percussion flake involves (1) a 'follow through' blow, combined with (2) the right amount of force relative to resistance, and (3) the right direction of blow when the resistance has been taken into account. Unless *all* these conditions are *simultaneously* met, the fractures that will result from two pieces of flint being hurled against each other could not possibly be mistaken for human workmanship. Were this not true, a pebbly sea-shore, after a storm, ought to yield thousands of *pseudo* 'humanly worked flakes'; and I have spent many hours on the shingle beach at Weymouth after a storm without finding one flake which could be seriously mistaken for a human artifact.

But we have seen that force applied by pressure has the same effect as force applied by percussion, *and it is by this means that Nature most often simulates the workmanship of man.* Geological deposits are subject to movements due to settling down, to landslips, to glaciation, and to other causes. A block of flint is firmly held in one part of the deposit and flints and other rocks held in another part of the deposit are pressed against it. Force is applied by pressure, and a flake with a bulb of applied pressure results. Even very large flakes with very large bulbs may be produced in this way.

Let us take another case. A flake is held firmly in the side of a slope, and down this slope slides a mass of debris containing other pieces of flint or other stones. The result will be that force is applied all along the exposed edge of the fixed flake, so that small flakes are pushed off. These will simulate humanly struck flakes, while on the firmly held piece of flint there will be seen flake scars that also suggest human workmanship.

How, then, can these results of pressure flaking by natural agency be distinguished from humanly made tools? Often they cannot. Consequently, many specimens that *may* be due to human workmanship, but which have been obtained from a geological stratum, have to be discarded as doubtful specimens.

Can any specimen from a geological stratum, then, be accepted as of human origin, unless it undoubtedly represents a definite and well-made implement of a type already known from the deposits? The answer is in the affirmative, for although flakes that have been produced by Nature cannot always be distinguished from those made by man, flakes that have definitely been made by man can often be distinguished from those made by Nature. Let me elucidate this statement.

Although Nature can press off flakes that are indistinguishable from others of human origin, and can also leave upon the block from which such flakes were removed flake scars that absolutely resemble human workmanship, such flaking will be all in *one* direction, owing to the nature of the conditions under which it was done. Long afterwards, a flake so trimmed by Nature may once again become imbedded and trimmed by pressure from another direction. But in the meantime the surfaces of the flake scars of the early period will almost certainly have become more or less weathered, so that their appearance will be different from that of the newer flake scars. Hence, although there may be evidence of trimming from more than one direction, it will be clear that the two periods of flaking were separated by a considerable interval of time.

When man—even in the most primitive stages of culture—trimmed a piece of stone to prepare it for use as a tool he almost invariably trimmed it from *several* different directions straight away. Thus, if a stone is found with evidence of having been flaked *from several directions*, and it can be shown that all such flaking was done at the same period (and not with long intervals separating the intervals of flaking) it is reasonably safe to assume that its flake scars are due to human workmanship. This supposition may be considered to become a certainty if, at the same place, not one but many specimens which satisfy this criterion are found associated together.

Besides these forms of fracture by natural agency, which simulate man's handiwork, there are other forms of natural fracture which do not do so and which therefore need never confuse the prehistorian once he has learned to recognize them.

Stones that are exposed to changes of temperature expand or contract according to whether the temperature is raised or lowered. If the temperature changes are *too sudden*, the strain is too great, and a fracture results; in exactly the same way that boiling water poured into a cold glass will break it.

Fractures in stone which are due to temperature changes are very common indeed and are termed thermal fractures. There are many forms of thermal fracture, but only one need concern us, for only one has a slight resemblance to human workmanship.

If a warm flint is exposed suddenly to very cold conditions—as when a severe frost comes on suddenly after a moderately warm day—the flint will often break in a way which forms a positive bulb on one piece and a negative bulb upon the other. Such positive and negative bulbs due to thermal action can always be distinguished from humanly made 'bulbs of percussion'. In the first place, a careful scrutiny will fail to reveal any point at which force was applied *along the edge of the flake* (or on the edge of a flake scar), whereas if a flake is removed by applied force, that force must have been applied from a point on the edge (see fig. 4*D* and 4*E*).

Secondly, such a thermal bulb, whether in positive or negative form, will, if closely examined, be found to have on its surface very asymmetrical rings like contour lines on a map. These lines are quite distinct from the much more symmetrical rings arising from applied force. This fact is illustrated in fig. 4*D*.

This discussion of flint fracture by man and by Nature could be continued almost indefinitely, but we must now leave it in order to consider other aspects of the interpretation of stone.

Every kind of geological deposit contains mineral and chemical constituents of one sort or another, many of which are soluble in water. If, therefore, any object lies in, or upon, a geological deposit which is exposed to, or which contains moisture (it does not matter whether it is humus, or sand, gravel, or clay), it is liable to be brought into contact with minerals in solution.

Different kinds of stone will react in different ways to the influence of the same chemical, or combination of chemicals, in solution. On the other hand, pieces of the *same* kind of stone will react differently to different chemicals, or combination of chemicals, in solution. It follows, too, that all sorts of different factors will play their part in controlling the speed with which reaction takes place. If the surface of a stone has been acted upon by two different chemicals in succession, the result on the stone will not be the same as if the second chemical were brought into contact with a piece of stone not previously affected by the first chemical. These statements are merely generalizations which indicate that, once a humanly worked piece of stone has found its way into a geological deposit, it may become subjected to all kinds of chemical influences which may very markedly alter its surface.

Flint is a stone which, owing to its composition, is remarkably susceptible to the action of certain chemicals. Furthermore, fresh flint contains a certain percentage of water, and if this dries out the nature of the flint changes considerably. Flint which has been altered in any way, either by chemical action, or by drying, is very susceptible to staining, and moisture which contains either minerals or chemicals in solution is a potent staining agent.

As a consequence of all this, fresh flint that has been broken up, either by man or by Nature, very seldom remains exactly as it was in its fresh condition, although the speed with which changes take place, as well as the exact nature of these changes, will vary according to the type of weathering to which it is exposed.

Very often these changes do not penetrate far into the flint, and if a piece of flint which shows a very altered surface is broken open, the interior is not infrequently found to be unaltered. The general name of 'patina' is given to the changed part of the flint, and the verb 'to patinate' is employed to describe the process of change.

Unstained patina is usually regarded as being invariably white, so that if a patina is not white, the colour is attributed to staining. Sometimes the staining is very superficial, sometimes it penetrates the whole of the patina.

The whole question of patina and patination is very little understood at present, but in spite of this, many geologists and prehistorians employ patina as a criterion of age. If a series of stone implements from a single deposit are found to be patinated in different ways they are often sorted into groups according to their state of patination, and the series is then subdivided upon this basis. A deeply patinated flint implement is considered to be much older than one less deeply patinated, and so on.

It is increasingly doubtful if there is any justification whatsoever for such methods, and until the subject of patina has been studied in very much greater detail, and is fully understood, the state of patination of stone implements *should not* be used for dating purposes, or for separating them into groups, even if they come from a single deposit.

Not a few cases are known of two broken halves of a single implement—which fit together perfectly—being found in the same deposit, only a few feet apart, on which the patinas are totally different.

Similarly, if two implements of flint were made by a prehistoric workman on the same day, one might have been made from a piece of freshly mined flint, and the other from a piece that had been exposed to weathering. If these two tools were subsequently imbedded in the same geological formation and subjected to identical chemical influences, they would not, necessarily, patinate the same way, because they were not made from identical material in the first instance.

I have treated this subject of patination at some length because the misuse of patina for dating purposes is very prevalent indeed in prehistoric studies.

I do not say that there may not be certain conditions under which it would be safe to employ patina as a criterion of age; especially when the subject has been properly studied, but at present it should only be used with the utmost caution, if at all.

So far, in this chapter, we have only been considering implements of stone and the fracture of stone. Prehistoric man also made considerable use of bone, antler, and to some extent of ivory, for his tools and weapons, more especially in certain of the later cultures towards the end of the Pleistocene. Under some conditions, particularly in acid soils, none of these materials survive, but under other conditions—for example, in cave deposits and in peat beds—implements made from these materials are beautifully preserved.

When any of these materials has been used to make a tool or implement, it is easy to recognize the fact, because of the shape and form of the specimen and also because the marks of cutting, polishing, and scraping can clearly be seen. The only non-human agency that sometimes leaves marks on these materials which could be confused with human workmanship are animals' teeth. Some of the larger rodents, and of course the various carnivorous animals, gnaw bones and antler. Occasionally, if a piece of one of these materials has been so gnawed, it is difficult to distinguish the marks from marks made by a stone tool. But of course animal-gnawing very seldom results in shapes that could be confused with humanly made implements.

There is one more subject connected with the interpretation of bone that we must consider briefly in this chapter, and that is the problem of 'fossilization'. Fresh bones contain not only water, but also animal fats and gelatine; but when bone is subjected to chemicals or minerals in solution, or is dried, it may become greatly changed. Under certain conditions a bone may become completely impregnated with minerals in a very short space of time; under other conditions it may retain a portion of its animal fats and gelatine for an almost indefinite period. Under still other conditions it may lose all its animal fats and gelatine and at the same time be subjected to such chemical action as will obliterate it completely; or, again, the whole bone may be entirely replaced by minerals, so that instead of having a bone that is impregnated with minerals we have an exact copy of the bone formed by the mineral itself.

The terms 'mineralization' and 'fossilization' are often employed interchangeably. Mineralization, strictly speaking, implies either impregnation with minerals or complete replacement; fossilization denotes that at least part of the animal fats and gelatine have been lost, but not necessarily that they have been replaced by anything else.

The state of preservation—mineralization or fossilization—of a bone, whether human or animal, does not alone give any real indication of its age. Frequently, however, a great age is attributed to a specimen simply because it is heavily mineralized or fossilized, and equally often a high antiquity is denied to some specimen because it is not heavily mineralized or fossilized.

Neither of these assumptions is justified on the basis of the present state of our knowledge.

The only use to which the state of preservation of a bone can be properly applied is a comparative one for use as contributory evidence. If, for example, it can be shown that in a given geological deposit bones are as a rule either fossilized or mineralized to some extent, and a perfectly unmineralized specimen is then found and there is *other* evidence of *a different nature* which also suggests that this bone does not really belong to the deposit, then its state of preservation can be used as contributory evidence. Taken alone, however, the degree of mineralization and fossilization of a specimen cannot be used as evidence of its age.

Nor does it by any means follow that because two bones from the same deposit are in a different state of preservation, they are of different age, as the following incident will show. At Bromhead's Site, Elmenteita, in 1927 we found two pieces of a human jaw some 30 feet apart, but in the same geological stratum. These two pieces fitted together perfectly and were unquestionably parts of the same jaw, yet one part was about twice as mineralized as the other.

During the past few years, some very important experimental work has been carried out by Dr. K. P. Oakley and his colleagues in connexion with fossil bones. This has come to be known as the 'Fluorine Test'.

Nearly all water in geological deposits is charged with a greater or lesser amount of a chemical called 'fluorine', and bones and teeth which lie in a damp deposit gradually absorb this chemical. Analysis of a very small amount of bone, drilled out of a fossil, will show the degree of fluorine content.

It sometimes happens that a geological deposit, such as a gravel bed, contains a number of fossil bones which are not all contemporary. Some of them may have become fossilized in some other deposit at a time long before the formation of the particular deposit in which they were found, and they may have been washed into that particular deposit in an already fossilized condition. Other bones, in the same deposit, may have been washed into the gravel when it was being laid down in an entirely fresh condition.

Clearly, it is most important to be able to find some method of distinguishing between the fossils of the two periods, and Dr. Oakley's researches have shown that in many cases this can be achieved by the test of fluorine analysis.

This type of investigation is only in its infancy, but it is likely to develop into a very important branch of prehistoric study as a means of checking conclusions based upon other lines of evidence.

To conclude this chapter we must briefly consider the significance of the state of preservation of a stone implement in determining its age.

It has already been mentioned that very many Stone Age implements are to be found in geological deposits such as river gravels, glacial outwash gravels, boulder clays, marine beaches, and so on.

Obviously, when Stone Age specimens have been incorporated by natural agencies in such a deposit they are liable to have been subjected to a greater or lesser degree of abrasion and damage, while, on the other hand, specimens which have become buried in a fine silt or clay soon after they were made will remain in quite a fresh condition. It follows, therefore, that the state of preservation of a stone implement is not in itself any indication of its age. But when a whole series of specimens are found in a single deposit and some of them are very much abraded and damaged, and others are in a much fresher condition, then it would *seem* to be a fair presumption that the fresher specimens are relatively younger than the more rolled ones in the same deposit.

Many prehistorians act upon this assumption and sort out stone tools found in a single geological deposit on the basis of their state of preservation alone, taking the more heavily rolled and weathered group as the older, and so on. In the majority of cases such a conclusion is probably justified, and yet it is a method which must be used with the utmost caution, as the following example will show.

At Warren Hill in Suffolk is a deposit which is very rich indeed in stone implements of many kinds, representing numerous culture stages. This deposit is a glacial outwash gravel, due to the melting of the ice during one of the major glacial advances over England. As this ice-sheet advanced, it picked up on its base stone implements from the land surface over which it passed, and also from the deposits through which it ploughed its way. Some of them were probably picked up many miles away, others only a few hundred yards from where they were eventually redeposited. Some of them were incorporated in the ice and were carried along intact, others merely adhered to the base of the ice-sheet and were much abraded in consequence.

As a result, at Warren Hill it is possible to find tools in every kind of state of preservation and belonging to every one of the cultures that antedated the advance of that particular ice-sheet, and no classification based upon the state of preservation would possibly result in a sorting out of the specimens belonging to the older cultures from those of the later ones, and we are provided with a valuable warning against making too much use of the 'state of preservation' for purposes of classification.

CHAPTER IV

The Uses of Stone and Bone Tools

IN the preceding chapter we discussed the fracture of flint and other
stone and the ways in which stone tools could be flaked. We also
noted how it was possible in most cases to distinguish between
stone deliberately flaked by man and stones flaked by natural
agencies. We must next examine the more important types of
stone and bone implements that were made and used by prehistoric
man and discuss their probable uses.

Students of Prehistory recognize many distinct specialized types
of stone implements to which they have given names. Sometimes
the names are purely descriptive of the shape of the tool, as, for
example, the word 'lunate', which is a name sometimes given to
a small crescentic type of stone implement. Other names are
intended rather to denote the use to which the particular tool is
believed to have been put by prehistoric man, as, for example, the
term 'scraper' for a tool type which was used for scraping.

In addition to the specialized tool types to which distinctive
names are given, prehistorians recognize that Stone Age man
frequently made use of rough, untrimmed flakes; such flakes nearly
always exhibit damage and chipping on one or more of the edges,
representing damage to the edge due to use. These flakes are
usually referred to as 'utilized flakes', but occasionally, when a
particular type of usage can be established, certain types of utilized
flakes are grouped together under a descriptive term such as
'fabricator'.

In the vast majority of cases a single site will yield a number of
different types of stone implement in association—sometimes also
accompanied by objects made from materials other than stone—
under conditions which show that they were all used by a single
family or group of people living together. Such an associated
group of implements is spoken of as an 'industry'. For example,
all the specimens found at a single level in a cave or rock-shelter
will be spoken of as the industry of that level, while the specimens
from other levels will be treated as representing different industries.

When a number of 'industries' have been found which are very
similar to each other we say that they belong to the same 'culture',

even if they are found hundreds of miles apart. But it has to be remembered that the fact that two industries belong to the same culture does not necessarily mean that they are of the same age. There is every reason to believe that some cultures survived longer in one region than in another.

Sometimes, too, a single culture persisted for an immense period of time without any real change or development taking place. When this happened we may have a whole series of industries belonging to this culture which are more or less identical but which were not contemporary. More often, however, a culture slowly and gradually developed and evolved, and as this process took place new tool types were invented and new techniques of flaking were evolved.

Under such conditions it is customary to divide the culture into what are termed 'stages', each stage being typified by the appearance of new variations of essential tool types or even of entirely new forms of tools. In such cases the earlier stages of the culture will differ both in age and in their content from the later stages of the same culture.

Some of the Stone Age cultures had a very extended range indeed, as, for example, the Chelles-Acheul or Hand-axe culture, which is found all over Africa, over most of South-west Europe, and over parts of the Near East and India. A widespread culture such as this is liable to have special local developments in the different geographical zones where it is found, and it is usual, nowadays, to preface the cultural name with a descriptive term indicating its geographical position. For example, we speak of the South African Chelles-Acheul culture and the East African Chelles-Acheul culture, to distinguish these variations from those of the area in which the culture was first named—in France. Naturally, it follows that Stage 3, shall we say, of the Chelles-Acheul culture in South Africa is not necessarily identical to, or the contemporary of, Stage 3 of the French Chelles-Acheul.

Not infrequently we find that two entirely distinct and separate cultures were present in the same area at the same time, sometimes even developing and evolving side by side in the same areas over a long period of time, in just the same way that in Africa today we have a European and an indigenous African culture existing side by side. When this happened in the past the results were not very different from those which occur under similar conditions today. Each culture tended to borrow certain ideas from the other, with the more primitive and less developed culture borrowing more, while the more evolved culture borrowed less or even nothing.

In the past, it has been customary among some students of Prehistory to refer to certain cultures as 'core cultures' and to others as 'flake cultures'. The idea underlying these terms was that some cultures (for example, the Chelles-Acheul Hand-axe culture) had a predominance of what were called 'core tools', while others (for example, the Mousterian) had a predominance of flake tools. *In reality there is no such thing as a 'core culture' or a 'flake culture'*, and the majority of prehistorians are today discarding the use of these misleading terms.

Similarly, in the past there has been a tendency to apply cultural names to describe certain techniques of making stone tools simply because certain cultures used those techniques to a marked degree. But as the various techniques for making stone implements had an immense range, not only in time but also in geographical distribution, and were not confined to any one culture, it has nowadays been realized that it is better not to use cultural terms for techniques of flaking.

For example, the Levalloisian culture of Europe made use of a very specialized technique in which a block of flint was carefully prepared with a view to knocking off one large flake of a particular type. For a long time the type of flake knocked off has been called a 'Levallois flake', and the type of core from which it was struck a 'Levallois core'. But, in fact, it is well known that those types of flake and core both occur in several cultures that are quite distinct from the Levalloisian and which probably have no connexion whatsoever with the Levalloisian. It is now, therefore, generally recognized that it is wiser to speak of the 'prepared core' technique and of 'flakes from prepared cores' so as not to confuse the Levalloisian culture with others, such as the Sangoan in West and Central Africa, or certain stages of the South African Chelles-Acheul, which made use of the same technique, but whose origin is probably quite distinct.

Before we proceed to discuss the principal tool types used by Stone Age man and to consider their probable uses, let us briefly consider the essential requirements of a primitive hunting people; we shall then be better able to understand the various types of Stone Age tool and see to what extent they fulfil these requirements.

A primitive hunter and his family need weapons for hunting and killing wild animals; sharp cutting tools which can be used for skinning and cutting up the animals when killed; cutting tools which can be used to shape wood for spear shafts, etc.; tools which can be used in the preparation of skins of animals as garments for protection against the weather; and sharp-pointed tools for digging up edible roots and for digging holes in the ground to serve as game pits.

One of the earliest known humanly made cultures occurs in Africa and goes by the name of Kafuan. This culture dates back to the very beginning of the Pleistocene and comes before the earliest stages of the Hand-axe culture. (In Europe pre-Chellean cultures probably exist, but they are still a matter of great controversy and will be discussed in the next chapter.)

The tools of the Kafuan culture are simple to a degree, and consist mainly of water-worn pebbles (or sometimes nodules of chert or lumps of quartzite) from which one or two flakes have been struck in order to make a sharp, jagged edge. What possible use could such exceedingly simple tools have served? To find an answer it is necessary to try to visualize life at that period.

Man had only just emerged from a sub-human stage and was still scarcely more than a wild animal. We can imagine him using broken branches of trees and even the larger limb bones of animals as rough clubs, but it is exceedingly doubtful if he had any real hunting weapon. Probably, for the most part, he lived upon nuts and fruits and upon such things as snails and small rodents, birds' eggs, and fledgeling birds, while he was also, probably, to some extent a scavenger.

There were plenty of large carnivorous animals about, and he could compete with the other scavengers for what was left from the kill of a lion or other large beast of prey. But—and it is a very important but—in order to do this he had to have some sort of cutting instrument, for neither man's teeth, nor his finger-nails, are of any use for tearing through the hide of an animal of any size.

With the jagged cutting edge of a Kafuan pebble tool, or the comparable tools of the pre-Chellean in Europe, man could have jaggedly cut through the hide of a dead animal and could have roughly cut up the meat into chunks of a size that could be eaten. So much, then, for the probable use of the simplest of all human stone implements, the Kafuan pebble tools.

The stone tools of the Hand-axe culture consist of hand-axes, utilized flakes, and, in the more advanced stages of the culture, of cleavers, bolas stones, and scrapers.

Hand-axes consist of roughly pointed tools varying in length from about four inches to as much as eighteen inches. The essential characters of a hand-axe are a sharp-pointed end (sometimes rounded), a cutting edge along one or both sides, and a butt which may be formed by a natural pebble or nodular surface or may have been trimmed into a further cutting edge. Experiments suggest that the hand-axe was a kind of general utility tool rather than a weapon—although some of the more advanced forms may possibly have served as weapons, hafted as spear-points.

Experiments have shown that with a hand-axe it is possible to dig up wild edible roots, to dig holes to serve as pit-traps, to dig along the burrows of rodents until the nest chamber is reached, to chop the smaller bones of animals when cutting up a beast, and, of course, to cut up meat. It is also possible, though rather more difficult, to use the cutting edge of a hand-axe to sharpen wooden stakes and as a clumsy skinning tool. Thus the hand-axe served for a number of the needs of a primitive hunting people.

It has also been shown by experiment that the irregular flakes knocked off in making a hand-axe can be used—more easily than the hand-axe itself—to sharpen wooden stakes and to cut skin and flesh; furthermore, on living-sites of the Hand-axe culture, close examination shows that a high proportion of the waste flakes bear evidence of such usage.

Since these flakes have not been particularly shaped into specialized tool types they are ranked as 'utilized flakes', but they probably represent as much an essential part of Hand-axe man's tools as do the actual hand-axes.

In the more advanced stages of the Hand-axe culture a tool type known as a 'cleaver' makes its appearance. Cleavers in many ways resemble hand-axes, but in place of a sharp point at one end (or a curved, sharp cutting edge, as the case may be) they have a more or less straight cutting edge at right angles to the long axis of the tool, and this cutting edge is usually very sharp. Experiments show that the cleaver makes an ideal skinning and flaying tool, and, once the cleaver was invented, it is probable that hand-axes were used less for skinning and more for other purposes.

Bolas stones consist of roughly spherical stones which may have been naturally shaped and later selected by man, or, in some cases, which show signs of having been carefully made by man. The bolas as a weapon for hunting is still in use in Patagonia and among some Eskimo tribes. The principle upon which it works is that the stones are attached to the ends of leather thongs. A variable number of stones, from two to five, may be used, and each stone is attached to its own thong, and all the thongs are linked together at one point.

Such a weapon is thrown at the legs of a running animal, and when the bolas comes against the legs of the animal—because the stones are of different weights and the thongs of different lengths —the thongs wind round at different speeds, and so become tangled up and bring the animal to the ground.

In the more advanced stages of the Hand-axe culture we also find roughly made convex and concave scrapers. Convex scrapers (by analogy with present-day people using stone tools, such as the Australian aborigines) were used for dressing and scraping the inner surface of hides for the purpose of turning them into leather. Concave scrapers, which consist of a rough flake from which a small notch has been chipped out on one side, make excellent tools for finishing off the shaft of a wooden spear or the handle of a club after it has been roughly shaped with a cutting tool, and were Stone Age man's equivalent of the carpenter's spoke-shave.

Both concave and convex scrapers occur in almost every known Stone Age culture, although the exact shape and form varies to some extent in the different cultures.

When we turn to the stone tools of the Clacton culture and of its probable derivative, the Tayacian, which we shall deal with more fully in a later chapter, it is not so easy to speak about definite tool types. This is in large part due to the fact that these cultures have not so far been intensively studied and also because the forms of the various tools do not in the main suggest any special uses so that descriptive names have not been given to them. A considerable variety of tool types does, however, occur, and an assemblage usually includes numerous scrapers, a number of pointed tools, and some excellent crude knives. There is also evidence to suggest that many of the cores and lumps of flint from which flakes were knocked off in order to make the smaller tools were themselves used as crude chopping tools.

The types of stone tools found in an assemblage representing an industry of either a Clacton or a Tayacian culture would serve most of the purposes we outlined as the hypothetical needs of a primitive hunting people, except that no weapon for hunting seems to be included. On the other hand, there is evidence from the type site of the Clacton culture—Clacton-on-Sea—that roughly pointed wooden spears were made.

By comparison with the Hand-axe culture, the Clacton-Tayacian complex is much less developed or specialized and it is reasonable

to believe that the makers of these cultures may have been much
less clever craftsmen and less skilled in the flaking of stone.

The Levalloisian culture has one very specialized tool type that
is commonly referred to as a 'Levallois flake'. This is a large flake,
generally pointed, that was knocked off a specially prepared core,
on which the face of the flake to be struck had been carefully
prepared beforehand by the removal of a series of small flakes.
Thus, when the large flake was knocked off, it required little or no
additional trimming to turn it into the required tool. It has been
referred to above as a very specialized tool because the making of
one involved a complicated and special process, but as a tool it was
probably just as much a general utility tool as the hand-axe of the
Chelles-Acheul culture. A proportion of 'Levallois flakes', however,
could have been, and probably were, hafted on to wooden shafts
to make formidable spear-points.

The 'Levallois flake' type of tool is not confined to the Levalloisian culture, but also occurs in a number of other cultures, as
we shall see in the relevant chapters.

Some stages of the Levalloisian culture also made use of hand-
axes, an idea that was probably borrowed from the contemporary
Chelles-Acheul culture, and there are also side-scrapers and
occasional burins or chisels. (Burins will be discussed later in
this chapter, as they are more typically tools of some other
cultures.)

Mousterian points and Mousterian side-scrapers are the most
typical tools of the Mousterian culture. The former are small and
roughly triangular and are usually carefully trimmed to a very
sharp point. Their exact use is not certain, but it is possible that
they were hafted on wooden shafts to make spear and lance-points.
Mousterian side-scrapers are merely a specialized cultural variant
of the ubiquitous scraper. At some stages the Mousterian culture
also has tools known as 'Audi points'. These are very like some of
the knife-blades of the Clacton culture.

The Mousterian culture, like the Levalloisian, at certain stages
also adopted the hand-axe idea from the Chelles-Acheul culture,
but these hand-axes are usually made by a different technique
from that of the Acheulean—a technique that included a great
deal of step-flaking.

In the North African variant of the Mousterian culture, known
as the Aterian, there is a further very specialized tool known as an
'Aterian point'. This is like a triangular Mousterian point, but has
a 'tang' at the base to facilitate hafting as a lance-head, and there

is little doubt that it served as a reasonably efficient hunting weapon.

In Europe, western Asia, round the Mediterranean basin, and also in parts of East Africa, there was a group of cultures, which we shall discuss in more detail in the appropriate chapter, which had a wider range of specialized stone tools than any of the preceding ones. This culture complex is sometimes referred to in general terms as the 'Blade and Burin complex'. The principal types of stone tools, in addition to scrapers, which we have seen are ubiquitous, are backed blades, burins, two-edged blades, sinew frayers, fabricators, *lames écaillées*, awls, and (in some but not all groups of the culture complex) small crescentic specimens known as lunates or crescents.

Backed blades are of infinite variety in shape and size, ranging from large specimens four or more inches in length to others barely two inches long. All are characterized by having one edge sharp and more or less straight, and the opposite edge either wholly or partially blunted. In their most typical form, these backed blades closely resemble the blades of modern penknives.

Experiments have shown that backed blades—even the smallest —are eminently suitable for skinning animals and for sharpening wooden points. (I have myself skinned and cut up a Thompson's gazelle—a creature about the size of a goat—with a single backed blade not quite two inches long.)

Such blades, with one side blunted so that finger pressure can be exerted, were probably never hafted. It seems likely that the two-edged knife-blades were hafted by means of gum or resin, much in the manner of the two-edged obsidian blades used by the native people of the Admiralty Islands today. A pointed two-edged blade so hafted serves admirably either as a knife or dagger.

Just as the backed blades or knives of the Upper Palaeolithic period may be regarded as the prototypes of the knife-blades we still use today, so the burins of the same period are the prototypes. of our woodworking chisels.

As we have seen, the backed blade with its sharp cutting edge and blunted back made an ideal tool for skinning and for sharpening wood, and indeed for all the purposes for which we use knives, but the edge of a flint (or other stone) knife-blade was too brittle to be used satisfactorily for working *across* the grain of wood, or for cutting bone or antler and other similar hard materials. For this purpose a sharp edge is needed, but it must also have thickness and solidity.

A very great variety of burin or chisel types has been recognized and described by prehistorians, but we need not concern ourselves in detail with them here. It will suffice to say that the essential element of a stone chisel or burin was the making of a thick-set, but sharp, edge at the end of a flake or blade by removing one or more small flakes longitudinally down one or both edges of the blade.

Experiment shows that with such a burin, wood can be cut across the grain, and that bone and antler can also be cut. This is very important—for it was only when the burin became a *common* tool of the Stone Age cultures that we find bone and antler and even ivory being utilized on a big scale to make awls, harpoons, arrow-points, etc. In other words, it was the invention of the burin that made it possible for prehistoric man to extend the range of materials over which he had mastery and which he could turn into weapons.

Before we pass on to the other tool types used by the 'blade and burin' culture complex, we must briefly refer to one other cutting tool which begins to make its appearance at this stage—that is the saw.

Many flakes and blades with irregularly serrated edges—due to damage in use—are often mistakenly labelled saws, but true saws do also occur. These consist of flakes or blades which have serrations along one cutting edge, made by the removal of tiny flakes in *alternate* directions. As we saw in the last chapter, experiment shows that a flint saw of this type can be most easily made with the finger-nail.

Awls are pointed tools in which the point has been prepared by careful flaking to a thick-set point rather than one with knife-like cutting edges. Experiment shows that they would have been very useful for piercing leather. 'Fabricator' is the name given to a rather special type of utilized flake which exhibits a peculiar crushed effect along one or more right-angle edges. These crushed right-angle edges on rough flakes are sometimes on the butt ends of waste flakes, sometimes along the edges of a flake struck from a core for the purpose of 'rejuvenating' it, and, in fact, on any kind of flake which presents a suitable right-angle edge. Experiment shows that just such crushing or bruising can be duplicated by using the right-angle edge of a flake to push off small flakes in the course of making the blunt back of a backed blade or of a crescent, etc.

A variant of this type of fabricator is the *lame écaillée*, which consists of part of a blade flake snapped at right angles to its long axis and with the right-angle edge between the fracture and the main flake surface used for pushing off flakes. In *lames écaillées* the crushed and battered edge is accompanied by a scaling of the flake surface in a characteristic manner which gives the tool its name. Experiment shows that the *lame écaillée* is an excellent tool for the quick manufacture of small backed blades and crescents.

Sinew frayers are specialized tools which occur in at least some of the Upper Palaeolithic cultures. A broken blade flake has small flakes removed along the broken edge *from* the multi-flake and *towards* the main flake surface, obliquely and irregularly. This results in an irregular jagged edge which experiment has shown to be an ideal tool for fraying sinew from animals in preparation of sinew-thread for sewing leather.

In some of the cultures of the Upper Palaeolithic, small objects called lunates (also sometimes described as crescents) occur. They vary in length from about two inches to less than half an inch and are characterized by having a straight and very sharp cutting edge on one side, and a curved and carefully blunted edge on the other. This type of tool becomes increasingly common in the Mesolithic period, where it is accompanied by many other small geometric forms, including trapezes, triangles, and U-shaped forms.

Discoveries in East Africa have shown that at least one of the uses of the lunate was as barbs for wooden arrow-points, and experiments have proved that with a wooden point barbed with lunates and hafted in a reed shaft it is possible to kill a small antelope relatively easily. After penetrating the target, the barbs lever out and remain in the wound, while the wooden head and shaft fall off so that they could presumably be refitted with further barbs.

By using a fabricator it is possible to make lunates, from suitable small blade flakes, at the rate of about one a minute. They can also be made by means of a small hammer-stone, by using a *lame écaillée*, or by means of the special micro-burin technique that was so extensively used in the Mesolithic period.

In some of the Upper Palaeolithic cultures which have the usual backed blades, burins, etc., there are also found beautifully made triangular, lozenge, and leaf-shaped tools worked carefully by pressure flaking over the whole or part of one or both faces. These very specialized tools probably represent spear, lance, and even arrow-points. They are most common in the Solutrean of Europe and in the Stillbay and Magosian of Africa.

In discussing the uses of burins and saws we have spoken of harpoons made from bone, antler, and ivory, and also of bone points.

Bone and antler, and to some extent ivory, points were extensively used in some Upper Palaeolithic cultures. Some of the bone points had split bases, some bevelled bases, and both types were probably used as the tips of either arrows or lances. The so-called harpoons, which became very common in the Magdalenian culture, consist of long points of bone or antler with very carefully made barbs and usually either a bulbous swelling or else a perforated hole near the base.

The use of the word harpoon to describe these weapons is liable to make the reader think that these weapons were essentially used for spearing fish, turtles, seals, and other aquatic creatures, because this is the usual idea of the use of harpoons.

The essential character of a harpoon is that the head is *loosely* fitted into a socket on the shaft and that the head is connected to the shaft by a long cord which is fastened to the harpoon at the perforation or at the bulbous projection. The principle is that after the head of the weapon has become imbedded in the flesh of the hunted creature it becomes detached from the shaft but remains linked to it by the cord.

While this type of weapon is of special value in catching fish, turtles, seals, and other water fauna, it is also still used by some hunting peoples for catching small antelopes and other small game. In such cases, when the wounded animal runs away with the head of the 'harpoon' sticking into it, it trails the shaft along behind it, since it is attached by a thong. Sooner or later the shaft gets caught up in vegetation and acts as an anchor, so that the hunter can catch up with the animal and kill it. It is necessary, therefore, to remember that the bone and antler harpoons of the Upper Palaeolithic may have been used for hunting as well as for fishing.

I have not in this chapter attempted to describe the uses of all the tool types of the Stone Age cultures of the Pleistocene, but after this general outline we may now conveniently pass on to a fuller discussion of the known cultures.

CHAPTER V

The Lower Palaeolithic Cultures

THE chapter of the earth's history known as the Pleistocene, which we have already discussed in an earlier section can be roughly divided into three periods: the Lower, Middle, and Upper Pleistocene.

The Lower Pleistocene may be taken to be the period from the beginning of the Pleistocene, up to, and including, the interglacial period between the Günz and Mindel glaciations and the comparable period of time elsewhere in the world. That is to say, in Africa and parts of Asia, it ends with the conclusion of the first interpluvial period (that between the Kageran and Kamasian pluvials), and with the final stages of the first interglacial period in the Himalayas.

The Middle Pleistocene covers the period from the beginning of the Mindel glaciation to the end of the Riss glaciation and, of course, the comparable period in the time-scale in other areas. In Africa, for instance, it covers the period from the beginning of the Kamasian pluvial to the end of the Kanjeran pluvial, while in Asia it covers the second and third major pluvials and second and third glaciations of the Himalayas.

The Upper Pleistocene covers the period from the end of the Riss glaciation, and comparable climatic phases elsewhere, to the end of the Pleistocene.

The evolution of human cultures in the Stone Age proceeded at an ever-increasing rate, and in consequence the story of the Upper Pleistocene is much more complicated than that of the Lower and Middle Pleistocene periods.

In this chapter, which deals with the true Lower Palaeolithic, we shall cover both the Lower and Middle Pleistocene periods, while two further chapters will be necessary to discuss the evolution of culture of the Upper Pleistocene period. Even on this basis only the barest introduction to the cultures can be given, and those who wish to know more must read some of the more specialized works listed in the bibliography.

The earliest known evidence of humanly made stone tools (in the Lower Pleistocene) is better documented in Africa than in Europe, and we will therefore start with that continent.

CULTURES OF THE LOWER PLEISTOCENE

(a) *The Kafuan and Oldowan Cultures.* In East Africa, and also in other parts of the continent, such as South Africa, Angola, and North Africa, there are to be found in geological deposits which belong to the Kageran pluvial, at the very beginning of the Pleistocene, pebbles (and sometimes also nodules of chert and lumps of rock) that have been very crudely flaked so as to give them one rough and jagged cutting edge. These tools are commonly referred to in the literature as 'Pebble Tools' because the vast majority are made from water-worn pebbles, but their essential character lies not so much in the fact that they were made from pebbles, as in the fact that very rough choppers were made from suitably sized pieces of raw material.

Man's teeth and finger-nails are not suitable for cutting and tearing the skin of animals, and it was probably only when he invented these rough chopping tools that he could really begin to become fully carnivorous in his habits.

A proportion of the forms attributed to the earliest Kafuan culture (a term first used by E. J. Wayland in Uganda) are not unquestionably of human workmanship, but there is no doubt whatsoever about the later Kafuan forms, nor of the Oldowan (see fig. 5) culture types which are developed from them.

There is evidence, too, from sites like Olduvai Gorge, that the earliest stages of the great Chelles-Acheul culture are directly evolved from the Oldowan. The Kafuan and Oldowan cultures of Africa are in fact not only pre-Chellean in the time-scale, but they are also ancestral to the Chelles-Acheul culture.

(b) *The pre-Chellean of Europe.* In Europe the evidence for the existence of stone tools in deposits of the Lower Pleistocene is still a matter of controversy. The late Mr. Reid Moir of Ipswich excavated many hundreds, if not thousands, of supposedly humanly worked flints from deposits known as the 'Stone Bed' and the 'Bone Bed' beneath the crag deposits of East Anglia. These two deposits beneath the crags are in reality old land surfaces of Lower Pleistocene age, and Mr. Reid Moir claimed to have identified a number of very early cultures from these deposits to which he gave the names of Icenian, Darmsdenian, and pre-Chellean.

In my earlier editions of this book I accepted Mr. Reid Moir's conclusions, but more mature consideration has convinced me that the available evidence does not warrant these subdivisions. It is more than likely that primitive humans were present in Europe

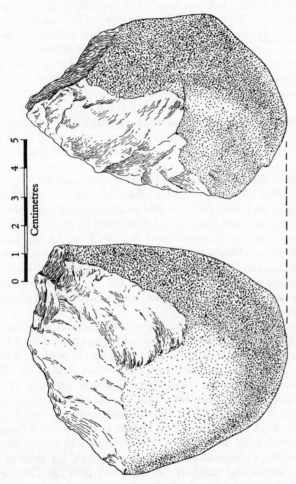

Fig. 5. Pre-Chellean tool of the Oldowan culture
From Leakey, *Olduwai Gorge*, by permission of Cambridge University Press

during the Lower Pleistocene, just as they were in Africa, and
certainly a proportion of the specimens from the sub-crag deposits
appear to be humanly flaked and cannot be regarded merely as the
result of natural forces, but the most that can safely be said at
present is that some evidence exists for a single pre-Chellean culture
in Europe during the Lower Pleistocene, as it is now defined (or the
Upper Pliocene, according to some of the earlier definitions).

A few of the specimens from the sub-crag deposits strongly recall
the 'Pebble Tools' of the Kafuan and Oldowan, but this resemblance may mean nothing more than that this was the obvious form
in which any human would make his first stone tools. Indeed, it
must be constantly borne in mind that although simple pebble
chopping tools *without any more elaborate forms* are typical of the
Kafuan and Oldowan, similar tools continued to be made and used
by the makers of much more advanced cultures, just as we ourselves still use candles although we also have electric light.

In Europe, after the crag deposits which overlie the so-called
Suffolk Bone Bed and Norfolk Stone Bed had been laid down, there
was a period of warm, wet climate which resulted in the formation
of what is known as the Cromer forest bed, in East Anglia, and
comparable deposits elsewhere. This warm period was the interglacial just before the Mindel glaciation, and in some text-books
this used to be regarded as the beginning of the Pleistocene period,
but on the basis of our present definition it comes at the end of the
Lower Pleistocene.

In my earlier editions I described a culture called Cromerian,
consisting in the main of immense flakes which are to be found in
quantity at low tide along the foreshore at Cromer, in Norfolk, and
which are supposed to be derived from the Cromer forest bed. If
this explanation is true, then these flakes represent an early and
primitive culture (possibly ancestral to the Clactonian). But a good
deal of doubt has been thrown on the question recently, and it is
still not certain that the Cromerian flakes are in fact derived from
the Cromer forest bed. It seems better, therefore, to regard the
authenticity of the Cromerian culture as 'not proven' for the time
being. Very careful and extensive excavations into the Cromer
forest bed, under the cliffs at Cromer, are needed before the
question can be fully settled.

On the other hand, there is some evidence of a very few crude
hand-axes being found *in situ* in the Cromer forest bed. These
specimens have been claimed to represent an early phase of the
Chellean stage of the great Hand-axe culture. They are not,

however, much more developed in form than the more advanced specimens of the Oldowan culture and are made from rough, rather elongate nodules of flint. More than anything else, these specimens appear to represent a European offshoot of the Oldowan culture, and they may be termed either European Oldowan or late pre-Chellean. In my earlier edition I referred to these implements as Chellean 1, but until a much larger series has been found it seems better to regard the Cromer forest bed specimens as pre-Chellean.

The so-called Harrisonian eoliths of the Kent plateau gravels are of very doubtful human origin, and the same must be said of most of the other material in Europe which has been claimed to represent stone tools of the Lower Pleistocene period (as now defined).

In Asia the famous deposits of the Choukoutien cave near Peking, which yielded the skulls of Peking man, were for a long time regarded as of Lower Pleistocene age. This, however, was based on the definition which regarded the Pleistocene as beginning at about the time that the Cromer forest bed was formed in East Anglia. On the basis of the new definition (now accepted internationally), which we are following in this book, the earliest deposits at Choukoutien are of Middle Pleistocene age, and we shall therefore consider the tools made by Peking man in the next section of this chapter.

The same is true of the earliest known culture from North India, the Soan, and, in fact, on the basis of the new definition, there is as yet no evidence of Stone Age tools belonging to the Lower Pleistocene period except in Africa, and possibly in England and Western Europe.

CULTURES OF THE MIDDLE PLEISTOCENE

(c) *The Chellean Stage of the Chelles-Acheul Culture.* The Middle Pleistocene period is taken to cover the period from the beginning of the second glaciation—the Mindel—and comparable climatic changes elsewhere, e.g. the Kamasian pluvial in Africa, up to and including the third glaciation, the Riss, and its contemporary climatic phases such as the Kanjeran pluvial in Africa. It thus covers a long period occupied by two major glaciations and one long interglacial period.

In Europe this period has been fairly intensively studied, and we have a clear picture of the culture sequences, although a good deal of detail still remains to be worked out.

We have seen that in Europe the deposits formed during the warm period preceding the Mindel glaciation contain elements of a culture which we have termed pre-Chellean, or European Oldowan. Naturally, the onset of the glaciation was not sudden or catastrophic but slow and gradual, and it was a long time, for instance, before the advancing glaciers reached East Anglia and the Thames Valley region. As the glaciation advanced, these regions were, for a time, still habitable under subarctic conditions, and it

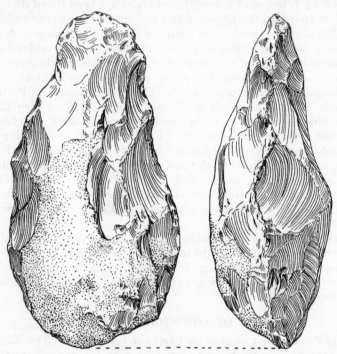

Fig. 6.   An early Chellean type of hand-axe
(reduced to about ⅔)

was at this time that the earliest stages of the Chellean culture appeared.

Unfortunately, when the glaciers, at length, came down southwards, they obliterated most of the old land surface and destroyed a great deal of evidence, but we can conclude that the Chellean culture was present during the period of subarctic conditions, because crude hand-axes of the culture were caught up in the advancing ice-sheets and scratched and carried considerable distances. When the glaciers finally melted in the next interglacial period, these tools were deposited in the glacial outwash gravels and also in river gravels, which were formed by rivers swollen with water from the melting ice-sheets.

In these deposits which were formed as the ice-sheets retreated, but which contain material that belongs to the period before the ice-sheets reached their fullest development (since it is evident that

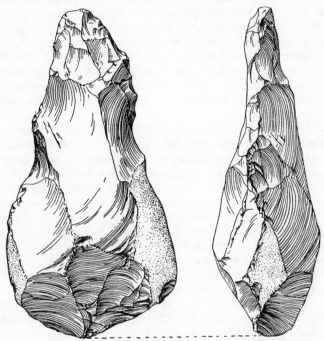

Fig. 7.   A late Chellean type of hand-axe
(reduced to ½)

it was caught up and often scratched by the moving ice), we find crude hand-axes representing the early stage of the Chelles-Acheul culture and, in addition, also a number of large oblong flakes which have, in the past, been classified as Clactonian Stage 1. We must briefly consider whether this view was really justified and upon what evidence it was based.

In an earlier chapter I have referred to the fact that there has been *a good deal of confusion between techniques of flint flaking and actual Stone Age cultures*, and it seems likely, from the evidence now available, that many of the specimens that were formerly attributed to Stage 1 of the Clactonian culture have nothing to do with the Clactonian culture at all. The true Clactonian culture, as we shall see presently, is characterized by rather peculiar assemblages of tools, but one of the most striking things about it is that nearly every flake was obtained by a technique which results in a large semi-cone of percussion instead of a rounded bulb of percussion. There is usually, also, a markedly wide angle between what is called the striking platform and the main flake surface. We know now that these characters were due to the use of a block-on-block technique of flaking which was *by no means confined to the making of the Clactonian culture.*

Unfortunately, these wide-angle flakes with large semi-cones of percussion were regarded—for a long time—as the 'hall-mark' of the Clactonian culture. The typical site of Clactonian culture at Clacton-on-Sea is ascribed to the interglacial period between the Mindel and Riss glaciations, and when, therefore, flakes with what was at that time regarded as the 'hall-mark' of the Clactonian culture—i.e. wide-angle, unfaceted striking platforms and large semi-cones of percussion—were found in deposits of the previous glaciation, they were regarded as representing an earlier stage of the Clactonian and described as Clactonian Stage 1. Moreover, they were separated from the hand-axes found in the same deposit, which were regarded, and rightly, as belonging to an early stage of the Chelles-Acheul culture.

Since the glacial deposits in which these hand-axes and flakes with wide angles and large semi-cones of percussion occurred were obviously very much churned up by ice action, it seemed reasonable to ascribe the association of the two types to this disturbance, and thus to account for their intimate association in this way, while attributing them to distinct and different cultures. It should, however, have been realized that among these so-called Clactonian Stage 1 flakes there were no real Clactonian tool types.

Subsequently, in Portugal, in North Africa, and in South Africa, well outside the range of the ice-sheets, similar primitive hand-axes, associated with large flakes with wide-angle butts and semi-cones due to the use of the block-on-block technique of flaking, were found together under conditions which made it impossible to think that their association was due to the mixing-up effect of ice action.

This led the Abbé Breuil and others to speak of a 'Clacto-Abbevillean', or Clacto-Chellean culture, although some, at least, of those who used these terms were emphatic that they did not mean to imply that the assemblages referred to were the result of any contact between the Clactonian and Chellean (or Abbevillean) cultures.

It is now clear that the Chellean culture (or Abbevillean, as French writers, following the Abbé Breuil, prefer to call it) must, in the light of our present knowledge, be regarded as a culture in which rough hand-axes are associated with numerous flakes resulting from a block-on-block technique. Such flakes are often indistinguishable from the *waste products* of a site of the true Clactonian culture, but must not, by themselves, be regarded as evidence of the Clactonian culture.

In Europe there is little evidence at present upon which any subdivisions in the Chellean stage of the great Hand-axe culture can be firmly established. This is in part due to the fact that the deposits in which most of the specimens are found are secondary deposits such as river gravels and glacial outwash gravels, in which specimens, possibly representing several distinct stages of the culture, antedating the formation of the gravels, were all caught up together.

It is also probably in part due to the fact that the climate of Europe during the time when the Chellean stage of the Hand-axe culture flourished was not very attractive, so that only a small proportion of the people who made the culture lived in what was the outermost fringe of their zone of occupation.

(*d*) *The Chellean Phase of the Chelles-Acheul Culture in Africa.* It was the African continent which was the centre of development of the great Hand-axe culture (with South-west Europe and parts of Asia as far as India as outlying provinces), and it is in Africa that the slow and gradual evolution of the culture can best be studied and understood.

In Tanganyika Territory, East Africa, there is a long and deep gorge known as Olduvai Gorge, which cuts through and exposes to view a series of deposits over 300 feet thick. These beautifully stratified deposits are not only rich in well-preserved fossil animal remains—which makes it possible to date them—but they also contain an incredible wealth of Stone Age tools at different levels, from the very base to the very top.

The main deposits at Olduvai fall into four divisions, known as Beds 1, 2, 3, and 4; Bed 1 being at the base. Beds 1 and 2 are regarded as belonging to the Kamasian pluvial period, which is roughly equivalent to the Mindel glaciation of Europe, if the history of glacial-pluvial correlation set out in an earlier chapter is accepted. Bed 3 represents an interpluvial period that occurred between the Kamasian and Kanjeran, and on the glacial-pluvial correlation hypothesis is roughly equivalent to the Mindel-Riss interglacial, while Bed 4 would be equivalent to the Riss glaciation.

The first unmistakable signs of the emergence of the Chellean stage of the Hand-axe culture are found at the base of Bed 2, and successive evolutionary stages can be found in three further clearly defined stratigraphical levels.

In the highest levels of Bed 2 the transition from the Chellean to the Acheulean phase of the Hand-axe culture takes place, but the main stages of the Chellean phase must be briefly summarized, before discussing this development.

Chellean Stage 1 is characterized by thick-set and very crudely made hand-axes which represent only a slight advance on the simple pebble tools of the Oldowan culture, many examples of which are also present, showing that the Chellean is a direct derivative of the Oldowan.

In Stage 2, however, there is evidence of much more careful and skilled tool-making, and the characteristic hand-axe of this stage is large and rather beaked and in some respects similar to the tools named 'rostro-carinates' in England.

Stage 3 is characterized by a great improvement in flaking technique, resulting in the making of large pointed hand-axes, no longer rostro-carinate in form, as the type tool (naturally, some rostro-carinate forms and also early crude types persist) in which the lower face is markedly flatter than the upper face, and usually with the butt quite straight and untrimmed.

In Stage 4 the flattening process continues and a considerable proportion of the hand-axes are trimmed carefully, even at the butt end.

In none of these four stages is any evidence of the use of the cylinder-hammer technique to be seen.

In South Africa there is at present little clear evidence upon which to base any subdivision of the Chellean stage of the Chelles-Acheul culture, and the term Stellenbosch 1 or South African Chelles-Acheul Stage 1 is used to cover all the typically Chellean as distinct from the Acheulean stage of the culture.

Various stages of the Chellean phase of the Chelles-Acheul culture occur in North Africa, some of which have been labelled Clacto-Abbevillian (see earlier) and some Chellean, and in fact evidence of the presence of the Chellean phase has been found over almost the whole continent of Africa.

The division of the great Hand-axe or Chelles-Acheul culture into Chellean and Acheulean phases is a fairly arbitrary one, and

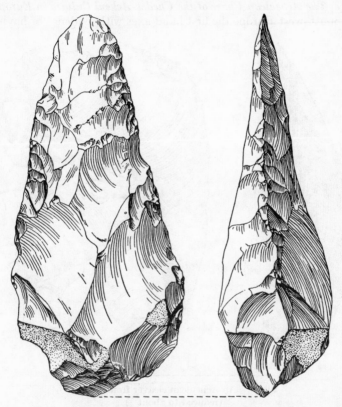

Fig. 8.   An early Acheulean hand-axe
(reduced to about ½)

the criterion usually accepted is the first appearance of the use of the cylinder-hammer technique to mark the start of the Acheulean phase.

It is exceedingly doubtful if the new idea spread so quickly as to come into use, simultaneously, all over the area where the Hand-axe culture existed, and consequently we may feel certain that later stages of the Chellean phase in some areas were contemporary with the earlier stages of the Acheulean phase elsewhere. In other words, the transition from the Chellean phase to the Acheulean phase of the great Hand-axe culture is probably not synchronous over the whole area of its distribution.

(*e*) *The Acheulean Phase of the Chelles-Acheul Culture in Europe.* In South-west Europe the first hand-axes with evidence of having

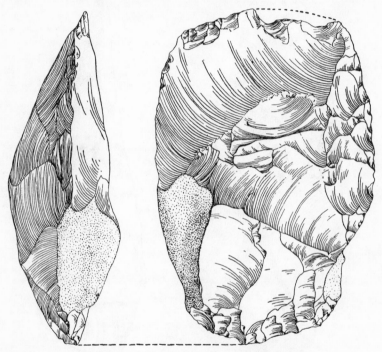

Fig. 9.   An Acheulean cleaver from Europe
(reduced to about ½)

been made by the cylinder-hammer technique (see fig. 8), which, as we have seen, is treated as the criterion for the Acheulean phase of the Chelles-Acheul culture, appear in the interglacial period between the Mindel and Riss glaciations, associated with a few cleavers (see fig. 9). These are classified in Europe as Lower Acheulean, but typologically they appear to be more advanced than the earliest stages of the Acheulean phase in Africa. Moreover, there is no evidence in Europe of a slow and gradual evolution from the Chellean phase to the Acheulean, but rather there is a sudden change. This can almost certainly be accounted for by regarding the appearance of the Lower Acheulean in Europe as an arrival from an area where the transition took place during the preceding Mindel glaciation; an area outside Europe.

Having arrived in Europe at the beginning of the Mindel-Riss interglacial, the makers of the culture remained in Europe and evolved a number of successive stages. By the time of the onset of the Riss glaciation a stage of evolution had been reached which is commonly called the Middle Acheulean in Europe, with a number of subdivisions.

Specimens typical of the Middle Acheulean are also to be found *in* deposits of the Riss glaciation, and some authorities consider that Acheulean man continued to live in Europe during the Riss glaciation, while the majority would probably account for the presence of Middle Acheulean specimens in Riss glacial deposits by regarding them as 'derived fossils' belonging, properly, to the previous interglacial, and caught up subsequently in the glacial deposits. This certainly seems to me the most likely explanation, since there does not appear to be any significant difference between Middle Acheulean assemblages in Europe which come from deposits of the Mindel-Riss interglacial and those which are obtained from the Riss glacial deposits.

Towards the closing stages of the Riss glaciation and at the beginning of the Riss-Würm interglacial the more advanced stages of the Acheulean, known as Upper Acheulean, appear. Although these Upper Acheulean stages in Europe are often regarded as a direct local derivative of the Middle Acheulean which occurs in the Riss glacial deposits, this explanation seems less likely, now that we have much clearer evidence of the uninterrupted evolution of the whole Chelles-Acheulean culture in Africa. It is more probable, in fact, that the Upper Acheulean represents a fresh wave of migration into Europe, when climatic conditions had sufficiently improved.

An important and significant feature of the Middle Acheulean in Europe is the evolution of the so-called 'S' twist ovates during the Mindel-Riss interglacial. These are small, somewhat oval hand-axes which, when viewed edge on, have the cutting edge in the form of an 'S' instead of more or less straight (see fig. 10). Industries with hand-axes having this characteristic appear in the African sequence at a somewhat later date, suggesting, very strongly, that this particular invention was brought back into Africa when the increasingly cold conditions of the advancing Riss glaciation drove the European Middle Acheulean people southwards in search of a more suitable climate.

(f) *The Acheulean Phase of the Chelles-Acheul Culture in Africa.* In Africa—as we have already seen—the most complete evidence of the slow and gradual evolution of the Chelles-Acheul Hand-axe culture is to be found at Olduvai Gorge.

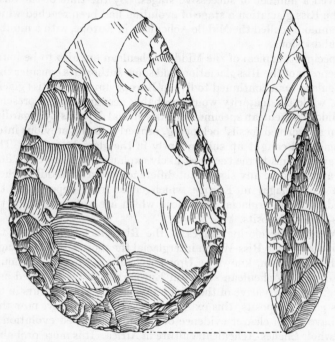

Fig. 10.—An Acheulean hand-axe from Europe with the so-called S-twist (reduced to ⅔)

At this site the transition from the Chellean phase to the Acheulean phase starts in the upper part of Bed 2, which, on the basis of the suggested glacial-pluvial correlation, corresponds to the closing stage of the Mindel glaciation.

Two transitional stages based on stratigraphical and typological evidence are recognizable at Olduvai; the first of these is more Chellean than Acheulean and might be called final Chellean instead of 'transitional', while the second is more Acheulean than Chellean and might equally well be called early Acheulean. We thus see evidence of the transition of the Chellean phase of the great Hand-axe culture into an Acheulean one in Africa, at a time when the makers of this culture were absent from Europe, owing to the inclement climate of the later part of the Mindel glaciation.

In East Africa the local evolution of the Acheulean culture, which started with the transitional stages towards the end of the Kamasian pluvial (Mindel glaciation), had reached a stage almost exactly comparable with the Lower Acheulean of Europe by the beginning of the Kamasian-Kanjeran interpluvial. It was at this time—as we have seen—that the Lower Acheulean moved into Europe to develop into the European Middle Acheulean during the Mindel-Riss interglacial. Meanwhile, in East Africa the climatic conditions during the interpluvial were far from good, and although a few of the makers of the Hand-axe culture may have remained in the area, there is no evidence of any cultural evolution during that interpluvial.

During the succeeding Kanjeran pluvial period a series of evolutionary stages can be traced, and, as we have seen, there is also evidence of the arrival of an intrusive stage—comparable to the Middle Acheulean of Europe, with 'S' twist, ovate hand-axes (see fig. 11)—which possibly reflects an influx of European Middle Acheulean people migrating back into Africa to avoid the Riss glacial conditions.

This does not, of course, mean that there was a direct migration from South-west Europe to East Africa of hand-axe makers who had already invented the 'S' twist. It suggests rather that a movement from Europe into North Africa brought the 'S' twist idea and that it gradually spread southwards among the Hand-axe culture people of Africa until it arrived in East Africa about half-way through the Kanjeran pluvial.

The final stage of the Chelles-Acheul culture in East Africa coincides with the end of the Kanjeran pluvial, although derived cultures (see the next chapter), such as the Kenya Fauresmith and the Sangoan, continued into the Kanjeran-Gamblian interpluvial (Riss-Würm interglacial) at a time when the final Acheulean and the Micoquian were developing in Europe.

In southern Africa the evolution of the Chelles-Acheul Hand-axe culture from the Chellean (or Stellenbosch 1) stage followed somewhat different and locally specialized lines during the Kanjeran pluvial. These local specializations included the development of the use of variations of the prepared-core technique, two of which are known as the 'Victoria West' and the 'Pniel' variations. These prepared-core techniques evolved locally, and in their later stages so closely resemble the Levalloisian prepared-core technique of Europe and North and East Africa (see next chapter) that it is still an open question as to whether it was an independent invention

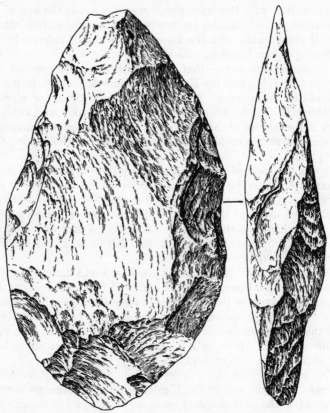

Fig. 11. An Acheulean hand-axe from East Africa with the so-called
S-twist
(reduced to about ⅔)

of the same idea, or whether the similarity of the specialized techniques in the advanced stages of the Chelles-Acheul culture in South Africa and the Levalloisian elsewhere were due to some sort of contact.

In northern and north-eastern Africa, from the Sudan to the Mediterranean, there are innumerable sites that yield industries of various stages of the Acheulean phase of the Chelles-Acheul culture, but as yet there is insufficient evidence from any one area to work out the detailed evolutionary sequence.

(g) *The Acheulean Phase of the Chelles-Acheul Culture in Asia.* In Asia the middle and later stages of the Acheulean phase of the Chelles-Acheul culture are represented at widespread sites in the Near East, and also as far as India, but much detailed work remains to be done to sort out all the evolutionary sequences in these areas, and there seems to be no reason to discuss the problem in detail here.

Throughout the area where stages of the Acheulean phase of the Hand-axe culture are known, from South-west Europe to Cape Town and across to India, there is evidence that, in addition to hand-axes, Acheulean man used the cleaver as a type tool and also made a variety of rough scrapers. Acheulean man in Europe seems to have used the cleaver far less than in Africa and Asia, but this is only a question of local variation of culture.

We have already seen in an earlier chapter that experiments suggest that the cleaver was used more for skinning and flaying, while the hand-axe served as a general utility tool. Hand-axes made from flint can be given a much sharper edge than hand-axes from other materials, and it is most noticeable that the industries in which cleavers are rarest are those where flint or chert was employed. This rather suggests that where the hand-axe could be used as a skinning tool, the cleaver was not commonly made use of.

The other important type tool of the great Chelles-Acheul culture (in addition to hand-axes and cleavers) is the bolas stone. In Africa the bolas stone is very commonly found in Hand-axe culture assemblages, and evidence suggestive of the use of these roughly spherical stone balls was found at Olorgesailie in Kenya. Similar bolas stones have been recovered from Chelles-Acheul sites in Portugal, but there is less evidence from the rest of South-west Europe and from those parts of Asia where the culture occurs.

(h) *The Clactonian Culture of Europe.* In Europe, and more particularly in England, there is excellent evidence of a clearly distinguishable and somewhat crude culture called the Clactonian, contemporary with the Lower and Middle Acheulean stage of the Hand-axe culture during the Mindel-Riss interglacial.

As we have seen earlier in this chapter, there have been suggestions of an early, or first, stage of the Clactonian culture during the Günz-Mindel interglacial and contemporary with the most simple

Chellean phase hand-axes. The evidence for a Stage 1 of the Clactonian as early as this was never very sound and depended largely upon the presence in certain deposits of flakes with 'wide angle, unfaceted striking platform and large semi-cones of percussion' which were for a long time regarded as the 'hall-mark' of the Clactonian culture.

We know, however, that these characters are really only evidence of the use of the 'block-on-block' flaking technique, which was also much used by the makers of the Chellean or Abbevillean phase of the Chelles-Acheul culture. Therefore, until a really good site with a typical Clactonian type of culture is found in the deposits of the Günz-Mindel interglacial or the Mindel glacial, it seems wiser to regard the old Clactonian Stage 1 as 'unproven' and to treat what used to be called Clactonian Stage 2 as the earliest known clear evidence of an independent culture contemporary with certain stages of the Chelles-Acheul culture in Europe.

The type site of the Clactonian culture from which it derives its name is at Clacton-on-Sea in England, where the industry occurs in deposits filling an old, low-level river channel, in part submerged beneath the present sea-level. The culture is also very well represented at a number of sites in the gravels of the 100-ft. terrace of the Thames, and an exceptionally rich site is known in the lower gravels of the Barnfield pit at Swanscombe. The culture is also found in the middle gravels of the 100-ft. terrace and at High Lodge in Suffolk. There is at present some difference of opinion as to the relative age of the various geological deposits concerned, though all belong to the Mindel-Riss interglacial, and it has been suggested by Oakley and M. D. Leakey in the report on the excavations at Jaywick, that the Clacton industries in the basal gravel of the 100-ft. terrace at Swanscombe are older than those in the submerged channel at Clacton-on-Sea and Jaywick, which are regarded as intermediate *in time* between the basal and the middle gravels of the Thames 100-ft. terrace.

A re-examination of all the evidence suggests very strongly, however, that (omitting the old Clactonian Stage 1, which is as yet not very certain, as we have seen) the oldest stages of the Clactonian culture of which we have really good evidence are those at Clacton-on-Sea and Jaywick; that the industries in the basal gravel of the 100-ft. terrace of the Thames come next, while those of the middle gravels of the 100-ft. terrace and of High Lodge come last.

This is based upon the view that the gravels which fill the sunk channel at Clacton-on-Sea and Jaywick were laid down when the sea-level relative to land was lower than it is today, at the very beginning of the Mindel-Riss interglacial and before the melting of the ice had raised the sea-level to a point much higher than at the present day, which we know happened at the height of the interglacial.

The Clacton and Jaywick channel deposits would thus represent the very beginning of the interglacial, and it is significant that there is no evidence whatsoever of the presence of Hand-axe man at the time that the Clacton submerged channel gravels were forming. In other words, the interglacial had not been in existence long enough for the arrival of Lower Acheulean man from Africa. The industry, too, of the Clacton and Jaywick deposits is distinctly less specialized and cruder than that from the basal gravels of the 100-ft. terrace of the Thames.

In order not to cause any confusion between the industry of Clacton-Jaywick and the old Clactonian Stage 1 (as yet not fully established), it would seem better to call it simply Clactonian 'A' (Old Clactonian 2).

As the interglacial developed, the sea-level rose in relation to the land, and the basal gravels of the 100-ft. terrace were formed in the Thames when it was graded into a much higher sea-level. The industries in this basal gravel may be referred to as Clactonian 'B' (Old Clactonian 2*a*).

At Swanscombe the basal gravel has not, so far as I know, yielded any Acheulean culture hand-axes at all, although Clactonian 'B' specimens are present in tens of thousands. This seems to show conclusively that the Clactonian culture is entirely distinct from the Acheulean and not (as some have suggested) the waste products of an Acheulean industry; for elsewhere, both in England and France, deposits of geologically the same age as the basal gravel of the 100-ft. terrace have yielded good Acheulean assemblages.

A small typical series of Clactonian 'B' tools is illustrated in fig. 12. These tool types include scrapers, crude knives with curved backs recalling the much later Mousterian Audi points, small triangular points, side, and end-scrapers, etc. All of these types are constantly recurring features of the Clactonian 'B' stage of culture.

Over the basal gravels of the 100-ft. terrace at Swanscombe is a layer of loam which contains a number of land snails and which seems to represent the beginning of the decline of the interglacial, when the sea-level was at its maximum and the waters of the river so sluggish that no gravel was being carried, while silt and earth

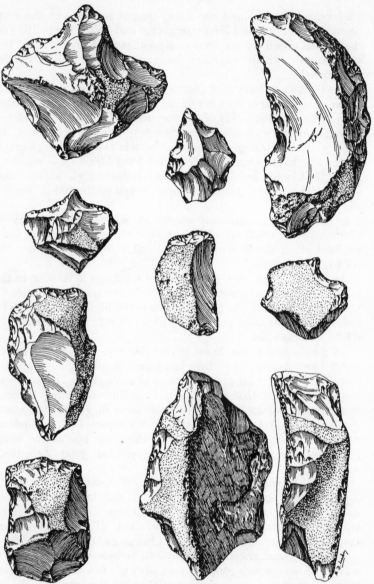

Fig. 12.   A series of Clactonian 'B' tools from the Lower gravel of the 100-ft. terrace at Swanscombe
(reduced to about ½)

were deposited, especially under the influence of the tidal movements. Above the loam-level are the middle gravels of the 100-ft. terrace, formed presumably when the sea-level had just begun to drop—thus rejuvenating the river—but at a time when the actual sea-level had not dropped so far as to make deposition upon the 100-ft. terrace impossible.

In these middle gravels the predominant culture is Middle Acheulean, a stage of the Hand-axe culture which belongs

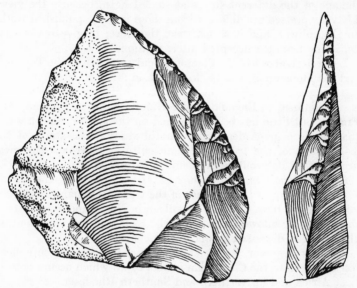

Fig. 13. A Clactonian 'C' side-scraper, recalling later Mousterian forms (reduced to $\frac{7}{8}$)

essentially, as we have seen, to the second half of the Mindel-Riss interglacial.

But these middle gravels also contain specimens which, by their typology, do not seem to belong to the Middle Acheulean but which are very similar indeed to the industry from High Lodge in Suffolk. The High Lodge assemblage consists in the main of developed Clactonian tool types, with certain marked tendencies towards the Mousterian culture (see Chapter VI) which suggests that the Mousterian may have its roots in the developed Clactonian. However, among the High Lodge specimens there are also a number of hand-axes which, *in form, but not in technique of manufacture*, recall the Acheulean.

In other words, it would seem as though the Clactonian of High Lodge (and of the middle gravels at Swanscombe) had been influenced by the contemporary presence of the Middle Acheulean people, and had borrowed certain tool types, which are, however, made by a different technique. We may, I think, safely call the Clactonian of the middle gravels of the 100-ft. terrace, and of High Lodge, Clactonian Stage 'C' (see fig. 13).

I have discussed the Clactonian sequence and the evidence for the age of the different stages at some length, because the views I have expressed are different from those in other published works on the subject, and it seems wise, therefore, to give reasons for departing from the accepted interpretation.

Later derivatives of the Clactonian culture, such as the Tayacian and the Mousterian, will be dealt with in other chapters.

The Clactonian culture, in the terms in which we have defined it, is not confined to England, and certainly occurs in Germany and France, but little has been published on the subject and it is one that needs a great deal more careful study. The study of the distribution of the true Clactonian culture is perhaps the most urgent of all Palaeolithic problems in Europe.

(*i*) *The Hope Fountain Culture in Africa.* In Africa there is no evidence, so far, of the presence of the true Clactonian culture; the misuse of the term Clacto-Abbevillean in North and South Africa should not be allowed to confuse the issue and this question has already been discussed earlier in this chapter.

There is, however, a very crude culture with certain superficial resemblances to the Clactonian in tool types which occurs both in East Africa and in Northern and Southern Rhodesia.

At Olorgesailie in Kenya, this culture (see fig. 14), which is in process of being studied and has not yet been described in detail, occurs in the same geological deposits as Stage 4 of the Acheulean phase of the Chelles-Acheul culture; i.e. it is contemporary with the late Middle Acheulean during the Kanjeran pluvial. On the basis of the pluvial-glacial correlation it is therefore rather later in time than the culture from the middle gravels of the 100-ft. terraces at Swanscombe. In the Rhodesias, industries which seem to belong to the same culture have been named the Hope Fountain culture. This culture is found *in situ* in Northern Rhodesia in undisturbed deposits, where it is contemporary with the Middle Acheulean, and in superficial and rather disturbed deposits of the type site of the Hope Fountain in Southern Rhodesia.

Too little is yet known about this crude culture to discuss its possible affinities with the Clactonian of Europe, but the possibility will have to be considered as to whether it does not represent an African variation of the culture or of its derivative, the Tayacian.

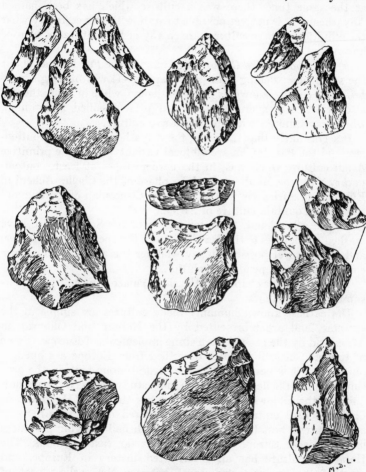

Fig. 14.   A series of tools of Hope Fountain type from Olorgesailie, Kenya, contemporary with the Acheulean culture
(reduced to ¾)

(*j*) *The Soan and Anyathean Cultures of Asia.* In Asia, during the interglacial between the second and third glaciations of the Himalayas and probably roughly contemporary with the Mindel-Riss interglacial deposits which contain the Clactonian culture in

Europe, there is a culture to which the name of Soan has been given. It is said to be contemporary with a stage of the Chelles-Acheul culture, of apparently Middle Acheulean facies. In Burma, at the same time, there was a culture which has been named Anyathean. It is not yet possible to state with any certainty what the affinities of these cultures are to any of the cultures of Europe and Africa.

(*k*) *The Choukoutien Culture of China*. In the Far East at about the same time, Peking man (see Chapter XI) was making a very primitive culture known as Choukoutienian, while in Java, there is also evidence of a crude culture, at present called Patjitanian, which has affinities with the Hand-axe culture.

It seems likely that the Soan, the Anyathean, the Choukoutienian, and the Patjitanian are all local variants of a single primitive Asian culture which was, in the earlier stages at least, contemporary with the Middle Acheulean phase of the Chelles-Acheul in Europe and Africa, as well as with the Clactonian of Europe and the Hope Fountain culture of Africa.

On the other hand, the later phases of the Soan culture have marked similarities to the Levalloisian of Europe (see next chapter) and it is not yet possible to say whether this was due to culture contact or to independent evolution.

To conclude this chapter on the early Palaeolithic cultures, let us summarize as follows:

The earliest known humanly made cultures are simple in the extreme, and are represented by the Kafuan and Oldowan in Africa and by the pre-Chellean stone implements of Europe. Some of the pre-Chellean cultures described from Europe are open to doubt, and it is best to group the earliest stone tools in the area simply as pre-Chellean until much more study has been carried out.

From the Oldowan of Africa emerges the great Hand-axe or Chelles-Acheul culture, which was centred in Africa, where its evolution can best be studied, but which had outlying provinces in South-west Europe and in Asia, as far east as India. The Hand-axe culture has an interrupted history in Europe, and most of the evolutionary stages between the earliest part of the Chellean phase and the beginning of the Acheulean phase are missing.

The Clactonian culture which was contemporary with the Early and Middle Acheulean in parts of Europe, is a distinctive culture, and much more work remains to be done on its evolution and distribution. A somewhat comparable culture, the Hope Fountain, is found in East Central Africa, where it is also contemporary with the Acheulean phase of the Hand-axe culture.

In the east of Asia a culture complex is slowly being revealed of which the Soan is the best known element. It is too early yet to say what is the relationship of this culture complex to either the Chelles-Acheul or the Clactonian cultures. It seems probable, and this will be discussed further in a later chapter, that the East Asia culture complex is linked with the *Pithecanthropus* and *Sinanthropus* type of man.

The table on p. 90 summarizes the Lower Palaeolithic cultures dealt with in this chapter.

CULTURES OF THE LOWER PALAEOLITHIC

	EUROPE Climate	EUROPE Cultures	AFRICA Climate	AFRICA Cultures	ASIA Climate	ASIA Cultures
Middle Pleistocene	3rd Glaciation (Riss)	Early Levalloisian (No cultures during maximum cold) (Derived tools in glacial deposits) Middle Acheulean	3rd Pluvial Kanjeran (Formerly Upper Kamasian)	Early Levalloisian Hope Fountain Upper Acheulean Intrusive Middle Acheulean Late Middle Acheulean	3rd Pluvial In Himalayas and some northern regions 3rd Glacial	Acheulean (Near East and parts of India) Soan (N. India) Choukoutienian (China) Anyathian (Burma) Patjitanian (Java)
	2nd Interglacial (Mindel-Riss)	Middle Acheulean evolving / Clactonian A, B, and C	2nd Interpluvial	African Middle Acheulean	2nd Interpluvial In some regions 2nd Interglacial	
	2nd Glaciation (Mindel)	No cultures during maximum cold (Derived tools in glacial deposits) Early Chellean	2nd Pluvial Kamasian (Formerly Lower Kamasian)	Transition from Chellean to Acheulean African Early Chellean Oldowan	2nd Pluvial In some regions of the North and in Himalayas 2nd Glacial	Chellean (Near East) Proto-Soan (India)
Lower Pleistocene	1st Interglacial (Günz-Mindel)	Pre-Chellean cultures	1st Interpluvial	Oldowan	1st Interpluvial and in some regions Interglacial	No cultures known
	1st Glacial (Günz)	No cultures known	1st Pluvial (Kageran)	Oldowan Kafuan	1st Pluvial and in some areas of the North and in Himalayas 1st Glacial	No cultures known

CHAPTER VI

The Middle Palaeolithic Cultures

IN the previous chapter we discussed the more important Stone Age cultures of the Lower and Middle Pleistocene period under the heading of Lower Palaeolithic cultures. In the present chapter we shall deal with a group of cultures which, in fact, have their roots in the closing stages of the Middle Pleistocene, but which flourished, for the most part, in the first half of the Upper Pleistocene, that is to say, during the interglacial period between the Riss and Würm glaciations and the interpluvial period between the Kanjeran and Gamblian pluvials in Africa, and the comparable period of time in Asia.

(a) *The Upper Stages of the Acheulean Phase of the Chelles-Acheul Culture in Europe.* We have already seen in the last chapter that the Middle Acheulean of Europe, which is divisible into several stages, probably developed independently in Europe from an Early Acheulean stage which was brought in from the African continent and that at least one of the special developments of the Middle Acheulean in Europe, the 'S' twist ovate hand-axe, was later carried back to Africa when the advancing glaciation drove the makers of the culture to seek warmer climates. We saw, too, that this 'S' twist variant appears as an intrusive element in the late Middle Acheulean of Africa, during the Kanjeran pluvial.

The Acheulean phase of the Chelles-Acheul culture reached its final stages towards the end of the Kanjeran pluvial in East and Central Africa, but in Europe we find that as the cold of the Riss glaciation gave way to milder conditions, an Upper Acheulean stage of the Chelles-Acheul culture appears in South-west Europe and continues throughout the first part of the Riss-Würm inter-glacial (see fig. 15). This fact suggests a migration into Europe of people who had already developed an Upper Acheulean stage of culture in Africa. In fact there is no evidence to suggest that the Upper Acheulean of Europe was derived locally from the Middle Acheulean of that continent, for there is a big hiatus between the two.

It is, of course, true that a large number of Middle Acheulean-type hand-axes and some cleavers are found in Europe in certain deposits which were formed during the Riss glaciation, and this fact has led some authorities to suggest that the makers of the Middle Acheulean in Europe continued to live in the area during the Riss glaciation. This is, however, exceedingly doubtful, and it

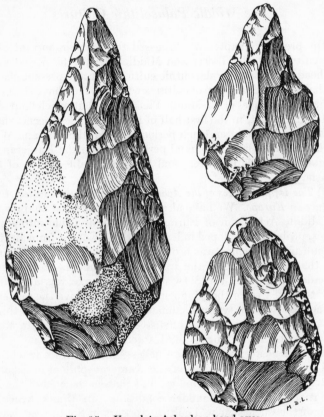

Fig. 15.   Very late Acheulean hand-axes
(reduced to about ¾)

is much more likely that the specimens so found simply represent material that belongs to the previous interglacial and that was caught up in the glacial deposits.

The Upper Acheulean of Europe is replaced after a time by a culture known as Micoquian (see p. 95), which appears to be the result of a culture contact between the late Acheulean and the Levalloisian.

(*b*) *The Levalloisian Culture in Europe.* The earliest evidence of the culture which is known as Levalloisian in Europe is found in deposits which were probably formed during the Riss glaciation. Since there is no evidence of the presence of this culture during the previous interglacial we cannot postulate that the specimens of early Levalloisian culture found in Riss glacial deposits belong to the previous interglacial (as we have done with the Middle

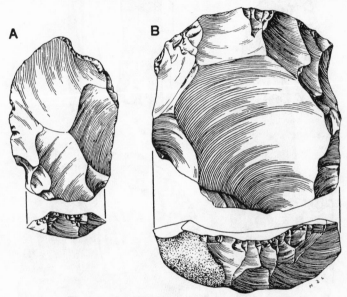

Fig. 16.   Levalloisian flake and tortoise core
(reduced to ½)

Acheulean specimens). Moreover, early Levalloisian assemblages of implements occur in deposits belonging to the Riss glaciation under conditions which are suggestive of living-sites, so that on the basis of available evidence it seems that these people, unlike the Acheulean men, did, in fact, inhabit parts of Europe during the Riss glaciation, but probably kept at some distance from the edge of the actual ice-sheets.

The Levalloisian culture in its early stages is represented by large flakes (see fig. 16*A*) struck from carefully prepared 'tortoise cores' (see fig. 16*B*), which are also found. The flakes represent simple tools blocked out on the core and then struck off by a single blow. A proportion of these Levalloisian flakes have slight secondary flaking, in cases where the prepared flake that was knocked off the tortoise core did not come off quite in the shape that the maker intended. A few of the Levalloisian flakes, too, were made into rough side-scrapers.

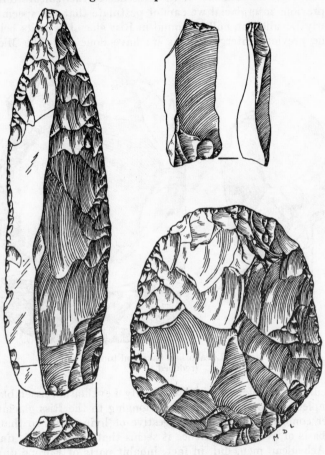

Fig. 17. Late Levalloisian tools and hand-axe
(reduced to about ¾)

The early Levalloisian of Europe has a rather different distribution from that of the Middle Acheulean of the preceding inter-glacial or that of the Upper Acheulean of the next, or Riss-Würm interglacial, and it extends considerably farther to the north and east and much less to the south and west.

When the makers of the Upper Acheulean culture came to Europe as the Riss glaciation receded, there was, for a time, an overlap of the Levalloisian and the Upper Acheulean cultures, which are found side by side in France and southern England during the Riss-Würm interglacial. Presumably as a direct result of this culture contact we find some industries of the more evolved Levalloisian of Europe in which the more typical Levalloisian cultural elements are associated with hand-axes. These hand-axes, however, are in the main NOT made by the Acheulean cylinder-hammer technique, but by a step-flaking technique (see fig. 17) reminiscent of the workmanship on Levalloisian side-scrapers. In other words, some of the makers of the more advanced stages of the Levalloisian were influenced by the presence of an Upper Acheulean culture to the extent of borrowing the hand-axe as a tool type, but they made it by their own technique.

Similar effects of culture contact can be seen in many parts of the world today. To give but one example: some African potters who have been in contact with European culture make earthenware cups and mugs which resemble their European prototypes in shape and in use, but not in technique of manufacture.

As the Levalloisian culture developed in Europe, and particularly at a stage known as Levalloisian 4, there was a tendency to modify the typical tortoise cores into cores from which long, roughly parallel, blade flakes could be struck (see fig. 17).

Industries of the Levalloisian in Europe which include hand-axes are sometimes referred to as Levalloisio-Acheulean.

(c) *The Micoquian Culture in Europe.* As might be expected from what we have just described, another effect of the overlapping of the Levalloisian and Upper Acheulean cultures in parts of Southwest Europe was that some of the makers of the Upper Acheulean culture were influenced by the Levalloisian. This resulted in the culture known as the Micoquian, in which hand-axes with long, narrow points predominate (see fig. 18)—hand-axes which were most certainly made by men highly skilled in the use of the cylinder-hammer technique of the Acheuleans. But the other elements of the Micoquian culture include prepared cores of the 'tortoise core' type as well as 'Levallois-type' flake tools, some burins, and many scrapers.

(d) *The Tayacian Culture in Europe.* A little-known but important culture in France during the Riss-Würm interglacial is that known as Tayacian. It is a crude and simple culture with certain elements which recall the Clactonian, and it is probably best to regard it as a late degenerate derivative of the Clactonian. Strong support for this view is given by the fact that during recent excavations by Mademoiselle Henri-Martin at the Grotte de Fontéchevade in France, a typical Tayacian culture is underlain by a level containing specimens which are truly Clactonian, suggesting a direct evolution of one from the other (see fig. 19).

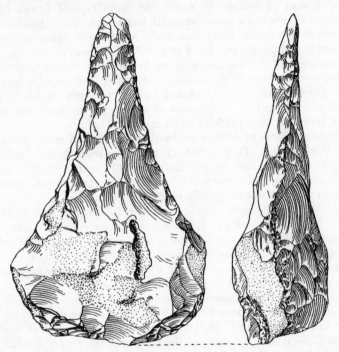

Fig. 18. A Micoquian hand-axe
(reduced to about ⅔)

The Tayacian is important because in these same excavations by Mademoiselle Henri-Martin fragments of two human skulls were found in a hearth in the Tayacian level. These skulls and their significance will be discussed in more detail in a later chapter. They give the Tayacian an added interest because they are the earliest fossil human remains so far found in France. If the skulls represent the makers of the Tayacian culture (a matter which will be discussed later, see pp. 204–5) then the Tayacian would become one of the very few Stone Age cultures of the Lower and Middle

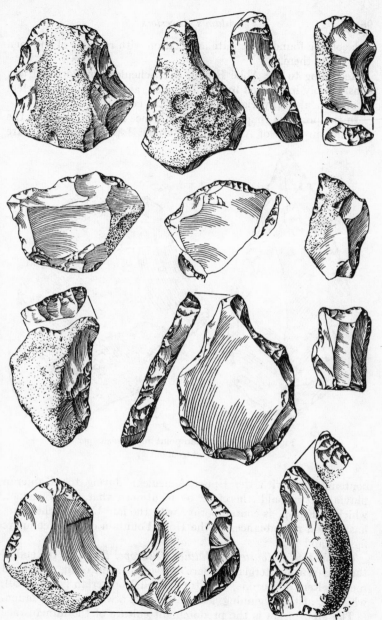

Fig. 19. Tayacian tools from La Micoque
(reduced to about ⅔)

Palaeolithic found in definite association with remains of the men who made them.

According to the Abbé Breuil, the Acheulean of Portugal was considerably influenced by the Tayacian, and he frequently refers to an Acheuleo-Tayacian culture in that country.

In the previous chapter, a brief reference has been made to the presence in parts of Africa of the crude Hope Fountain culture

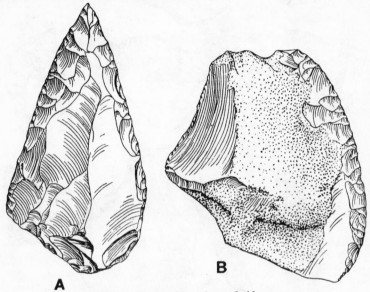

Fig. 20.   A Mousterian point and side-scraper
(reduced to about ⅝)

contemporary with the Upper Acheulean during the Kanjeran pluvial. It should therefore be mentioned that the Tayacian, which in Europe is contemporary with the late Upper Acheulean, has certain resemblances to the Hope Fountain culture (compare figs. 14 and 19).

(e) *The Early Mousterian Culture of Europe.* Towards the end of the Riss-Würm interglacial there appears, in some of the caves and rock-shelters of Europe, a culture called Mousterian (see fig. 20), which is, at the beginning, associated with a warm-climate fauna.

The Mousterian is the predominant culture of the human race known as Neanderthal man (see Chapter XI), and because of its association with this peculiarly brutish and well-known race of fossil man it has been studied in considerable detail. Moreover, it is a culture which is found in the main—but not exclusively—in rock-shelters in Europe, which makes it relatively easy to discover and excavate living-sites and obtain not only good assemblages of specimens, but easily interpreted evidence of position in the culture sequence.

The early or, as it is sometimes called, the 'warm' Mousterian has strong resemblances, in certain respects, to the Clactonian of High Lodge, from which it was in all probability originally derived. That is to say, it is perhaps a highly evolved and specialized derivative of the Clactonian, while the Tayacian is a degenerate offshoot of the same culture.

The Mousterian culture found with the Krapina skulls and in association with a warm fauna—including *Rhinoceros merki*—is an example of the early Mousterian culture which in many ways recalls the late Clactonian of High Lodge. There have even been suggestions that the Krapina site may be as old as High Lodge (the end of the Mindel-Riss interglacial), but the weight of the evidence points rather to the end of the Riss-Würm interglacial. The culture found with the Ehringsdorf skull in Germany, in association with a warm fauna belonging to the very end of the Riss-Würm interglacial has many resemblances to the late Clactonian of High Lodge, thus supporting the view that the early 'warm' Mousterian is a derivative of the Clactonian. The later stages of the Mousterian of Europe will be dealt with in the next chapter, for they belong strictly to the Upper Palaeolithic period.

It should be noted here that there are a few writers who suggest that the term Upper Palaeolithic should be confined to the Aurignacian, Magdalenian, and Solutrean cultures of Europe, but that view is not accepted or followed in this book (see introduction to Chapter VII).

Having briefly reviewed the Middle Palaeolithic cultures that occur in Europe during the first part of the Upper Pleistocene (the Riss-Würm interglacial), we must pass to the Middle Palaeolithic cultures of the African continent.

(*f*) *The Late Upper Acheulean Culture in Africa.* In parts of the African continent the final stages of the Acheulean phase of the Chelles-Acheul culture persist into the beginning of what we are calling the Upper Pleistocene period—that is to say, into the first part of the interpluvial between the Kanjeran and the Gamblian. This seems to be particularly true of the North African littoral, which, in this respect, has a culture sequence much more like that found in South-west Europe than that of the rest of the African continent.

The late Acheulean of Kharga in Egypt probably also belongs to this period, and the living-site is there concentrated around a series of springs which apparently were in the process of drying up, but which still produced water at a time when the climate was beginning to get drier. The late Acheulean of Tunis and Morocco probably also belong to the last interpluvial.

(g) *The Early and Middle Stages of the Sangoan Culture of Africa.* Towards the close of the Kanjeran pluvial period, as the climate of a large part of Africa became increasingly dry, we find that a culture appears in certain parts of the continent of Africa to which the name of Sangoan has been given. It is with the early stages of this culture that we are concerned in the present chapter.

The early Sangoan is found in those parts of Central and South Africa which, for one reason or another, were still reasonably well watered at a time when the rest of the continent was rapidly drying up. Thus, in North Angola and the Congo, where the huge river systems of the present day shrank to much smaller streams, there appears to have always been some flow of water, even at the height of the Kanjeran-Gamblian interpluvial.

Similarly, in the land surrounding Lake Victoria and along the banks of such great rivers as the Zambesi, there was water available at a time when many other parts of Africa were uninhabitable. Naturally, game animals tended to concentrate in these areas where they could still find grazing and water, and it was in these regions that the early stage of the Sangoan culture was evolved by Stone Age men who had gone thither partly to follow the animals upon which they lived and partly because they, too, had to have water to drink.

A study of the early stages of the Sangoan culture, in which large and crude hand-axes and picks are associated with a certain number of much more evolved forms tending towards the later lance-head type, together with the use of the 'prepared-core' technique, leads one to suspect that the roots of the Sangoan culture will one day be traced to the South African variant of the Chelles-Acheul culture. This, as we have already seen, was a culture in which the 'prepared-core' technique was being used at an early stage.

Geographically, too, it is not difficult to envisage a movement from South Africa into the well-watered regions of Angola and

thence down the Zambesi and northwards into the Congo, and up
to the region of the Central African lakes.

The early and middle stages of the Sangoan culture belong
essentially to the dry interpluvial period before the onset of the
Gamblian pluvial, and all except the very earliest stage belong to
what was formerly called the 'Tumbian' culture. This term has
been discarded in Africa, by agreement, because it had been used
loosely to cover a range of cultures extending from the end of the
Middle Pleistocene to Neolithic times, which had only one element
in common, the presence of lance-heads made of stone. We now
know that whereas these types first occur sporadically in the early
and middle stages of the Sangoan, they continued to be made and
used in much later times, and that *by themselves* they provide no
evidence of the cultural stage to which they belong.

There are many local variants of the early and middle stages of
the Sangoan, in exactly the same way that we find regional variations of the Chelles-Acheul culture, but the culture is characterized
everywhere by the association in any typical *in situ* assemblage of:

(1) Large crude picks and crude hand-axes reminiscent of the
early Chellean.

(2) Much more carefully made hand-axes which, taken individu-
ally, would be regarded as Acheulean.

(3) Large discoidal scrapers.

(4) A small proportion of lanceolate hand-axes and some actual
lance-heads.

(5) The use of an evolved form of the 'prepared-core' technique
which yielded triangular points and also parallel-sided blade flakes.

(*h*) *The Fauresmith Culture in Africa.* During the same period
that the early and middle stages of the Sangoan culture flourished
in Angola and the Congo, as well as in the area round the Central
African great lakes, another offshoot of the Hand-axe culture was
evolving in other regions, notably in East Africa and in parts of
the Rhodesias and South Africa.

In East Africa the culture is only found in deposits belonging
to the dry period between the Kanjeran and the Gamblian pluvial,
and it is noteworthy that the area of distribution is confined to
high altitudes round such mountain masses as Mount Kenya, the
Aberdare range, the Mau range, and Kilimanjaro (which even
during the interpluvial had a certain amount of rainfall), and along
the banks of a few rivers whose sources were in these mountainous
areas.

Farther south, the early stages of the Fauresmith culture are to be found in the areas near major rivers, in deposits of the inter-pluvial period; but the culture persists, and its more evolved stages belong to the early part of the Gamblian pluvial, and will be discussed in the next chapter.

The Fauresmith culture, as we have seen, has its origin in the great Hand-axe culture in the same way as the Sangoan, but it differs from it in many ways. The typical tools of the Fauresmith culture are flat and rather ovate hand-axes, small triangular and heart-shaped hand-axes, little pointed hand-axes, small and well-made cleavers (see fig. 21) (true cleavers, as distinct from large *tranchet* axes, do not seem to occur in the Sangoan), numerous bolas stones and a high percentage of flake tools made on flakes derived from 'prepared cores'.

The Kenya Fauresmith is at present regarded as being directly derived from a contact between an incoming branch of the true Levalloisian and a later stage of the Acheulean. On the other hand, in South Africa the evidence suggests that the Fauresmith is a direct derivative of the later stages of the specialized South African Acheulean which had already developed the use of the 'prepared-core' technique.

More recently, however, it has been shown that later stages of the Acheulean culture in South Africa (Stellenbosch 4 and 5, as they are sometimes called) which belong, in time, to the closing stages of the Kanjeran pluvial, already show a strong tendency towards the true Fauresmith culture (they are certainly the origin of the South African Fauresmith). It is not impossible that the Fauresmith of East Africa may represent, in fact, a movement of a branch of the makers of the later South African Acheulean stage of culture, into an area which already had its own indigenous population of late Acheulean people. If this is the case, then it would be simply a matter of chance that at about this time a branch of the northern Levalloisian culture arrived in East Africa, where the makers of the Fauresmith culture were also using the 'prepared-core' technique.

(*i*) *The Tayacian Culture in North-west Africa.* Some authorities recognize the presence of a Tayacian culture in Morocco,[1] and if this is the case, it most probably reached this area via Portugal, across the straits from the Iberian peninsula, since the Tayacian is widely recognized in Portugal. It may be noted here that the Abbé

[1] Since writing this I have visited Morocco and the evidence for a Tayacian culture there is not at all convincing.

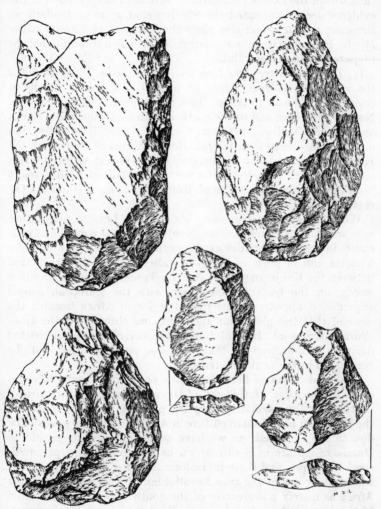

Fig. 21.   Fauresmith cleaver, hand-axes, and flakes from Kenya
(reduced to about ½)

Breuil, in his table of the culture sequence, places the Tayacian as contemporary with the early stages of the Hand-axe culture, and thus within the Lower Palaeolithic. But this interpretation of the evidence does not appear to be wholly sound, more particularly as the same author would also place the Tayacian of Europe in the Mindel-Riss glaciation; an interpretation which I would not be prepared to accept as valid.

(*j*) *The Early Stage of the Levalloisian Culture in Africa.* So far as the available evidence shows at present, the true Levalloisian culture is confined, in Africa, to a small area along the coast of North-west Africa and to the north-east and east, including Egypt and the Nile Valley, Abyssinia, Somaliland, and East Africa. In other words, except for a very limited area west of the Nile, in the Kharga region, and for a coastal strip in North-west Africa, it seems to lie in an area bounded in the west by the Nile and in the south by a line through the centre of Tanganyika. We will discuss the eastern area first.

Within this area a true early stage of the Levalloisian culture appears at the very end of the Kanjeran pluvial period and continues in suitable localities as, for example, in the area near Lake Victoria and in parts of the Nile Valley, during the dry period between the Kanjeran pluvial and the Gamblian pluvial. In other words, on the basis of correlation with the European glacial sequence, it appears in this special region of Africa towards the close of the Riss glaciation and continues throughout the Riss-Würm interglacial. Its evolution and its derivatives which existed during the first part of the Gamblian pluvial period, will be considered in the next chapter.

It should be noted here that some prehistorians who have no special knowledge of this out-of-the-way corner of the African continent still passionately deny the presence of a true branch of the European Levalloisian culture in Africa. This view seems to be due to the fact that, as we have seen, the later stages of the Hand-axe culture in South Africa have a comparable 'prepared-core' technique, and these prehistorians prefer, therefore, to treat what is here called the true Levalloisian of East and North-east Africa as merely a derivative of the South African manifestation of the 'prepared-core' technique. Examined carefully, however, this view cannot be sustained, and it seems certain that the arrival of the Levalloisian culture, in its typical form, in this one corner of Africa can be traced to movements from the north via Palestine, where the true Levalloisian was well developed.

In the true Levalloisian of this corner of the African continent—in which several distinct stages can be recognized—we find an assemblage of artifacts—whether it be at Kharga or at Muguruk in Kenya—which includes no hand-axe elements whatsoever, a good array of tools made from flakes struck from prepared cores with little or no marginal retouch, no bolas stones, and only a few rare scrapers. Flakes showing evidence of the block-on-block technique also occur.

In the western coastal zone of North Africa, Ruhlmann and others have recognized what they regard as a true Levalloisian, underlying the Aterian (see Chapter VII) which in this coastal zone is said to be only represented by the more evolved stages of the Aterian. It is not yet clear whether the assemblages which are attributed to the Levalloisian in this part of North Africa are truly Levalloisian,[1] or whether they are more comparable to an early stage of the Aterian. Since, however, these authors recognize an early Levalloisian in the same area, contemporary with the early and middle Acheulean stages of culture, we may for the moment accept the possibility that a true branch of the Levalloisian culture occurs here. It would appear to have no link with the branch of the Levalloisian that came into Egypt and the Nile Valley and thence to East Africa via Palestine, and it may have arrived from Europe at a time when there was a land bridge at the western end of the Mediterranean, or across the narrow straits.

(k) *The Pseudo-Stillbay Culture of East Africa.* In East Africa there is a curious local culture which is geologically contemporary with the East African Fauresmith and early Levalloisian, to which the name of Pseudo-Stillbay has been given, because certain of its rarer elements, taken out of their context, could easily be mistaken for specimens of the true Stillbay culture (stratigraphically much later).

The Pseudo-Stillbay (see fig. 22) can only be regarded as a very specialized local variant of the Levalloisian, and is characterized by the association of three characteristic types. These are:

(1) Small, thick-set triangular points, seldom exceeding one and a half inches in length, made from flakes struck from small 'prepared cores' in the Levalloisian tradition, with the secondary trimming confined to the upper face. In proportion to their size these little triangular tools are always very thick and give a general impression of crude workmanship.

[1] As a result of a recent visit to N. Africa I am satisfied that a Levalloisian culture does occur there.

(2) A relatively small proportion of triangular points worked carefully all over both faces, usually (but not always) with the bulb of percussion carefully trimmed away. These look as though they have been made by pressure flaking, but careful examination shows that this is not the case.

(3) The presence of very rare, small hand-axes, seldom more than three inches long.

(*l*) *The Cultures of the Middle Palaeolithic in Asia Minor.* Whereas it has been possible to make use of the correlation between the glacial and interglacial periods of Europe and the pluvial and interpluvial periods in Africa in deciding upon which cultures to discuss in the present chapter, we are in some difficulty when we turn to Asia Minor, since at present there is very little upon which a time correlation either with Europe, or with Africa, can be based.

Careful examination of the available evidence seems to suggest, however, that the Tayacian, the Upper Acheulean, the Micoquian, and Lower Levalloisio-Mousterian stages of culture all fall within the period, with the first two cultures belonging to the downward half of the climatic curve of the period, the Micoquian coming at the bottom of the curve, with the Levalloisio-Mousterian marking a fresh rise in the curve, as the Würm glaciation of Europe and the Gamblian pluvial of Africa were approaching. This last culture, however, probably continued into the beginning of the next period.

(*m*) *The Tayacian Culture of the Near East.* The Tayacian is the oldest of the Near Eastern Stone Age cultures which seem to be within the period now under discussion. It does not differ significantly from the Tayacian of the south of France and needs no special comment, except to record that its stratigraphical position beneath the Upper Acheulean and Micoquian is exactly the same as in Europe, and that it is very crude, without any trace of influence from the Hand-axe culture.

(*n*) *The Upper Acheulean of the Near East.* The final stages of the Acheulean of this area are characterized by the presence of a very large number (nearly two-thirds of the total) of small implements other than hand-axes, made on flakes and including many scrapers and rough choppers as well as a few burins.

As we have already seen, scrapers and other small flake tools continually occur in both the Chellean and Acheulean stages of Hand-axe culture elsewhere, so that their presence here is not of itself significant, but the relative proportions seem to be highly significant, for they suggest that the makers of the Upper Acheulean in Palestine were developing in a cultural direction rather

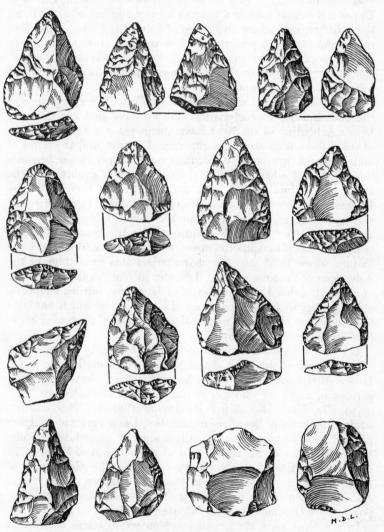

Fig. 22.   A series of Pseudo-Stillbay tools from East Africa
(reduced to ¾)

different from that taken by their fellows in other areas. It is also probably of the very greatest significance that in this area Upper Acheulean man had become a cave dweller, whereas in all the other regions where this stage of culture is found, Acheulean man seems to have preferred to live in open station sites, only seldom occupying caves or rock-shelters as permanent homes, though he occasionally took temporary shelter in them and left a few implements behind.

(*o*) *The Micoquian Culture of the Near East.* The significance of the two unusual characteristics that we have just noted in the Upper Acheulean of the Near East; the increase in the proportion of small flake tools such as scrapers and burins, and the habit of making use of caves and rock-shelters as *permanent* homes, becomes more apparent when we study the next stage of evolution of the Hand-axe culture in the same area. This has been called by Professor Garrod 'Upper Acheulean (Micoquian)'. In other words, this authority regards it as a further evolutionary stage of the Upper Acheulean, but with affinities to the Micoquian of Europe.

In fact, the Micoquian element is not very marked, and the feature which most strongly characterizes this final stage of the Acheulean of the area is the still greater increase in the proportion of elements other than hand-axes, i.e. scrapers, burins, choppers, etc., together with the appearance of a type of tool which was later to become one of the hall-marks of a new culture, *the backed knife-blade of the Chatelperron type.*

It seems not unreasonable to believe that we may perhaps have evidence here of the birth of the culture which used to be called Lower Aurignacian, but which has since been renamed Chatel-perronian, a culture whose origin has hitherto been obscure.

(*p*) *The Lower Levalloisio-Mousterian Culture.* This culture, while of essentially Levalloisian affinities, has a very much higher proportion of its tools very carefully shaped by secondary chipping than is the case of the more classical Levalloisian of Europe. In this respect it much more closely resembles the Mousterian of Europe and, as we shall see in the next chapter, there is also evidence in Europe of a Levalloisio-Mousterian which is contemporary with the more classical Mousterian.

In the Near East, the Levalloisio-Mousterian seems to start at about the time the so-called 'warm' Mousterian appeared in Europe, but the later stages of the culture in Palestine continue and are roughly contemporary with the classic Mousterian of the European zone (see next chapter).

(*q*) *The Other Asiatic Cultures of this Period.* Although the Soan, Anyathian, and Choukoutienian cultures of North India, Burma, and China, respectively (which have already been referred to in the previous chapter), may have derivative stages which belong to the period with which we are dealing in this chapter, the evidence is not very clear, except in the case of China, where the uppermost levels of the Choukoutienian culture would appear to belong, in time, to the period which corresponds to the Riss-Würm interglacial in Europe.

In those parts of India where the later stages of the Acheulean culture occur, the evidence of age is almost non-existent, but the probability is that the final stages of the Acheulean continued there into the period covered by the present chapter.

To conclude this chapter we may summarize as follows:

In Europe, the period from the end of the Riss glaciation to the beginning of the Würm glaciation was one during which Stone Age man flourished exceedingly. The final stages of the Upper Acheulean were replaced by a derivative culture known as the Micoquian, in which Levalloisian influences seem to be present.

The Levalloisian culture itself spread over a wide area of Europe and underwent a series of evolutionary stages. The early Mousterian and the Tayacian, both probably derived from the Clactonian, also appear on the scene for the first time.

In Africa, the Acheulean stages of the Hand-axe culture give way, in the main, to two derivative cultures, the early stages of the Sangoan and the Fauresmith. These two cultures occupy different parts of the continent, and the areas chosen by each group seem to have been determined by geographical considerations. In the earlier part of the period there are occasional survivals of a very late stage of the Acheulean culture, while in the north-east area and certainly as far south as East Africa the true Levalloisian of Europe appears as an intrusive culture.

A specialized culture known as the Pseudo-Stillbay has a limited distribution and appears to be a local evolution from the early Levalloisian.

In the Near East the later stages of the Acheulean evolve along rather unexpected lines to produce a culture in which small flake tools composed of scrapers, a few burins, and a few backed blades of Chatelperron type predominate over hand-axes. There is some reason to believe that these, in fact, represent the birth of the culture complex of which the Aurignacian, Chatelperronian, and Capsian are among the ultimate derivatives. This culture, known for the present as 'Upper Acheulean (Micoquian)' (although its relationship to the Micoquian of Europe is not very great) is suddenly replaced, at the end of the period under consideration, by an early Levalloisio-Mousterian, which represents the arrival of a new element. There is at present no clue as to what happened to the former culture, which was rapidly losing its Hand-axe culture characteristics.

Over the rest of Asia the evidence for this period is negligible.

The whole period is one of great importance because it witnessed the birth of new cultural elements in each continent, which were destined to affect the whole picture of the culture complex of the Upper Palaeolithic period.

The table opposite sets out the contents of the chapter graphically.

CULTURES OF THE MIDDLE PALAEOLITHIC

EUROPE	*Climate*	Third Interglacial (Riss—Würm Interglacial) (Warm and Wet)
	Cultures	←——Upper Acheulean Micoquian——→ Warm Mousterian ←————Tayacian———— ←——Early Levalloisian————→ Upper Levalloisian Tayacio-Acheulean (Portugal)
AFRICA	*Climate*	Third Interpluvial (Kanjeran — Gamblian Interpluvial) (Cultures mainly concentrated by large lakes, big rivers, permanent springs and high up mountain massifs)
	Cultures	←——Late Acheulean (N. Africa)——→ ←——Fauresmith (E. and S. Africa)————————→ ←—Tayacian (N. Africa)——→ ←——Levalloisian (N. and E. Africa)————→ ——Sangoan (Central Africa)—————→ Final Acheulean——→ Pseudo-Stillbay (E. Africa)——→
ASIA	*Climate*	Third Interglacial in Himalayas, etc. (Relatively warm and wet in many other parts of Asia)
	Cultures — *Near East*	Upper Acheulean Micoquian Lower Levalloisio-Mousterian Tayacian
	Cultures — *Far East*	Upper Soan Upper Anyathian Upper Choukoutienian

CHAPTER VII

The Upper Palaeolithic Cultures

IN the preceding chapter we discussed a group of cultures, some of which have their roots in the Lower Palaeolithic, but which occupy the period roughly from the end of the Riss glaciation in Europe to the beginning of the Würm glaciation and to a comparable period in the geological time-scale in Africa and Asia. These cultures were grouped together as Middle Palaeolithic, and occupy the earlier part of the Upper Pleistocene period.

Before we proceed to discuss the cultures which I propose to group together as Upper Palaeolithic, it will be necessary to discuss these terms Middle and Upper Palaeolithic further and to re-define them. They were first used at a time when the study of Prehistory was in its infancy, and it is no longer possible to employ them with the meanings which they originally had.

The Stone Age, as a matter of convenience, is divided into Palaeolithic or Old Stone Age, Mesolithic or Middle Stone Age,[1] and Neolithic or Newer Stone Age. The term Mesolithic was interpolated between Palaeolithic and Neolithic at a relatively recent date, when it was realized that there were a number of Stone Age cultures which could not properly be classed either as Palaeolithic or Neolithic, and which, in fact, served to bridge the gap between these two major divisions.

So far as the Palaeolithic is concerned, this was divided into Lower, Middle, and Upper Palaeolithic at a time when the sequence of Stone Age cultures appeared to be very simple indeed. The term Lower Palaeolithic was taken to be practically synonymous with the Hand-axe culture, i.e. with the main divisions of Chellean and Acheulean, although its use was later extended backwards to include what were called the pre-Chellean cultures. Some workers treated the term Lower Palaeolithic as being so completely synonymous with the Hand-axe culture that they invented the somewhat meaningless term of 'pre-Palaeolithic cultures' for cultures which antedated the dawn of the Chellean.

Similarly, in those early days the term Middle Palaeolithic was

[1] N.B. Where the term Middle Stone Age is used in South Africa, it is NOT synonymous with the Mesolithic (see later).

confined to the Mousterian culture and was, to all intents and purposes, treated as a synonym. The term Upper Palaeolithic was used for the post-Mousterian Palaeolithic cultures of Europe, which were known to be made by men of *Homo sapiens* type and was, to all intents and purposes, confined to what are sometimes called 'the blade and burin cultures'.

These early and simple definitions of the divisions Lower, Middle, and Upper Palaeolithic can no longer be accepted, since it would then be necessary to invent new terms to cover Palaeolithic cultures which did not fit in with these definitions. For example, if we accepted the term Lower Palaeolithic as synonymous with the Hand-axe culture, where could we place the Clactonian, which, while demonstrably older than most of the stages of the Hand-axe culture, does not, itself, belong to this culture complex? Clearly, since Palaeolithic in simple English means 'Old Stone Age', and Lower Palaeolithic clearly refers to the earlier part of the Old Stone Age, the Clactonian culture must be classed in the Lower Palaeolithic. This has, in fact, been done in Chapter V.

Now, since some sort of dividing line must be drawn between Lower and Middle Palaeolithic, it seemed better not to attempt to make it coincide with the end of any particular culture, but rather to make the division at a given point in the geological time-scale. As a matter of convenience, therefore, the end of the Middle Pleistocene was taken to coincide with the end of the Lower Palaeolithic, and stages of a culture such as the Acheulean, which survived *in some areas* after this period, were grouped with the Middle Palaeolithic, which, as we have seen, was a very important period in Stone Age history, since it witnessed the birth of so many new ideas. The early, or 'warm' Mousterian and the Tayacian evolved from the Clactonian. The Fauresmith, Sangoan, and Micoquian evolved from the Acheulean. The Upper Acheulean in the Near East apparently gave rise to the roots of the Chatel-perronian-Aurignacian complex, while the Levalloisian, which had just started towards the end of the Lower Palaeolithic, saw its main development during the Middle Palaeolithic (as we have defined it) and played a large part by means of culture contact in the evolution of some of the new cultures listed above.

Under the old definitions, as we have seen above, the term Middle Palaeolithic was treated as synonymous with the Mous-terian, but the term Mousterian itself was very loosely used, and covered, among other cultures which we recognize today, the Levalloisian, the Aterian, the older 'warm' Mousterian, the classical

Mousterian, and the Levalloisio-Mousterian hybrid culture. The term was even used to describe the Sangoan, because that culture included some specimens with a Levalloisian appearance.

Clearly, we can no longer treat the term Middle Palaeolithic as synonymous with Mousterian, and therefore in the preceding chapters we have used it to cover the cultures of the *period* from the end of the Riss glaciation to the beginning of the Würm. But by so altering the meaning and re-defining this term we can only include in the Middle Palaeolithic the early, or 'warm', Mousterian, and all the rest of the Mousterian—coming as it does within the period of the Würm glaciation—will have to be included in the Upper Palaeolithic.

This will appear revolutionary to many prehistorians who would like to retain the Mousterian in the Middle Palaeolithic. Let us therefore see if this would be feasible in the light of our present, much greater, knowledge of the Stone Age of Europe, Asia, and Africa.

In East Africa the equivalent of the Würm glaciation is the Gamblian pluvial period, and from the very beginning of this period we have two cultures evolving side by side, one of which is a so-called 'blade and burin' culture and the other the Levalloisian and some of its derivatives. We could thus, on one hand, have the Middle Palaeolithic of Europe contemporary with the Upper Palaeolithic in Kenya, while at the same time the Levalloisian elements in Kenya, which are contemporary with the 'blade and burin' culture, would be classed as Middle Palaeolithic. This, in effect, would mean that in one and the same place we had cultures side by side which we had to describe respectively as Middle and Upper Palaeolithic!

Having thus defined the position and made it clear that in this book the term Upper Palaeolithic is NOT being used with the limited meaning it used to have in the early days of Prehistory, we can turn to a review of the Upper Palaeolithic cultures.

(*a*) *The 'Cold' Mousterian Culture of Europe.* From the beginning of the Würm glaciation until its closing stages, the dominant Stone Age culture in Europe was the Mousterian, which, as we have seen in the last chapter, had appeared upon the scene during the preceding interglacial period where it was associated with a warm-climate fauna.

The Mousterian proper was almost certainly derived from the Clactonian, and in fact there would be some justification for calling the 'warm' Mousterian 'final' Clactonian were it not for the fact that it is much more evolved than any of the other Clactonian stages known to us, so that it seems best to treat it as early Mousterian.

As we have seen, the early Mousterian was contemporary with the later stages of the Levalloisian and also with the final stages of the Acheulean and Micoquian, and inevitably there was a great deal of influence upon the Mousterian by these other cultures. The net result seems to have been that different groups of Mousterian people evolved their culture during the Würm glaciation along a number of distinct lines. Some groups adhered to a form of culture which derived straight from the so-called 'warm' Mousterian and which shows no influence of either Acheulean or Levalloisian elements. Thus the classical Mousterian has no hand-axe elements and no Levalloisian elements.

On the other hand, the careful excavation by Peyrony of Le Moustier itself (type site of this culture) has shown that the shelter there was occupied at various times not only by the makers of the classical Mousterian culture, but also by what he calls Moustero-Levalloisian and Moustero-Acheuleo-Levalloisian. At many other sites in France, too, we find that among the industries formerly classified as Mousterian there are at least three distinct variations of the Mousterian culture to be recognized. One of these is the classical Mousterian, another is a Mousterian with many Levalloisian elements but with scarcely any hand-axes, and the third is a basically Mousterian culture with strong elements both of the Hand-axe and the Levalloisian cultures.

As regards this last group, it is not certain whether the hand-axe element is due to an actual *direct* influence of the late Acheulean on the Mousterian, or whether it is due to the fact that, during the preceding period, part of the Levalloisian culture had been much affected by the Acheulean and had adopted hand-axes as a tool type, so that a contact between the Levalloisio-Acheulean and the Mousterian could account for Peyrony's Moustero-Acheuleo-Levalloisian.

What is both significant and important to note is that the hand-axes which occur in Acheuleo-Mousterian and Acheuleo-Levalloisian industries are almost entirely made by a different technique from that used by true Acheulean hand-axe makers, and show no evidence of the cylinder-hammer technique having been employed.

The essential tool types of the classical Mousterian are triangular points and side-scrapers and a wide variety of utilized flakes. In the Moustero-Levalloisian and the Moustero-Acheuleo-Levalloisian we find, in addition to these, a proportion of hand-axes, mostly small and heart-shaped or triangular, a few rare burins, and a number of tools of a type known as 'Audi points'. The 'Audi point' is a tool somewhat recalling a crude and large backed blade and is, in fact, a crudely made 'knife with blunt back'.

Before the evidence from other continents showed that, in fact, true Chatelperron-type knife-blades had been invented elsewhere, much earlier, it was thought that the 'Audi point' of France was the parent of the backed blades of later cultures in the same area, but this no longer seems likely.

During the first part of the period we are discussing, the greater part of Europe, especially in the north, was too cold for any human occupation, and it was only as the ice-sheets retreated that some of the later cultures moved northwards.

(b) *The Chatelperronian Culture of Europe* (formerly called Lower Aurignacian). Towards the close of the Würm glaciation there arrived in South-west Europe a culture which is characterized by large backed blades made on large blade flakes, burins, and end-scrapers (see fig. 23). This culture differs markedly from any of the Mousterian cultures, and replaces them rather suddenly; it is now called the Chatelperronian, but for years it was known as Lower Aurignacian, since it was believed to lead up to the Aurignacian of Aurignac, which was then called Middle Aurignacian.

Unlike the Mousterian culture or any of its European variants, which were all made by Neanderthal man (see Chapter XI), the Chatelperronian was made by *Homo sapiens*.

We have seen in the last chapter that the so-called late Acheulean (Micoquian) of Palestine and the Near East is of special interest because its hand-axe elements are in very small proportion to the rest of the assemblage, and it was suggested that the roots of the Chatelperronian might, in fact, be found in this culture in the Near East. It is therefore of special interest to note that whereas hand-axes are exceedingly rare in the Chatelperronian they are not entirely missing. The famous Combe Capelle skeleton, found with the Chatelperronian (or former Lower Aurignacian) in France, had a hand-axe buried with him, and although it is possible that the Chatelperronian culture makers had given up making and using the hand-axe as a tool type (since they had invented other tools which better served the purposes for which hand-axes were generally used) they still remembered their origin in a Hand-axe culture and used hand-axes as some kind of symbol or in ritual ceremonies.

This idea need not be as far-fetched as at first sounds, for we know
from modern native tribes that peoples who use iron for all normal

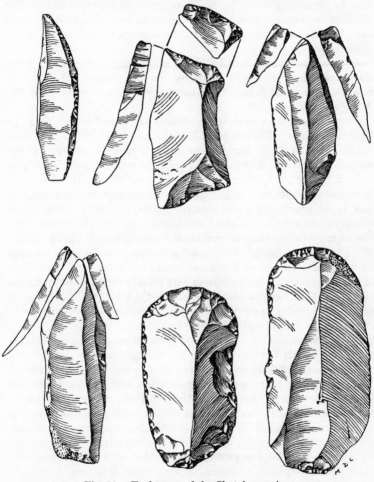

Fig. 23.   Tool types of the Chatelperronian
(redŭced to about ¾)

purposes sometimes use stone flakes and knives for ritual purposes
such as circumcision.

It was with the coming of the Chatelperronian to Europe that
art first appeared (see Chapter VIII) as well as a regular use of
bone to make simple tools, such as awls for piercing leather.

(c) *The Aurignacian Culture* (formerly called Middle Aurignacian). The Chatelperronian is followed in South-west Europe by the Aurignacian, while in South-eastern Europe (so far as the available evidence shows) the Aurignacian succeeds directly upon the Mousterian, without any intervening Chatelperronian or similar culture.

If, as seems likely, the Chatelperronian came into Europe from Palestine, then sites will certainly, in due course, be found in South-east Europe, where the Chatelperronian occurs beneath the Aurignacian.

But whereas we can only guess that the possible origin of the Chatelperronian of South-west Europe was in Palestine, we have ample proof that the Aurignacian came from that country. If the distribution of the Aurignacian is plotted on a map, it is seen to extend from Palestine and Syria to the west coast of France. The Aurignacian culture, like the Chatelperronian, includes among its tool types some well-made backed blades, but they are in much smaller numbers than in the Chatelperronian, and the characteristics of the Aurignacian culture are the association of vast numbers of high backed, keeled, and nosed scrapers; end-scrapers on long blade flakes, numerous burins of many varieties, and a number of blade flakes utilized as knives but mostly without blunt backs (see fig. 24). There is also a considerable increase in the use of bone and similar materials for tools, while art developed very considerably (see Chapter VIII).

(d) *The Solutrean Culture.* This very interesting culture of South-west and South Central Europe is characterized by leaf-shaped tools worked over one or both faces by pressure flaking into what may have been large, simple arrow-heads and javelin-heads. In France, where it was first found, the Solutrean occurs in rather an evolved form, but in South Central Europe earlier stages have been recognized. In addition to the special leaf-shaped tools which are characteristic (see fig. 25), the culture has burins, end-scrapers, a few backed blades, and clearly has affinities with the Aurignacian.

Its actual origin is, however, by no means clear yet. There are some who believe that it may have evolved in South Central Europe as a result of an Aurignacian group of people coming into contact with a late Acheuleo-Mousterian group and being influenced by them. There are others who regard it as a spontaneous development from a part of the Aurignacian. Either explanation seems possible.

(e) *The Gravettian Culture* (formerly called Upper Aurignacian).

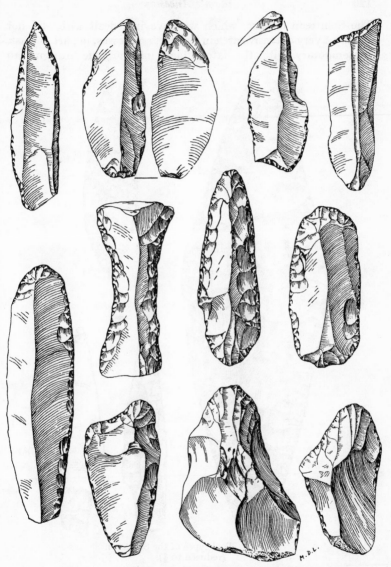

Fig. 24. Tool types of the Aurignacian (formerly called Middle Aurignacian)
(reduced to ¾)

The Solutrean culture, which we have just dealt with, did not occupy a very extensive area in Europe, and it was, in part at least, contemporary with the later stages of the true Aurignacian

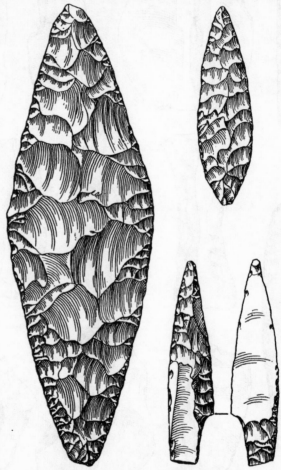

Fig. 25. Tool types of the Solutrean
(reduced to ⅞)

(formerly called Middle Aurignacian). In time, it also overlapped the beginning of what used to be called the Upper Aurignacian, now called Gravettian.

This culture has all the appearance of being a derivative of the

Chatelperronian, but so far as Europe is concered, there seem to be some stages missing in the evolution from Chatelperronian to the Gravettian. This may well be due to our present incomplete

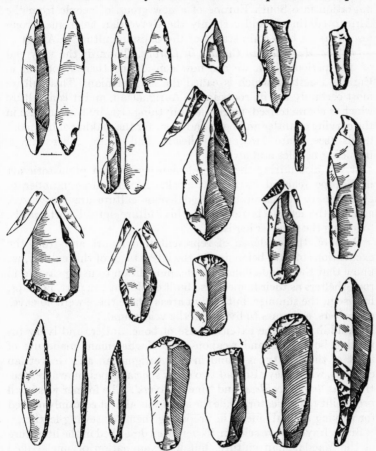

Fig. 26.   Tool types of the Magdalenian and Gravettian
(reduced to ⅔)

knowledge, and it would not be surprising if sites were found—outside the area of Aurignacian dominance—where Chatelperronian could be shown to evolve slowly into the true Gravettian.

In most ways the Gravettian can be regarded simply as a refined and more highly evolved Chatelperronian, with the large Chatelperronian type of backed blade giving place to small, narrow, parallel-sided backed blades, as well as to a variety of specialized burins (see fig. 26). There is, however, another school of thought which sees in the Gravettian culture evidence of a migration into South Europe of a new group of people from the African continent, and certainly the Gravettian has some strong resemblances to certain stages of the Capsian culture in Africa.

(*f*) *The Magdalenian Culture in Europe.* Towards the very end of the period which we are now considering there appeared in Europe a culture which is called the Magdalenian. This culture most certainly has its roots in the Aurignacian, and it is a culture which is characterized, more than anything else, by the increase in the carving of antler and bone and ivory for the making of harpoon-heads (see Plate II*a*), arrow-heads, and many other things, including needles and awls.

It was also during the Magdalenian period that prehistoric art in Europe reached its highest peak. A very large number of evolutionary stages of the Magdalenian culture are recognized, and, as the ice-sheets retreated, this culture spread northwards, following the reindeer herds.

Both on the evidence of representation in art and from the excavations of sites belonging to the later stages of this culture, we know that the Magdalenian people, in addition to using caves and rock-shelters as their homes, also built crude huts; in part, perhaps, for use in the summer, but also in areas where there were no caves or shelters, as homes to live in all the year round.

In addition to the extensive use of bone, antler, and ivory for making both tools and weapons, the Magdalenians made use of most of the tool types found in the Aurignacian and Gravettian cultures, while they also had two other special types known, respectively as '*lames écaillées*' and 'sinew frayers'. The former was in all probability a fabricator, while the latter was almost certainly needed for fraying animal sinews in preparing them for sewing leather.

Sinew frayers have seldom, if ever, been described in the literature of the Magdalenian culture, but an examination of unclassified specimens from type sites shows that this tool, which also occurs in East Africa at about the same time, is well represented at some Magdalenian sites.

(*g*) *The Cresswellian Culture.* A regional offshoot of the Gravettian culture extended into parts of England during the closing stages of the Pleistocene, and it is regarded as sufficiently distinct to be given a separate name, derived from the site where it was first recognized, Cresswell Crags, in Derbyshire.

AFRICA

When we turn to the African continent we find that the complexity of cultures, which is a feature of all the Upper Palaeolithic, is such that it will be necessary to divide our survey and discuss different regions of the continent separately.

(*h*) *The Aterian Culture.* This culture was formerly known simply as the Mousterian of North Africa, but that name was applied to it at a time when the main distinctions between Mousterian and Levalloisian were still not clarified and when the Levalloisian of Europe was itself usually described as Mousterian. Then, in 1920, Reygasse gave the new distinctive name of Aterian to this culture, having recognized that it contained many elements which had no counterpart in the classical Mousterian. The name has gradually been accepted more and more generally and the culture itself has been divided into a number of stages as well as regional phases.

As Miss Caton-Thompson has shown in her 1946 study of the Aterian, this culture is characterized by the presence of tanged points (unmistakable arrow-heads), and spear blades up to nine inches long, in association with other elements, such as side and end-scrapers and a very high proportion of prepared cores of general Levalloisian type (see fig. 27).

If we were certain that the origin of the Aterian was to be sought for in the European continent, then we should, in terms of modern knowledge, have to seek its roots more in the Levalloisian or perhaps in the Levalloisio-Mousterian of South-west Europe than in the Mousterian. But we have already seen in earlier parts of this book that the Levalloisian culture was not the only one to evolve a highly developed prepared-core technique, and that the Sangoan (which, incidentally, was also once labelled Mousterian) has in fact a great many of the essential elements of the Aterian. This is particularly true of the later stages of the Sangoan and of its derivative, the Lupemban, which will be discussed later in this chapter.

If we examine the general distribution of the Aterian and its evolutionary stages we find that it is much more widespread, as well as appearing earlier, in North-west Africa than elsewhere along the northern coastal strip, although evolved and later stages of the culture eventually reach Egypt.

Since there is considerable doubt as to whether there was a land bridge linking North-west Africa with Europe after the Riss glaciation, it becomes almost impossible to seek an origin for the Aterian in Europe unless we postulate that it was derived from a very early stage of the European Levalloisian which crossed into North Africa *before the Riss-Würm interglacial*. It is equally unlikely that it has its origin in a movement westwards from Egypt, since there is no early Aterian in the eastern part of the region in which this culture occurs.

We may, therefore, feel justified in examining the possibilities that the Aterian has no direct connexion with the Mousterian or Levalloisian of Europe at all, but is an indigenous African culture, with its roots in some older African culture.

We know that during the Kanjeran-Gamblian interpluvial (the Riss-Würm interglacial) the Sangoan was very widely spread over the vast regions to the south of the Sahara, including the Congo, Uganda, and Angola. We believe that in Africa, during this period, the Sahara was probably considerably drier than it is today and would therefore have proved an effective barrier to a migration northwards. But as the change of climate which gave rise to the Würm glaciation in Europe and the Gamblian pluvial in Africa set in, the Sahara would once again gradually have ceased to present a barrier to migration, and it would have been very easy for a branch of the evolved Sangoan to start to move up into Morocco and Tunisia and give rise to the Aterian. It is therefore of the utmost importance to see what similarities we can find between the later stages of the Sangoan and the Aterian.

In point of fact, the resemblances are remarkable. The prepared cores of the Aterian are indistinguishable from those of the later Sangoan; both cultures have a proportion of hand-axe types surviving; both have the long pointed lance-heads carefully worked over both faces (the Upper Sangoan has these in much higher proportion than the Aterian), while the tanged points of the Lupemban, a derivative of the Sangoan occurring in Angola and the southern Congo, provide an exact parallel to the points of the Aterian. Both cultures also have a few small, leaf-shaped, biface tools recalling the Solutrean of Europe or the Stillbay of East and South Africa.

(*i*) *The True Mousterian.* In discussing the Aterian culture earlier in this chapter, the view has been expressed that a true Mousterian may not perhaps occur in the same area, and that all of what has been classed as North African Mousterian is in reality Aterian in one or another of its many stages and regional variations. At the same time it is essential to note that some authors who are conversant with the Aterian still maintain strongly that the Aterian is preceded along the coastal zone of North-west Africa to the west

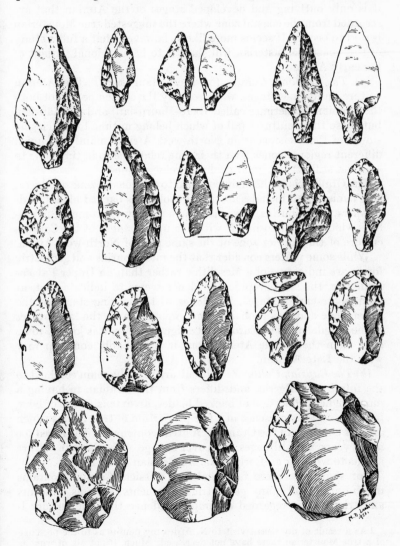

Fig. 27. Tool types of the Aterian
(reduced to about ⅔)

by a true Mousterian without Aterian elements.[1] If this view is correct, then it does not necessarily invalidate the view that the Aterian proper has origins in the south and not in the north, for it is only outlying and developed stages of the Aterian that are recorded from the coastal zone where the suggested true Mousterian is said to occur. It seems more likely, however, that a fuller study of this coastal Mousterian will show it to be a regional variant of the early Aterian.

(*j*) *The Oranian Culture* (or Ibero-Maurusian). The Aterian culture, in its final stages, was probably the contemporary of both the Oranian (sometimes called Ibero-Maurusian) and the Capsian, but these three cultures (all of which belong in time to the closing stages of the Pleistocene in North-west Africa) mainly occupied different regional zones, and their true relationship in time, one to another, still needs a great deal more elucidation.

The Oranian is in the main confined to the coastal zone of Algeria and Tunis, and it includes among its tool types backed blades, end-scrapers, micro-burins, crescents, and a variety of geometric micro-liths which appear to link it with the upper stages of the Capsian culture of the interior zone of the same part of North-west Africa.

While some writers consider that the micro-burins and geometric forms are indicative of a Mesolithic rather than an Upper Palaeo-lithic age, the stratigraphical evidence seems to indicate that, at least in its earlier stages, it belongs to the closing stages of the Pleistocene and was probably contemporary with the later stages of the Magdalenian in Europe. Stratigraphically, it is known to be later than the Middle Aterian, but it is probably contemporary with the Late Aterian.

(*k*) *The Capsian Culture*.[2] This culture is in the main confined to the interior of Algeria, and differs from the Oranian in having a much higher proportion of backed blades, an extensive use of bone for awls, and the presence of a fair proportion of true burins which are less common in the Oranian. A great controversy has raged for many years, and still rages, both over the age of the Capsian culture and as to whether an Early or Lower Capsian exists or not.

For some, the mere fact that the classical Capsian contains micro-burins and many geometric implements, such as crescents and triangles, is regarded as ample evidence that the culture is

[1] As a result of my recent visit to N. Africa my doubts as to the presence of a true Mousterian there have not decreased. Much, if not all, of what is called Mousterian appears to be nearer to the Levalloisian.

[2] See Appendix.

Mesolithic and does not belong to the Upper Palaeolithic. This view seems to be based, in the main, on an out-moded point of view which treats the term 'Upper Palaeolithic' as synonymous with the so-called 'blade and burin' cultures of Europe and which uses the Prehistory of Europe as the yardstick by which all other cultures in other continents must be measured.

Since micro-burins and geometric tools first appear in Europe in the Mesolithic, any culture which has these elements—so the argument goes—must be labelled as Mesolithic or later. This view tends to ignore the evidence of stratigraphy and fauna, both of which seem to indicate clearly that the Capsian of North Africa starts in the closing stages of the Pleistocene and therefore should rank as Upper Palaeolithic just as much as the later Magdalenian.

There is also some—albeit disputed—evidence that an early Capsian occurs in North Africa which is probably as old, at least, as the Middle Aurignacian of Europe, and those who oppose this view most strongly do so on the ground that it cannot be a true early Capsian as it includes microlithic elements. As we shall see later in this chapter, the presence or absence of microliths is no criterion of age in the African continent, whatever it may be in Europe.

We must next turn to the Upper Palaeolithic of Egypt.

EGYPT

(*l*) *The Sebilian Culture of Egypt.* The Sebilian culture, first found at Sebil by Vignard, and later shown to have an extensive range elsewhere in Egypt, has its roots in the Levalloisian, and three distinct stages—Lower, Middle, and Upper Sebilian—are recognized.

Owing to the essentially microlithic character of the later stages of this culture, there are many who have refused to regard it as of Upper Palaeolithic age, but the recent review of the evidence by Miss Caton-Thompson leaves little room for doubt that even the Upper Sebilian should be regarded as contemporary with the later stages of Upper Palaeolithic of Europe.

The Sebilian sequence demonstrates a slow and gradual change from a Levalloisian to a very specialized microlithic culture, in which micro-burins play a very important part. An interesting feature is that the whole culture is mainly based upon a prepared-core technique, and that even its microlithic elements are made from flakes mostly produced from very small prepared cores and seldom from true blade cores. Another characteristic of the

Sebilian is the use of deliberately broken or snapped flakes, and the widespread habit of trimming away the bulbar end of the flakes used for tools.

(*m*) *The Levalloisio-Khargan and the Khargan Cultures.* These cultures are in some respects similar to the Sebilian, but with predominantly round rather than angular forms of flakes and with evidence of being derived from a Levalloisian. The use of deliberately snapped flakes is an important characteristic of the Khargan, corresponding to the similar development in the Middle Sebilian.

(*n*) *The Late Aterian Culture.* Whereas the earlier stages of the Aterian culture are missing in Egypt, there seems to have been an invasion by a very late and somewhat specialized branch of the Aterian culture towards the end of the Upper Palaeolithic period.

From Egypt we must proceed to East Africa to study the next important region where the development of the Upper Palaeolithic cultures is well exemplified.

EAST AFRICA AND THE SUDAN

In the East African zone we find the contemporary and parallel evolution of three distinct cultural elements. These are: (1) the Kenya Capsian (formerly called Kenya Aurignacian); (2) the Developed Levalloisian and its derivatives the Stillbay and Magosian; (3) the later stages of the Sangoan (formerly called Middle Tumbian).

(*o*) *The Kenya Capsian Culture.* Whereas the available evidence concerning the Capsian culture in North-west Africa suggests that it appears towards the closing stages of the Upper Pleistocene (and continues in derived forms right through to Neolithic times), the position in East Africa is very different.

From the very beginning of the Gamblian pluvial period there appears a very well-developed culture (see fig. 28) in which the dominant tool types are: (*a*) backed blades; (*b*) end-scrapers; (*c*) burins of many forms; (*d*) sinew frayers; (*e*) crescents; and (*f*) triangular fabricators. The cores are all of the true blade-core type. Some of the blades show faceted striking platforms, but these should not be confused with the faceted striking platforms found on flakes derived from prepared cores of the Levalloisian type. The presence of long blades from blade cores with faceted striking platforms can be shown, by a study of the cores, to be due to the fact that a core from which a series of blades had been struck in one direction was often then turned through a right angle and further blades struck off, with the fluted surface, from which the first series of blades were derived, used as a striking platform.

The Kenya Capsian passes through a long series of evolutionary stages, starting with Lower Kenya Capsian and followed by Upper

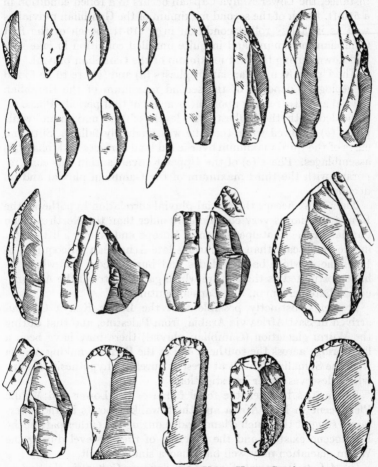

Fig. 28. Tool types of the Upper Kenya Capsian
(reduced to about ⅔)

Kenya Capsian; of which phases (*a*), (*b*), and (*c*), are the best known.

Unlike the Capsian of North Africa, which is mainly to be found in surface sites, in shell mounds, and at little depth in rock-shelters, the Kenya Capsian is known both from well-stratified geological deposits of the Gamblian pluvial, from many high-level beaches of lakes formed during the different maxima of the Gamblian pluvial, and also from very well-stratified deposits in rock-shelters. For instance, the Lower Kenya Capsian occurs in a rolled condition in a 510-ft. beach of the second maximum of the Gamblian pluvial as well as in a less rolled condition in a 710-ft. beach of the first Gamblian maximum, and in quite unrolled condition in lake silts laid down during the first maximum of the Gamblian pluvial.

The Upper Kenya Capsian of phases (*a*) and (*b*) are to be found in geological deposits of the second maximum of the Gamblian pluvial and also resting upon the beaches of that period. Phase (*a*) coincided with the highest lake levels of this maximum, while phase (*b*) followed while the lake was gradually falling. Silts and clays of the third maximum overlie old land surfaces with phase (*b*) assemblages. Phase (*c*) of the Upper Kenya Capsian was contemporary with the third maximum of the Gamblian pluvial and its decline.

Thus, if we accept the glacial-pluvial correlation hypothesis, the Kenya Capsian is very considerably older than the North African Capsian or the Chatelperronian of Europe and is only a little later in the time-scale than the curious late Acheulean (Micoquian) of Palestine in which backed blades and burins occur and which we have postulated as the culture which gave rise to all the Aurignacian, Chatelperronian, and Capsian cultures.

It seems distinctly possible that the Lower Kenya Capsian arrived in East Africa via Arabia, from Palestine, and that during the Würm glaciation (Gamblian pluvial) there may have been a land bridge across the southern end of the Red Sea linking Arabia with the Somalias. This is at present purely an hypothesis, but one which deserves closer investigation.

Similarities between the fossil fauna of the Lower and Middle Pleistocene in East Africa and the Siwalik deposits in India certainly suggest that such a land bridge during the earlier part of the Pleistocene existed; and the lowering of the sea-level during the Würm glaciation may well have had a similar result.

(*p*) *A Late Degenerate Stage of the Sangoan Culture in the Sudan.* A recently published paper indicates the presence of a crude culture, with general similarities to the Levalloisian, at Singa in the Sudan. The illustrations tend to suggest that this may in fact be a degenerate form of late Sangoan. Further work is needed.

(*q*) *The East African Developed Levalloisian Culture.* Throughout

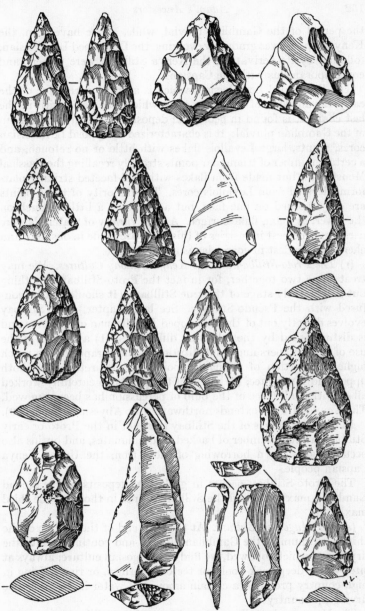

Fig. 29. Tool types of the Stillbay, from Ethiopia
(reduced to about $\frac{2}{3}$)

the period of the Gamblian pluvial, while, as we have seen, the
Kenya Capsian was gradually evolving, the Developed Levalloisian,
followed by its derivative, the Kenya Stillbay, were present and
contemporaneous with the Capsian.

The Developed Levalloisian, which is a direct derivative of the
early Levalloisian of the same area, which was dealt with in the
last chapter, is found in geological deposits of the first maximum
of the Gamblian pluvial. It is characterized by typical Levalloisian
cores, points, large Levallois flakes with little or no retouch, and
a certain number of triangular points strongly recalling the classical
Mousterian, but made from flakes with well-faceted striking platforms derived from Levallois cores. The majority of these points
are only worked on one face, but a few have a little retouch on
the lower, or main, flake surface. A wide variety of materials were
used, and the best industries of this stage are made in obsidian and
chert, the crudest in coarse lavas and quartzite.

(*r*) *The Proto-Stillbay and the Kenya Stillbay Cultures.* We may
treat these two together, for in fact the Proto-Stillbay is nothing
but a very early stage of the true Stillbay. (It should not be confused with the Pseudo-Stillbay. See last chapter.) The Stillbay
evolves directly out of the Developed Levalloisian of this area and
is distinguished by the following differences: (1) a decline in the
use of side-scrapers and a substitution of end-scrapers; (2) a much
higher proportion of triangular points having retouch on both
upper and lower face; (3) a few of the points so carefully worked
all over that all trace of the bulb of percussion has been removed.
The Kenya Stillbay extends northwards into Abyssinia (see fig. 29).

In the later stages of the Stillbay (but not in the Proto or early
Stillbay) a small number of backed blades, lunates, and burins also
occur, suggesting a borrowing of ideas from the Upper Kenya
Capsian people.

The Proto-Stillbay occurs in geological deposits of the second
Gamblian maximum and the Stillbay proper in those of the third
maximum.

(*s*) *The Magosian Culture.* At the very end of the decline of the
third maximum of the Gamblian pluvial, and continuing into the
dry period which followed, we find the Magosian culture; always at
sites where deep rock pools, or tectonic springs, or rivers rising in
high country provided a certain amount of water in an otherwise
drying-up country.

The Magosian is really a debased form of the Stillbay (see fig. 30),
but with the true Stillbay bifacial points becoming very scarce and

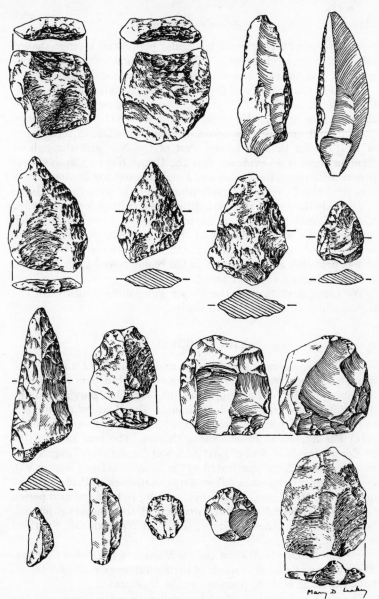

Fig. 30. Tool types of the Magosian from Kenya
(reduced to ¾)

being replaced by very small triangular points and lozenge-shaped bifacially worked specimens. The proportion of lunates, end-scrapers, and burins is also much higher than in the Stillbay proper.

(*t*) *The Upper and Final Sangoan* (formerly called Middle Tumbian). In parts of East Africa, and more particularly in the area on the east side of Lake Victoria, there is an overlap of the Kenya Capsian and the Upper Sangoan (see fig. 31), while in those parts of East Africa that lie to the west of the Nile and throughout Uganda there is no evidence that the Upper Kenya Capsian ever penetrated; there, the Upper and Final Sangoan are contemporary first with the Developed Levalloisian and later with the Stillbay.

Towards the end of this period there is a culture formerly called 'Upper Tumbian', which is at present little known but which appears to be a late offshoot of the Upper Sangoan and which, when properly studied, might have to be given a distinctive name. It was probably contemporary, in the region round Lake Victoria, with the Magosian of drier areas.

We must next turn to the Upper Palaeolithic cultures of the region which embraces the Rhodesias.

THE RHODESIAS

(*u*) *The Rhodesian Upper Sangoan and the Bembesi Cultures.* The former is a local variant of the Sangoan which occurs in deposits belonging to the first maximum of the Gamblian pluvial and the dry period before the second maximum. The Bembesi culture is a variant of the Upper Sangoan and is found in Southern Rhodesia.

(*v*) *The Rhodesian Proto-Stillbay Culture.* The true Levalloisian of Egypt, the Nile, and of East Africa as far south as Tanganyika, never seems to have penetrated to the Rhodesias (see Chapter VI), and the Upper Sangoan is followed by the Rhodesian Proto-Stillbay in both the Rhodesias. It belongs, mainly, to the semi-arid period between the second and third maxima of the Gamblian pluvial, but also occurs in the vicinity of the great rivers during the third maximum of the pluvial.

(*w*) *The Rhodesian Stillbay and the Rhodesian Magosian Cultures.* These are merely local variants of the East African equivalents and have the same relative positions in the time-scale.

The next region which must be dealt with is the Congo and the northern part of Angola. This is a region of great rivers and extensive forest, and it is ecologically very different from most of the other parts of Africa.

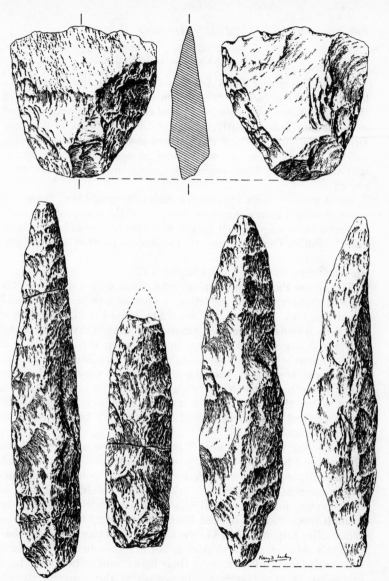

Fig. 31. Tool types of the Upper Sangoan from Kenya
(reduced to $\frac{4}{9}$)

THE CONGO AND ANGOLA

(x) *The Upper and Final Sangoan Cultures.* In the Congo, for a long time, all the various stages of the Sangoan, as well as some of the later cultures, were classified together as Tumbian and regarded as Neolithic. Subsequently, as the result of the work of Jacques, Breuil, Cabu, and Lowe, it was realized that many different stages existed in the area, some of them of considerable antiquity, and the names of Djockocian, Tshitolean, and Lupemban were coined.

Subsequently, work in northern Angola revealed that there was a direct evolutionary sequence from the main stages of the early Sangoan to a stage which in the old parlance would have been called Middle Tumbian, and it was suggested that the cultural term Sangoan should be employed for the various stages up to and including this stage (see Chapter VI).

The Upper Palaeolithic period (with which we are dealing in the present chapter) saw the evolution of what we now term Upper and Final Sangoan. These stages are characterized in the Congo and northern Angola by the vast numbers of beautifully made lance-heads and less well-made picks, in association with a number of cruder forms which were common in the earlier Sangoan, such as large discoidal scrapers, some hand-axes, and a very high develop-ment of the tortoise-core technique. This became developed to a point where the cores, taken out of their context, as well as the flakes derived from them, would unhesitatingly be attributed to a Levalloisian culture.

(y) *The Lupemban Culture.* Towards the close of the Gamblian pluvial the Final Sangoan gives way to a derived culture which includes among its characteristic tools tanged points, many pre-pared cores of a type which, taken alone, would be classed as Levalloisian, numerous small bifacial lance-heads and picks, and a small proportion of backed blades, trapezoidal forms and cres-cents. The Lupemban as known at present is more evolved than the early Aterian of North Africa, but it seems distinctly possible that both these cultures, with their many similarities, may have originated from a common side branch of the Sangoan culture somewhere in the northern part of the Congo, where our knowledge of Stone Age cultures is still very limited.

Finally, as far as Africa is concerned, we must turn our attention to South Africa before we examine the position in Asia.

SOUTH AFRICA

In South Africa the term 'Middle Stone Age' has been used as a sort of 'omnibus term' to embrace a whole series of cultures, the stratigraphical and cultural inter-relationship of which is still far from fully worked out. The term itself is at any rate a most unsatisfactory one, for *Middle Stone Age* is an English translation of 'Mesolithic', and would therefore seem to imply that all the so-called 'Middle Stone Age' cultures of South Africa were post-Upper Palaeolithic in date. Actually, there is good reason to believe that a part, at least, of the so-called 'Middle Stone Age' culture of South Africa belongs truly to the Upper Palaeolithic period as we have defined it, though not, of course, to the 'Upper Palaeolithic cultures' as the term was once used to cover exclusively the so-called 'blade and burin' cultures.

The term Middle Stone Age as used in South Africa is also unsatisfactory from another point of view, because some writers have treated it as though it were synonymous with a very different term, Middle Palaeolithic, simply because in the early days of Prehistory, when the term Middle Palaeolithic was first coined, the 'Mousterian' (used in its widest sense to include the Levalloisian) was then the only culture put into the Middle Palaeolithic, and the so-called Middle Stone Age cultures of South Africa were seen to have certain similarities with Moustero-Levalloisian types.

Such lack of clear definition of terms has led to a great deal of confusion as to the true significance and position of what the South African prehistorians call the Middle Stone Age.

It is very misleading as we have seen earlier, to use terms which have a 'time significance' such as 'Upper Palaeolithic' or 'Middle Stone Age' as though they had a cultural significance, for when other contemporary cultures are found that do not fit into the cultural definition that has been given to a term which should signify a time-stage, the issue becomes very confused.

(z) *The Late Fauresmith Culture.* We have already seen in the previous chapter that a culture called the Fauresmith emerged as one of the derivatives of the earlier Hand-axe culture, towards the end of Middle Palaeolithic times, in South Africa. It is a culture characterized by an association of many small hand-axes with numerous unifacial flake-tools made by the prepared-core technique, and very closely parallel to the Levalloisian of Europe. We have shown that there is reason to believe, however, that the special development of the prepared-core technique in South Africa has no connexion with the Levalloisian of Europe but was an independent parallel evolution.

During the period which we are now considering, the Upper Palaeolithic—the period from the beginning of the Würm glaciation in Europe (the Gamblian pluvial in Africa) to the end of the Pleistocene—some late stages of the Fauresmith culture seem to have survived in South Africa, with a tendency for the hand-axe element to become smaller and more rare.

(*aa*) *The Stillbay Culture.* The Stillbay culture was first recognized and given its name in South Africa, but, as we have seen, regional variations occur in other parts of the continent. The South African Stillbay seems to belong to a fairly late period in the Upper Palaeolithic, but is, nevertheless, most probably truly Upper Palaeolithic in age, although its final stages may extend into the post-Pleistocene.

(*bb*) *The Mazelspoort, Mossel Bay, Howiesonspoort, Modderpoort, Koeningse, Glen Grey, Pietersberg, and Cape Flats Cultures.* Under the omnibus term of 'Middle Stone Age cultures' the above and sundry other cultures have been named in South Africa, and it seems impossible in the present state of knowledge to sort out the relationships of each to the other, or to determine to what extent they are separate and distinct cultures or merely regional variants of one or the other within the group.

Some of these cultures would seem to be nothing more than local variants of the Stillbay; others may be direct specialized derivatives of the Fauresmith, while there is also a possibility that the influence of the Lupemban of Angola (itself a derivative, as we have seen, of the Sangoan) may not be wholly absent. This possibility is suggested by the tanged points of Noordhoek, which are associated with a variety of other tool types which also occur in the Lupemban, such as backed blades, lunates, and 'spear-points'.

(*cc*) *The So-called 'Tugela Industry' of Natal.* Under the name of the 'Tugela industry' several very interesting assemblages of implements from the Natal coast have been described. I examined a representative selection of these in South Africa and have since had a further series sent to me for study, and I am convinced that this 'Tugela industry' represents a variant of the Upper Sangoan. The presence of an Upper Sangoan variant on the Natal coast raises an interesting problem of distribution. It seems likely that a branch of the Sangoan people followed the Zambezi river to the sea and then spread southwards along the coast, but never extended far inland in South Africa. It is interesting to note, however, that

Wayland, who found the original Sangoan at Sango Bay in Uganda (from which the culture got its name), has recently reported a Sangoan variant in Bechuanaland.

(*dd*) *The South African Magosian.* We have already seen that in East Africa and the Rhodesias, variants of the Magosian culture are to be found at the very close of the Pleistocene period, and recently the occurrence of this culture has also been noted in South Africa. It is not yet clear, however, whether the South African Magosian represents a local derivative from the local Stillbay or whether it is, in fact, evidence of a movement southwards of the Magosian culture from the Rhodesias.

If it is a local derivative from the South African late Stillbay, then it is probably post-Pleistocene in age, but it may well be found to be due to a southward movement of the Rhodesian Stillbay, in which case it may perhaps prove to be contemporary with the late Stillbay of the Cape and of Upper Palaeolithic date, in the sense in which we are using the term in this book.

To conclude this chapter on the Upper Palaeolithic, we must next turn to Asia.

THE NEAR EAST AND SYRIA

(*ee*) *The Upper Levalloisio-Mousterian.* In Palestine and neighbouring countries the Levalloisio-Mousterian, which, as we have seen in the last chapter, was strongly developed during the first part of the Upper Pleistocene (i.e. the period corresponding to the Riss-Würm interglacial), continues well into the period covered by what we are calling Upper Palaeolithic, and was, in fact, roughly contemporary with the main development of the Mousterian and Mousterio-Levalloisian of Europe.

In Syria the work of Mr. Rust at Jabrud has resulted in a very detailed publication of the culture sequence. Part of his list consists of the following:

(8) Lower Jabrudio-Mousterian.
(7) Pre-Micro-Mousterian.
(6) Levallois-Mousterian.
(5) Micro-Mousterian.
(4) Younger Acheuleo-Mousterian.
(3) Young Acheuleo-Mousterian.
(2) Younger Jabrudio-Mousterian.
(1) End Mousterian.

It is likely that all of these are merely variants, or possibly sub-stages, of the final evolution, in that area, of the Levalloisio-Mousterian of Palestine. It must be noted that in his own table of correlation Rust suggests that it is only (1), (2), (3), and (4) above that are the equivalent of the Upper Levalloisio-Mousterian of Palestine.

At any rate, it may be said that during the earlier part of the period with which we are concerned—the time corresponding to the greater part of the Würm glaciation of Europe—the dominant culture of the Near East was some form of late Levalloisio-Mousterian and that such rare hand-axes as occur in this culture are more in the Levalloisian tradition than in that of the Acheulean, as far as technique of trimming was concerned.

(*ff*) *The Lower Aurignacian.* Throughout this area the Levalloisio-Mousterian appears to be followed by what has been called a 'Lower Aurignacian', which is characterized, at least in Palestine, by burins, end-scrapers, some backed blades of Chatelperronian type, and what is called the 'Emireh point'. It is not at all clear at present whether this 'Lower Aurignacian' is merely an early stage of the true 'Middle' Aurignacian, or whether it should be regarded as Lower Aurignacian in the old sense in which the term was formerly used in France for what is now called Chatel-perronian. On the whole, the balance of evidence seems to point to its being a very early stage of what became 'Middle' Aurignacian or, as we prefer to think of it now, true Aurignacian.

It must be noted that in Palestine, at Mugareh-el-Wadi, Layer 'F' yielded both a 'Lower Aurignacian' culture and an Upper Levalloisio-Mousterian culture in the same horizon, while Turville-Petre found a similar state of affairs at Mugareh-el-Emireh. On the other hand, Neuville found a fine level of 'Lower Aurignacian' with Emireh points at Jebel Kapzeh without any association with Upper Levalloisio-Mousterian, and the same is true of Rust's results in Syria.

It has been suggested that these two cases of admixture in the same level may be explained by regarding them as derived from two distinct levels.

Another explanation which cannot, however, be ruled out is that these two cultures overlapped in time, and that certain caves were occupied seasonally by people of two entirely distinct cultures, so that elements of both cultures were dropped on the floor and eventually became incorporated as a single deposit in the cave.

(*gg*) *The 'Middle' Aurignacian.* Following the Lower Aurignacian

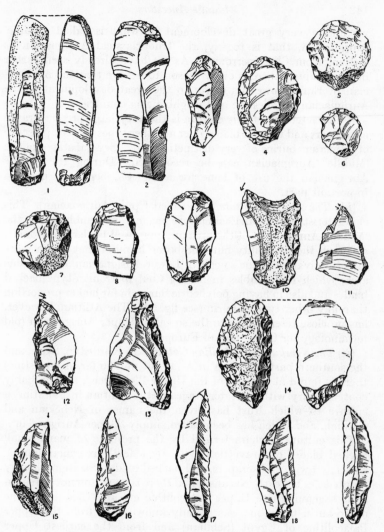

Fig. 32. Tool types of the Atlitian from Palestine
(From *The Stone Age of Mount Carmel*, Vol. I, by Garrod & Bate.
Oxford University Press)
(reduced to about ⅔)

we find a very great development of what is called 'Middle' Aurignacian, that is to say, the true classical Aurignacian as distinct from Chatelperronian. As we have already seen earlier in this chapter, there is every reason to believe that the Aurignacian of Europe owes its origin to the great development of the Aurignacian in Palestine and neighbouring countries.

A characteristic of this culture is the very large preponderance of scrapers and utilized blades over all other types and the presence of numerous burins of very distinctive type. Several stages of the 'Middle' Aurignacian can be recognized. During the Middle Aurignacian the use of bone for awls, etc., begins to play an important part.

(*hh*) *The Atlitian Culture* (also called Upper Aurignacian). This characteristically Near East culture has many resemblances to the 'Middle' Aurignacian of the area and may well be derived from it, although the possibility must be borne in mind that it is a more direct derivative of the so-called 'Lower Aurignacian' of the same area, which it resembles in having Chatelperronian-type backed blades and also in having polyhedric burins in far higher proportion than any other type of burin (see fig. 32). The Atlitian, however, has no close resemblance to the so-called Upper Aurignacian (old terminology) or Gravettian of Europe.

(*ii*) *The Nebekian and Fatilian Culture.* In Kurdistan, Syria, and the southern part of Russia in Asia (but not, so far, in Palestine) there is found at the end of the Upper Pleistocene, and probably contemporary with the later stages of the Atlitian in Palestine, a culture to which Rust has given the names of Nebekian and Fatilian, and which has been called simply 'Upper Aurignacian'.

This culture is characterized by the presence of many small backed blades of Gravettian type, by a few rare 'micro-burins' associated with end-scrapers, and backed blades. Stratigraphically it antedates the early Natufian, and there is no reason not to regard it as a genuine late Upper Palaeolithic culture. The use of the micro-burin technique was already known both from the Upper Palaeolithic of Egypt (Sebilian) and from the earliest Upper Palaeolithic of East Africa, the Kenya Capsian, and its presence in this culture in Syria need not be regarded (as some, including Rust, would suggest) as positive evidence of a Mesolithic age.

In many respects this late Upper Palaeolithic culture of Syria, Kurdistan, and South Russia resembles the Grimaldi industry in the south of France, and it has also resemblances to some of the early Capsian industries of North Africa.

INDIA AND BURMA

(*jj*) *The Upper Palaeolithic.* In northern India and Burma it would seem, from the available evidence, as though the Soan and Anyathian cultures continued to evolve slowly and still survived in modified forms during the Upper Palaeolithic period. In other parts of India there is some evidence of a 'blade and burin' culture, resembling perhaps the Fatilian of Syria and Kurdistan, but the evidence is too vague at present and much work is needed.

THE FAR EAST

(*kk*) *The Ordos Culture.* In China, during the later stages of the Upper Pleistocene, there was a culture which is called the Ordos culture, which seems to be a mixture of very late and evolved Levalloisian elements with some strain of the Aurignacian culture.

(*ll*) *The Ngandong Culture.* In late Upper Pleistocene times in Java the Patjitanian culture is replaced by the Ngandong of somewhat indeterminate affinities.

To summarize this very lengthy chapter on the Upper Palaeolithic cultures is far from easy, but briefly, the position would seem to have been somewhat as set out below.

So far as our present knowledge goes, the dominant cultures in Europe and the Near East during the greater part of the Würm glaciation—and the corresponding period in areas where glaciation did not extend—were the Mousterian and the Levalloisio-Mousterian, both of which were made by men of Neanderthal type (see later). Nevertheless, it seems likely that somewhere in the Near East at about the same time there was another culture developing out of the late Acheulean (Micoquian) of Palestine, which, as we have seen in the previous chapter, had elements foreshadowing the emergence of the Aurignacian and Chatelperronian and kindred cultures. It is even possible that this evolution had advanced quite considerably by the beginning of the Würm glaciation of Europe, in some area of the Near East, at present unknown.

The Mousterian and Levalloisio-Mousterian of Europe, Palestine, and Syria were superseded, rather suddenly, towards the end of the Würm glaciation (and the corresponding period in the Near East) by, first of all, the Chatelperronian (in Europe) and the so-called 'Lower Aurignacian' with Emireh points, in Palestine, etc.

Possibly the Aurignacian superseded the Levalloisio-Mousterian in the Near East several thousand years earlier than the arrival of the Chatelperronian in France, and there was a gradual movement into Europe from Asia Minor.

In Europe the Aurignacian (Middle Aurignacian) was followed by the Solutrean, which may well have come from a mixing of the cultures of the invading Aurignacian with a late stage of the Mousterian somewhere in Central Europe; but the Solutrean had only a limited range. In the meantime, elsewhere, the Aurignacian was evolving towards the Magdalenian culture, while the Chatelperronian (formerly called Lower Aurignacian) possibly evolved locally in parts of South Europe, through the Grimaldian into Gravettian, in areas where the force of Middle Aurignacian influence was not too strong.

This view is, however, not always accepted and there are some who would prefer to see, in the Gravettian, evidence of a direct invasion from North Africa. This seems, however, very improbable and it is more reasonable to regard the Gravettian as a local evolution of the Chatelperronian in areas where Middle Aurignacian influence did not exist, and to believe that it then spread and extended into Middle Aurignacian zones of influence.

In the Near East, however, things went somewhat differently. The true, or Middle, Aurignacian was followed by the Atlitian in Palestine and Syria, and in Palestine it persisted until the Mesolithic Natufian culture appeared, while in Syria an early Natufian is preceded by a culture which must be regarded as an evolved development from the Chatelperronian into something very similar to the Gravettian on the one hand and the Kenya Capsian on the other.

In Asia, apart from the Near East and South Russia, we have at present all too little knowledge of developments in Upper Palaeolithic times; they have been outlined, but need no summary.

In Africa we have an even more complex picture than in Europe or Asia, with regional developments along distinctive lines.

The early Sangoan flowers into a strong culture in Angola, the Congo, and the Sudan, and possibly influences the development of the Aterian in North Africa and some of the cultures of South Africa.

The Fauresmith persists in South Africa for a time during this Upper Palaeolithic period and may possibly be the parent of some of the other Upper Palaeolithic cultures of the so-called 'Middle Stone Age' in South Africa.

In North Africa, on the western side, the Aterian (with possibly some true Levalloisio-Mousterian along the coast) dominates the scene at the beginning of Upper Palaeolithic times, and is followed by the Capsian and Oranian. In Egypt, on the other hand, the late Levalloisian persisted for a time and then evolved into the Sebilian.

In East Africa the whole period is marked by the contemporary development of two distinct cultures. The Kenya Capsian appears on the scene at the very beginning of the period, and it seems reasonable, on the available evidence, to regard it as having arrived from some unknown part of the Near East and to have had its roots in the curious late Acheulean (Micoquian) of Palestine, etc. This, however, presupposes a land bridge (or a sea crossing) somewhere at the south end of the Red Sea, for there is no evidence at all for such a movement through the narrow Suez isthmus.

While the Kenya Capsian was evolving in East Africa over the whole long period, the Developed Levalloisian, which has its roots in the true Levalloisian of the slightly earlier period, evolved by easy stages through Proto-Stillbay and Stillbay to Magosian. In both the latter cultures there is evidence of the influence of the Kenya Capsian.

It is not yet clear whether the Magosian of the Rhodesias and parts of South Africa was a local parallel evolution from the Stillbay of those areas, or whether the Magosian of East Africa moved southwards.

The table on p. 146 sets out in summary form the cultures treated in this chapter.

CULTURES OF THE UPPER PALAEOLITHIC

EUROPE

Climate

Fourth glaciation (with several maxima)

(Würm glaciation and its decline)

Cultures

←—Cold Mousterian—→   Chatelperronian   ↗ Gravettian—→

←—Mousterio-Levalloisian—————→   ↘ Creswellian—

←Solutrean→

Aurignacian

←—Mousterio-Acheulean—————→   Levalloisian   ↘ Magdalenian—

AFRICA

Climate

Fourth Glacial Period   (Several maxima)

(Gamblian pluvial and its decline)

Cultures

North Africa

←—Aterian—————→   Upper Aterian   ←—Capsian—

←—Mousterian—→   Oranian—

←Sebilian—

←—————Levalloisio-Khargan—————→   Khargan—→   Final Aterian of Egyp

E. Africa

Lower Kenya Capsian—→   Upper Kenya Capsian————→

Developed Levalloisian—→   Proto-Stillbay—→   Stillbay—→   Upper Stillbay—→   Mago

S. Africa

Late Fauresmith→   Middle Stone Age Complex (Stillbay, Howiesons Poort, Modderspoort, etc.)→Mago

Angola

←—Upper Sangoan—→   Final Sangoan—→   Lupemban—

ASIA

Climate

Fourth Glaciation in the Himalayas (Cold and damp)

Cultures

Near East

←—Upper Levalloisio-Mousterian

Lower Aurignacian—→   Middle Aurignacian————→   Upper Aurignac

←—Final Soan   Atlitia

Far East

Upper Anyathian   Fatili

CHAPTER VIII

Palaeolithic Art

IT is only under exceptional conditions that really early art is preserved, and although many thousands of examples of Palaeolithic art are now known, these must represent only a very small proportion of the art that was executed by Stone Age man in Palaeolithic times.

The only preserved art of Palaeolithic age belongs to the closing stages of the Würm glaciation and the corresponding period in the time-scale elsewhere, but this does not necessarily mean that art was not practised before then. Indeed we may, I think, be reasonably sure that some crude form of art was being practised earlier, which has not been preserved.

We can, indeed, imagine that long before man started to paint with colours or engrave with specially made graving tools, he must often have made rough drawings in sand, in the earth, and on clay, with his finger-tips or a piece of wood. Naturally, however, such examples of early art would hardly ever survive. We have, however, a few rare examples of drawings made with the finger-tips on wet clay, on the ceilings and walls of a few caves (for example, on the ceiling of the Peche-Merle cave), and these examples serve to fortify our belief that art in these forms must have been fairly common before painting and engraving were thought of.

The few preserved examples of finger-tip drawing are only to be found under most exceptional conditions. Those of Peche-Merle, for example, are on a clayey patch of the ceiling of a deep underground cavern, where the clay has not only remained moist ever since the drawings were made (and therefore not crumbled), but where the position of the drawings was such that there was little risk of their obliteration by later users of the cave, as would have occurred to drawings on the clayey floor or walls. Moreover, the cave entrance was blocked by a rock fall towards the end of Palaeolithic times, and so sealed in, until a new entrance was formed by subsidence in relatively recent times.

In addition to works of art executed with the finger-tips on such soft surfaces as clay, etc., the other, and more common, forms of prehistoric art may be subdivided into:

        (*a*) Engraving.
        (*b*) Drawing and Painting.
        (*c*) Sculpture.
        (*d*) Modelling.

There are examples of both engraving and the use of colour among the earliest preserved Palaeolithic art of Europe, but it seems likely (but not proven) that primitive engraving preceded the use of colouring materials.

We will therefore briefly consider engraving first of all.

As we have already seen in the chapter on the uses of stone tools, Palaeolithic man made a special tool called a 'burin' which, although it had other uses, was probably the principal tool for the making of most engravings of the incised-line type. There is a very great degree of variation in the nature of the incised-line engravings, depending upon the particular usage of the period. On the whole, the early engravings tend to be more deeply cut, with rather wide lines, while in the later stages of Palaeolithic art we find the use of very thin lines—barely scratches.

Engraving was not only carried out on the walls of caves and rock-shelters but also, to a very considerable extent, upon small pieces of stone (see Plate II*b*) and on pieces of bone, ivory, and antler. Often, especially in Magdalenian times, objects such as harpoon-heads, arrow-straighteners, etc., made of bone or ivory were beautifully ornamented with line engravings.

Within the general category of engraving, mention must also be made of 'pecked', as distinct from incised-line, engravings. These are particularly common in South Africa, but at present there is no certainty that they are not much later in age than the Palaeolithic.

Turning next to drawing and painting, we find that it can be divided into colour-drawing, true painting, and spray-painting. All these groups—because of the use of colour—are usually classified in books on Prehistory as 'paintings'.

That colour-drawing, as distinct from painting, was indulged in to some extent is proved by the discovery of sharpened 'crayons' of mineral colouring materials, and indeed close examination of preserved prehistoric art reveals a few examples that, when examined closely under a lens, show that they were made by this method rather than with a liquid paint. But dry colour, naturally,

Plate II

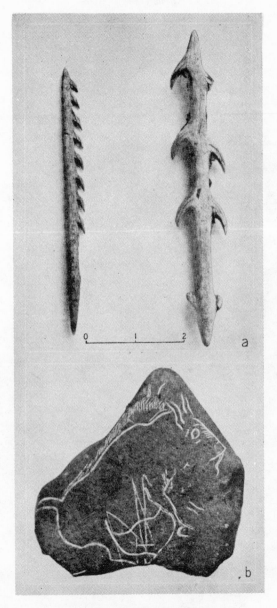

(a) Harpoons of the Magdalenian culture
(b) An engraving on stone by Magdalenian man

Plate III

Bas-relief of a horse by Magdalenian man, from the sculptured frieze at
Cap Blanc, Dordogne, France

Plate IV

An example of prehistoric painting

Plate V

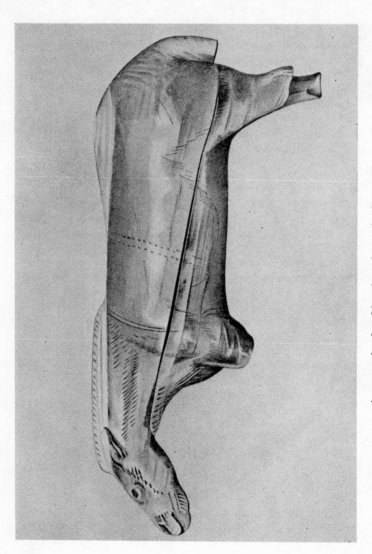

An example of prehistoric sculpture in the round

is less easily preserved than true paintings, and the examples are not numerous.

Colour-painting was carried out by grinding various mineral colouring materials to a fine powder and mixing them with various media such as fat and probably also water and the juices of certain plants. Palettes of stone on which colours have been mixed have occasionally been found, as well as hollow segments of bones which appear to have been containers for powdered paints.

In part, at least, painting was done with the finger-tips, and most of the broad-line paintings in outline were almost certainly done in this way. But simple brushes may also have been used, and we know from the study of modern primitive tribes that effective, but simple, brushes can be made from various fibrous plants and from bits of animal fur, while a sharpened point of wood or the quill of a feather can also be used to apply paint in thin lines, if the paint has been mixed fairly thick. The so-called 'punctuation' painting, where an outline was drawn with a series of coloured dots, was almost certainly done with such a 'brush'. An example of prehistoric painting is seen in Plate IV.

It is interesting to note that the idea of spray-painting seems far from being a modern invention and probably dates back to Upper Palaeolithic times. The commonest examples of such spray-painting are 'negative' hands, where the artist has placed his hand against a bare patch of rock and then 'sprayed' paint with his mouth in such a way that when his hand was removed the outline of his hand and fingers remained as a blank amidst a splash of colour.

It is also distinctly possible that some of the painting in pre-historic polychromes was applied by this simple spray-painting technique, for the overlap of colour in some of these paintings, when examined closely, certainly suggests spraying.

It should be noted before we leave the subject of paintings and engravings that a combination of more than one technique is sometimes found.

Palaeolithic sculpture may be divided into bas-relief and sculpture in the round. Some of the bas-relief work of Upper Palaeolithic times, such as the frieze of horses at the Cap Blanc rock-shelter in France (see Plate III), are of outstanding artistic merit. It is not easy to be certain just what tools were used for this purpose, but we may guess that large, crude hand-picks were used in the blocking-out process and that burins were used to finish off the details. Paint was sometimes used with sculptures of this sort.

Sculpture in the round was mainly confined to the carving of small objects, among the most interesting of which are the exaggerated human female figures often referred to as 'venuses'. Figures of animals also occur, see Plate V.

Although the only sculptures of this sort that have survived are those in stone, bone, ivory, and antler, it can be imagined that wood was also freely used for the purpose of carving, and it is more than likely that sculpturing in wood long antedated the first attempts in harder and more durable materials.

Although left to the last, there is no reason to believe that the art of modelling was a later discovery of prehistoric man, but, like the drawings in clay, etc., with the finger-tips, this type of art only survives under very exceptional conditions.

If we may judge from the efforts of children and of present-day primitive peoples, it seems probable that Stone Age man at a very early date experimented in modelling animals, etc., in clay and mud. But such objects, if only sun dried and not baked (or even when baked, unless made of a very good clay mixture), in the ordinary course of events do not last. A few rare example of Palaeolithic modelling have, however, survived. Some of these, such as the famous clay bisons of the Tuc d'Audoubert, are really models in bas-relief, showing only one side carefully modelled. But there are also a few little models in the round, such as those from Vestonitz.

Having outlined the forms in which Palaeolithic art is found, it is perhaps necessary, very briefly, to indicate some of the evidence that the art we are dealing with really does belong to the Upper Palaeolithic period, since the question is repeatedly asked, 'How can you tell that this art is so old?'

In the first place, a proportion of the art represents animals which we know are extinct, and yet they were clearly drawn or painted by people who were familiar with them as living animals. Moreover, we know approximately when such animals as the woolly mammoth did disappear and that gives us a forward dating limit. Secondly, in many, but not of course in all cases, examples of mural art have been found buried beneath occupation levels in caves and rock-shelters which can be dated, by their content of tools and fossil animal bones, to various definite periods of the Upper Palaeolithic. Clearly, if a painting or engraving or bas-relief on the wall of a cave is buried by an accumulation of deposits containing, say, Magdalenian culture, the art cannot be later than that culture. Or, again, blocks of rock from the ceiling or walls of a cave, with paintings on them, have fallen and become imbedded in deposits found on the floor of the cave containing datable cultural material. The paintings must therefore be either contemporary with or earlier than this culture. Yet another line of argument that can be used is through the discovery of samples of colouring materials, crayons, and palettes in deposits of a certain culture, and the correlation of these colours and crayons with some of the art on the walls.

Of course, too, there is all the mass of small objects of art, of bone and ivory, and small stones which are found *in situ* in different Upper Palaeolithic cultural levels and are clearly contemporary with the cultures. When paintings and engravings in identical styles are also found on the walls of caves, the small objects can be used to date the mural decorations.

There is really therefore no doubt whatsoever as to the genuineness of Upper Palaeolithic art, although there are some sites usually ascribed to this period, where the evidence is not yet quite clear.

If we turn to a consideration of the places where Palaeolithic mural art can be found, we notice that the sites fall into three main categories:

(*a*) Dark caves and passages where nothing can be seen without the aid of artificial light.

(*b*) Open rock-shelters, with which we may include slightly overhanging rocks, which are not quite strictly shelters.

(*c*) On flat slabs of rock and the tops of boulders.

In addition to this, small objects of art can be found in a variety of sites of Upper Palaeolithic times, including open station sites, such as Vestonitz.

The art which occurs in dark caverns and in the passages leading to them presents us with a whole series of problems. Why were these dark and often very inaccessible places chosen for the manifestation of art? How did the artist manage to work in the dark, or, if not, what was his source of light? Did he paint entirely from memory?

The first of these questions we will examine at the end of this chapter when we discuss the significance of prehistoric art, but the other two must be dealt with here.

Little hollowed-out stones, with evidence of charring, have been found again and again in the painted caverns of France and elsewhere, and these are interpreted as lamps, by analogy with those of modern Eskimos. A lamp such as this presumably consisted of a wick of moss floating in marrow-fat, but it must have required several to provide enough light to paint by, and, at the best, painting under such conditions cannot have been easy.

As to whether prehistoric man painted from memory or not, it is by no means impossible that he made 'sketches' from life on bits of tree bark or other perishable material, and then copied from these sketches on to the walls of the caves. But if he worked thus, no positive evidence has remained.

It is also possible that some of the examples of engraving on small bits of stone and bone fragments, that are found from time to time, were not so much works of art in themselves, but 'artists' note-books'; work done in the field from living models for use later when executing art in the caverns.

But all this is really guesswork, and we have no positive proof of the correctness of our answers to these problems.

Even in the deep caverns and passages, only a small part of the art that was originally present is ever preserved to the present day. This is due to the action of damp, of air currents, of rock-weathering, and many other causes. We even find that in caves that have been sealed in and inaccessible from Palaeolithic times until rediscovered in modern times—such, for example, as Lascaux—it is only the paintings on certain parts of the walls that are perfectly preserved, while other apparently excellent wall surfaces show no clear paintings, yet the faint traces of colour on them show that they, too, once carried paintings that have been lost.

In open rock-shelters prehistoric art is only present if it consists of engraving or bas-relief sculpture or, so far as paintings are concerned, if the rock is of a particularly hard kind whose surface is hardly affected at all by weathering in such a short time (geologically speaking) as 25,000 or more years.

Paintings were probably common on the walls of most rock-shelters, but we only find them in the very few regions where suitably hard rock has saved them from scaling away.

Even less suitable for the preservation of early art are the exposed tops of rounded or flat boulders. Under such conditions, where the sites are subject to even greater weathering by sun and wind, we can only find engravings preserved, and of these only those which were fairly deeply incised.

One of the apparently curious things about Palaeolithic art is the fact that we find such vast numbers of superimposed figures on the same rock-surface; paintings or engravings made by successive artists at different periods. This, at first, seems all the more surprising when near by we see what seems to us an equally good 'canvas' with no paintings on it at all. But if we remember that it is only on some surfaces that art has survived, we then realize that the apparently empty canvas next to an area with a series of superimposed paintings, was probably also covered with paintings at one time. We can then more readily understand how it became necessary to paint over earlier art.

In practice, the fact that early man did so frequently paint over someone else's earlier work is of great value to the prehistorian. By studying the various styles of art in their relation to each other, it becomes possible to work out a sequence of styles from any given site. Then, if we find out whether or not the same sequence is repeated at other sites, it is possible to discover if the sequence also has a chronological significance. Very often it has.

It is for this reason that it is of very great importance to make quite certain of the relative positions of paintings, when there is superposition. This is not very difficult if the superimposed paintings are in a different colour, but often requires very critical examination if pigments of the same colour have been used by successive painters.

In studying styles of art many different aspects of the problem have to be considered. In certain styles there is a tendency to draw everything in a formal profile, so that animals are shown with only two legs. There are certain styles also in which great attention to detail is paid, hooves, ears, and sex organs are clearly indicated; or again there are styles which are naturalistic and others which are very conventionalized. It is not possible, however, to discuss the question of styles in detail in a book which is only meant to give a general introduction to the Palaeolithic period and which is not intended as a text-book on prehistoric art. Such a text-book is, however, very urgently needed today.

We must next briefly summarize the main cultures with which Palaeolithic art is associated.

In Europe the earliest art appears to be associated with what used to be called Lower Aurignacian, and is now known as Chatelperronian. The true (or Middle) Aurignacian and the Gravettian (old Upper Aurignacian) cultures are also associated with art, while the Magdalenian culture in Europe seems to be linked with the period when Palaeolithic art reached its finest development. The Solutrean people, whose culture, as we have seen, appears in an intrusive form between the Gravettian and Magdalenian in some areas, do not appear to have been great artists, so far as the available evidence shows.

In North Africa there are many engraved and painted sites, but most of them are probably of an age later than the Upper Palaeolithic. Some at least were probably carried out by the makers of the early stages of the Capsian and Oranian cultures, towards the closing stages of the Pleistocene.

In East Africa some of the prehistoric art is almost certainly of Upper Palaeolithic date, although most of it seems to be younger. Until more work has been done it is not possible to be certain.

In Southern Rhodesia it seems certain that some of the earliest art is associated with the Rhodesian Stillbay culture, but much of the rest is probably of later age.

Similarly, in South Africa, the greatest part of the art is almost certainly attributable to the makers of such cultures as the Wilton and Smithfield, which are both post-Upper Palaeolithic, but a little of the earliest art may well go with the Stillbay culture or some of the other so-called 'Middle Stone Age' cultures. Much more work is needed.

In Asia I know of no record of art that is certainly of Upper Palaeolithic age, but this is probably due to the fact that suitable sites for the preservation of early art have not yet been found. It would be surprising indeed if the Middle Aurignacian people of Palestine did not produce art, but if they did, it does not seem to have survived.

We must, in conclusion, briefly review the theories that have been advanced to explain the various forms of prehistoric art.

First of all, we must consider the art which is found on the walls and ceilings of deep, dark caves and passages, often at a considerable depth underground. We have already seen that prehistoric artists, in order to have painted or engraved successfully in these dark places, must have provided themselves with some sort of illumination, and we have noted the fact that primitive 'lamps' are often found—sometimes in large numbers. A strange thing about this 'art in darkness' is that it was often executed not only in places where no natural light could reach it but often in incredibly difficult places within the caves; in crevices, on narrow ledges, and on the ceiling; places where the physical act of painting must have been very hard to carry out successfully.

The commonest explanation of this art, hidden away in dark caverns and in inaccessible places, is that it was a manifestation of the magico-religious. It is argued, and not without a large measure of justification, that if it was meant to be seen and admired it would hardly have been executed in the places where we find so much of it: in the dark, on the ceilings, and in inaccessible crevices. Also, if it was meant to be looked at, it would seem to have been rather senseless to superimpose one painting on another, again and again, so that it requires extreme patience to follow out the details of any given animal.

Among modern primitive peoples we can, perhaps, obtain ideas which may or may not correctly indicate an answer to our problem. For example, we know that among some stock-owning tribes today, as well as some primitive hunting peoples, there is a magic practice which is supposed to 'tie up' or 'safeguard' an animal until the person who has 'tied it up' himself frees it. Thus the Kikuyu, if a goat or sheep is found to have been lost out grazing when the evening tally is made, will take the herdsman's club and perform a simple magic rite whereby the missing animal is identified with the club. The club is then hidden in the darkest part of the owner's hut under the bedding, and it is believed that by this simple magic act the missing animal is 'tied up' so that it will not fall a prey either to carnivora or to thieves until it is located by the owner next morning. Somewhat similarly the Wanderobo will 'tie up' a wounded animal they have been tracking, when night falls, in order that it may not escape during the night but may be easily found next day.

If we allow ourselves to suppose that Stone Age man entertained similar ideas and beliefs, it is not impossible to see a similar practice in the paintings of animals—some of them clearly wounded animals —in deep caves. We can imagine a hunter who has been following a wounded bison all day going to the local artist with a request that he should 'tie up' the animal till daybreak, by painting its likeness in some very inaccessible dark cavern. By making the image or likeness of the animal as inaccessible and secure from prying eyes as possible he might have thought to safeguard the actual beast from carnivora or from other hunters, until he found it.

Or, again, some of the painted scenes depict pregnant female animals; or male following female, in search of a mate. From the analogy of the ideas of some modern primitive peoples it is possible to interpret these as symbols in a fertility cult destined to help, by magic means, the proper increase of the wild animals which were the chief source of food for the Palaeolithic hunters. In the case of this interpretation, however, there would seem to be less reason, certainly less obvious reason, for painting these scenes in the darkness.

The famous site of Trois Frères with the so-called Sorcerer—a curious semi-human masked figure—is usually regarded as providing clear evidence of a magico-religious cult linked with prehistoric art, and it is widely believed by prehistorians that solemn ceremonies conducted by a sort of 'priest magician' took place in this painted cave. This may or may not have been the case. It does seem certain, however, that most of the art in the dark caverns and passages cannot be explained simply as the desire for self-expression.

On the other hand, there are cases where actual scenes are depicted, that one cannot help feeling were, in a sense, commemorative and due to a desire to record an actual event that happened.

Concerning the art on the walls of caves and rock-shelters that were also habitation sites, in most cases there seems much less reason to seek a magico-religious interpretation.

A frieze of horses in bas-relief, such as those of the Cap Blanc shelter, must have taken a long time to complete, and there seems little reason to believe that they were not the work of an artist indulging in self-expression and, at the same time, decorating his home. There are many parallel cases in modern ethnology where the walls of mud huts, which are the home of a man with an artistic temperament, are decorated without any magico-religious significance being involved.

Where actual scenes are portrayed, as in some sites in Tanganyika Territory, it may also be possible that the commemorative aspect of the paintings played a part with the decorative. Such a dual function in art is, after all, still very common.

When we turn to the examples of art executed on small movable objects, either slabs of stone, or bone, or actual objects of everyday use, the problem of the significance takes on a different complexion. It seems distinctly probable that, to some extent, the engravings of animals, or just heads of animals, on bone fragments and small stone slabs, may be regarded—as we have already mentioned—as a sort of artist's note-book. Nevertheless, we cannot ignore the possibility that art in this form may also have been for the purpose of 'tying up' an animal until the hunter could find it. One can easily imagine a hunter going to an artist and getting a 'likeness' of the wounded animal he had failed to catch up with engraved upon a stone, and then taking the stone back with him to his own rock-shelter to hide. A man might well use the same stone again and again for such a purpose, since the fact that one engraving was superimposed over another would not affect the efficiency of the magic, but might indeed enhance it, if the previous time the stone had been so used it had 'apparently' been effective. On the other hand, it is hard to see why an artist who was making 'note-book sketches' should have gone on using the same piece of stone or bone over and over again, until it requires hours of work to sort out which line belongs to which animal.

Where art is found on actual objects of daily use, most of it was probably purely decorative, though again one can conceive of its being, to some extent, also commemorative. A hunter who had used his favourite spear-thrower with effect against a particularly difficult quarry might well decide to commemorate the fact by engraving its likeness on his weapon.

CHAPTER IX

The Problems of Human Evolution

IN this chapter I propose to discuss, in very general terms, the problems that face us in the study of human evolution and also to outline the methods by which scientists distinguish between the different types of fossil man that are found.

In the three succeeding chapters we shall then be in a better position to discuss respectively fossil apes, fossil humans of extinct type, and fossil remains of *Homo sapiens,* and the evidence which these fossils yield to help us in forming a picture of how present-day man was evolved.

Today there are to be found living in the world a number of quite different creatures which all belong to the main zoological order of Primates. Living members of this group range from the little, big-eyed tarsius of the Far East and the little galagos (or bush babies) of Africa to man himself, and also include all the lemurs, monkeys, and great apes in between these two extremes.

Most of the members of the order have tails, man and the great apes being the only exceptions, while man alone of all the living members of the order Primates can walk fully erect. Yet anyone who has carefully studied the details of the anatomy or of the dentition of the different Primates cannot fail to be struck by the numerous points of similarity—varying in degree, of course—which cause scientists to treat all these creatures as being more closely related to each other than they are to members of other zoological groups such as the carnivora or the rodents or the ungulates.

In other words, to anyone who has studied the subject, it is very clear that all of these creatures were evolved from some common stock in the dim past, and the chief problem of the study of human evolution is to sort out all the evidence and trace back the ancestry of the various divisions of the group by means of fossil evidence, in order to get at the truth. Fortunately, every year sees more and more discoveries of fossils which have a bearing upon the problem, but, needless to say, a great deal still remains to be discovered.

Instead of the popular conception of scientists being engaged in the search for '*the missing link*' the truth is that whole lengths of the chain are still missing, and often when we do discover one of the many missing links we find it hard to decide just whereabouts in the chain it properly belongs.

Before we proceed to discuss just how fossil human and other remains—often fragmentary—can be interpreted, let us briefly look at the living apes and man.

Four genera alone of great tailless apes survive today: the gorilla and chimpanzee in Africa and the orang outan and gibbon in Asia. Each of these genera have certain characteristics in which they resemble man more than the others do, and also other characteristics in which they differ more from man. None of them could ever be regarded as representing a close cousin of man, nor could any of them qualify as representatives of a stage of evolution through which man had passed in his gradual rise to his present position.

People will stand in front of a chimpanzee in a zoo, or a stuffed gorilla in a museum, and say: 'I just could not believe that I am descended from that!' Scientists do not believe it either, nor do they ask anyone else to believe it; but they do claim that the great apes and man had a common ancestor long ago. But man on the one hand and apes on the other represent different branches and different specializations that have arisen from that common stock.

Here let me pause to discuss a misconception that is still widespread and which has been fostered to a not inconsiderable extent, in the past, by scientists themselves. It has been all too common to write or speak of the great apes as PRIMITIVE members of the ape-human stock, and from this to argue that physical characters that occur in the apes are also PRIMITIVE characters, and as such, characters which one might expect to find in pre-human fossils that were in the direct line leading to man himself. I myself have to plead guilty of having misused the term 'primitive' in my first edition of this book, and so contributed to building up a wrong picture.

The great apes of today are all characterized by having what is called a 'simian shelf'—a ledge of bone that unites the two halves of the lower jaw on its inner aspect. This simian shelf has for years been regarded as a sort of 'hall-mark' of primitiveness in Primates, and it has been assumed for years that it was present in some of the earlier stages through which man passed, in the course of his evolution, and was subsequently lost. Similarly, the great apes all have very long arms in proportion to their legs, and this was regarded as PRIMITIVE; it was assumed, and still is in some quarters, that man passed through a similar stage, in which he had very long arms and that he later reduced the length of his arms, as he evolved. The evidence today, which we shall discuss more fully in the chapter on fossil apes, indicates clearly that scientists were wrong in regarding these characteristics as primitive just because they were found in the apes, who were regarded as 'primitive' cousins, and it now seems certain that both of these characters, as well as a good many others, must instead be regarded as extreme specializations in the apes; characters which markedly separate them from man and which we must expect to find less and less accentuated as we trace back the ancestors of the present great apes to the point where their branch and ours join.

If we turn from the living great apes to the living races of man, as we find them in the world today, we see that the differences between some of the extreme variations of the species *Homo sapiens* (for all living humans today belong to that species) are so great that we might almost be tempted to regard them as distinct species. For instance, if we were to place an Australian aboriginal, with his relatively massive brow ridges and his deep-set nasal bridge, side by side with a South African bushman, a Chinaman, and a man of the tall, fair-haired Nordic type we should be struck first of all by the dissimilarity of detail, before the similarity of general structure made itself apparent. But of course, in actual fact, the divergences between the existing extreme variations of the species *Homo sapiens* are not nearly so great as are the differences between the various races of domestic dog, such, for example, as the St. Bernard, the Dachshund, the Pekingese, and the Greyhound.

When we see a typical example of any of the major and better-known racial variants of *Homo sapiens* we have little difficulty in saying 'that is an Australian aboriginal', 'that is a Mongoloid', and so on; and our opinion is formed by a rapid and often quite subconscious assessment of a wide range of characters which together combine to form the picture of a particular racial type. Most people know and recognize the more common racial types, whether of man or of dogs or of any other racial group, from their appearance in the flesh, but it has to be remembered that the flesh of the face and head and the whole body are built up and moulded by the structure of the bony skeleton.

In the study of fossils, whether human or otherwise, the scientist has to work without the benefit of the form of the flesh that once covered the bones, or the colour of the skin, or the nature of the hair; nevertheless, by proper study and understanding it is just as possible to say with certainty 'this is the skull of a certain type of man' and 'this is the skull of another type', and to compare and study them as well as to distinguish clearly between one type and another, as it would be if they were in the flesh.

It is even possible to give a correct diagnosis on incomplete material, for detailed study shows that different racial types have, during the course of their differentiation, developed specializations in parts of the skeletal anatomy that can be used to identify them with relative certainty. Naturally, when dealing with racial variants within a species, there are times when the results of interbreeding make positive identifications of skeletal material, to any given racial subdivision within that species, very difficult. This applies as much to humans as to any other form of animal life.

On the other hand, since, as we have shown, the differences between well-defined racial groups can be seen and identified even from skeletal material, it is clear that differences between different species should be more easily distinguishable, and those between distinct genera even more so.

The division of animal groups into genera, species, and races is, of course, an arbitrary one. A commonly held criterion, so far as living animals are concerned, is that fertile interbreeding between races of a single species is possible, while between distinct species of a single genus crossing may result in offspring which, however, will be infertile or mules. Some people go further and say that crossing between different genera will not even result in conception, let alone in the birth of offspring, even infertile. These criteria do not always hold good, and a case is on record from South Africa of a calf being born from the crossing of an eland with a domestic cow, animals which are regarded scientifically not only as different genera but as belonging to different sub-families.

Moreover, when it comes to fossils, we cannot apply the tests of fertile interbreeding, etc. (even if they were of positive value), in deciding whether two clearly distinct fossil types are merely racial variants of a single species, or different species, of a single genus, or whether they belong to different genera. Here the personal interpretation of the value of the evidence before the individual scientist inevitably plays a large part, so that we find, again and again, that fossil human and sub-human remains are classed by some scientists as races of a single species and by others as having specific or even distinct generic rank.

This is inevitable in view of our present state of knowledge, but it does not invalidate the fact that there are many different types of fossil man and of his pre-human ancestors and cousins that differ very markedly indeed from man as we know him today.

Since we know very well the essential skull and skeletal characters of *Homo sapiens*—having available for study a vast mass of material representing the living races of that species—it is not very difficult to decide in respect of fossil human remains whether a skull is or is not *Homo sapiens*.

As we shall see in another chapter, there are many Stone Age fossil remains that we can say with certainty are of the same species as present-day man, and we can subdivide these *Homo sapiens* fossils into a number of racial types and also recognize some evidence of racial cross-breeding. But, with the fossil human remains that we can say with certainty do *not* fall within the species *Homo sapiens*, we have greater difficulty when we try to decide whether they are merely distinct species of the genus *Homo* or whether they represent one or more distinct genera.

The human type that is known as Neanderthal man, for example, is regarded, by some, as merely a distinct species of the genus *Homo* —*Homo neanderthalensis*—while others consider that the differences between the Neanderthal type and *Homo sapiens* are so great as to indicate membership of a different genus which they call *Palaeoanthropus*. This does not matter very much at present; what is important is to be able to distinguish between the Neanderthal type of skull or skeleton and that of *Homo sapiens* on the one hand, and of the other extinct human types on the other.

An experienced physical anthropologist who has handled a very large number of skulls of the living races as well as of fossil men, and who is well acquainted with the essential characters of the different races and species can often tell at a glance to what racial group of the species *Homo sapiens* a given skull belongs, or can say that the skull he is examining is not *Homo sapiens*. He does this by an appreciation and understanding of the morphological characters without having to stop and make detailed measurements and comparisons.

Such visual methods can be, and are, of course, supplemented where necessary by the more precise and accurate method of measurement and comparison of measurements and by the use (if required) of the statistical approach in order to determine whether the observed and measured differences fall within or without the normal range of variation within a given race or species. But there are many important characters for which at present no means of exact measurement have been devised, *and it must be remembered, therefore, that the measuring of skulls must remain the servant and not the master of the physical anthropologist.* The mere fact that two things (whether skulls or teeth or pieces of wood) have the same length and breadth and height does not mean that they have the same shape or are morphologically identical. Far from it.

Let us now for a moment consider some of the characters that differentiate races within the species *Homo sapiens* and which also distinguish all the races of that species from the races of other species of *Homo*, and examine briefly how the physical anthropologist works.

If we examine and compare a series of skulls which belong to some of the better defined races of living man we will be struck at once by the very great differences between them (see Plate VI), whether looked at from the side or from in front or from above. The shape of the brain-case or cranium is seen to vary considerably between typical examples of one race and another, while there will be a lesser degree of difference between the skulls of individual members of the same race, if it is fairly pure and has not been much affected by inter-racial cross-breeding. A glance at Plate VI will immediately make this clear, whether we look at the full-face view, the profile view, or the view from above.

But the shape of the brain-case, by itself, is not enough to determine racial identity. The sum total of all the characters visible must be taken into consideration in deciding the race to which a given skull belongs, that is, the shape of the brain-case, that of the nasal bones, the angle of the face, the shape of the lower jaw, etc. It follows, therefore, that the more incomplete a specimen is, the less certain can we be in deciding upon *racial* identification.

The shape of the brain-case alone is, in fact, not even always sufficient to say whether a skull is of the species *Homo sapiens* or not, still less to differentiate race, but it does help to classify skulls to some extent, and therefore (as a matter of convenience) physical anthropologists have invented terms to describe skulls of different shapes. A skull which is broad in comparison to its length is called brachycephalic, one which is long and narrow is called dolichocephalic, whilst skulls of intermediate form are called mesocephalic. The exact classification is determined by measurement, and here again the divisions are arbitrary: if the ratio of breadth to length is over 80 per cent we say the skull is brachycephalic, if it lies between 70 and 75 per cent we say it is dolichocephalic, and if it lies between

75 and 80 per cent we call it mesocephalic. Skulls whose length-breadth ratios are below 70 per cent are termed ultra-dolicho-cephalic.

Similarly, there are terms to classify the measurements that can be taken of the nasal aperture, the eye-sockets, etc.

Several different races may be brachycephalic, but if they are truly different it will be found that they differ significantly in respect of some other character. For example, some skulls of Congo pygmies are quite as brachycephalic as the German skull shown at the top of Plate VI, but the differences in facial angle, in nasal height, etc., would be such that no possibility of confusion would occur.

It cannot be emphasized too often that no single measurable character of any skull will serve, by itself, to distinguish one racial type from another, and that it is only by a critical examination of the combination of all the measurable characters that results of any value can be obtained. Even so, there will be occasions when the visual assessment of some morphological character which has escaped measurement—or expression in terms of measurement—may have to be called in to help supply the correct answer.

As has been stated earlier, there are certain characters, not always measurable, which, taken together, serve to distinguish *Homo sapiens* from extinct species and genera of mankind, and we must now briefly consider some of the more obvious and important of these.

First of all, let us consider what are called brow-ridges, the raised area of bone at the base of the forehead, just above each eye-socket (see Plate VII).

The brow-ridge over each eye is made up of two component parts in *Homo sapiens* and allied forms. One part in each case starts just above the nose and extends sideways and slightly upwards to overlap the second part, which, on either side, starts at the extreme edge to right and left of the eye-socket respectively, and extends inwards and slightly downwards. Thus, above the centre of each eye-socket, there is an overlap of the two elements. This can be clearly seen in Plate VII in the two upper photographs which represent the brow-ridges of an Australian aborigine skull and of a German.

In all *Homo sapiens* skulls brow-ridges occur, and in all cases, so far as we know (except where some pathological condition has intervened), the brow-ridge above each eye-socket is made up of two elements as described above. In some living races of *Homo*

Plate VI

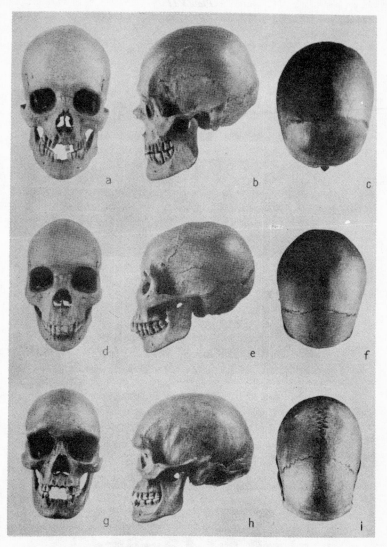

Skulls of various types of modern man to illustrate the range of variability of the shape of the skull. (*a, b, c*) Nordic; (*d, e, f*) Negro; (*g, h, i*) Australian aboriginal

Plate VII

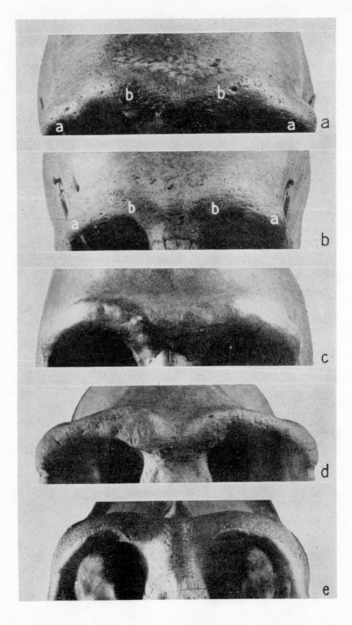

Brow ridges in various types of men and apes. (*a*) Australian aboriginal; (*b*) Negro; (*c*) Neanderthal man; (*d*) Gorilla; (*e*) Chimpanzee

Plate VIII

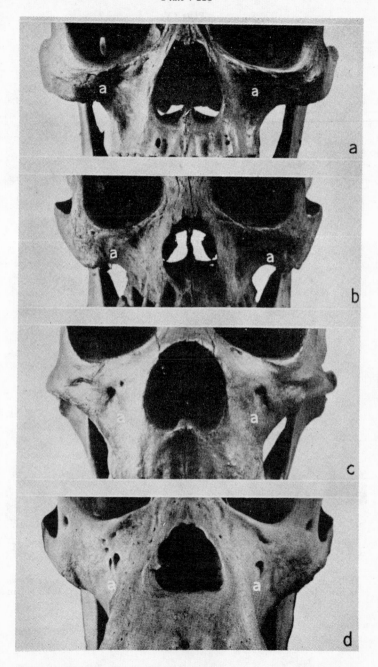

The canine fossa in *Homo sapiens* and its absence in some other primate groups. (*a*) Nordic; (*b*) Negro; (*c*) Neanderthal man; (*d*) Gorilla

Plate IX

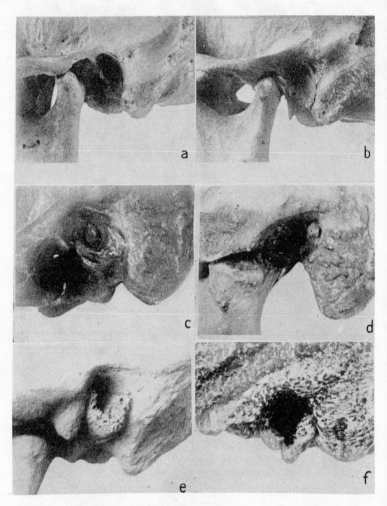

Different types of tympanic plates in man and the apes. (*a, b*) *Homo sapiens*; (*c*) Neanderthal man; (*d*) Piltdown man; (*e*) Gorilla; (*f*) Peking man

Plate X

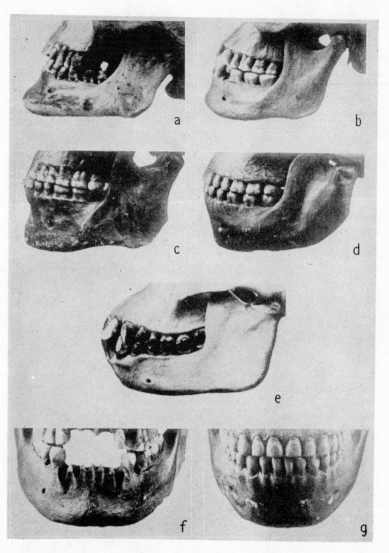

Different types of mandibles. (*a*) Nordic; (*b*) Negro; (*c*) Predmost;
(*d*) Neanderthal man; (*e*) Chimpanzee; (*f*) Nordic; (*g*) Neanderthal man

sapiens, such as the Australian aborigines and also among individual members of many other living races, the brow-ridges may be very large and massive, while in others, such as some negro races, they are represented merely by a slight swelling of the bone.

In some prehistoric races of *Homo sapiens* too, as in Cromagnon man, the brow-ridges are very strongly developed, but they have this same distinctive form in which the ridge over each eye is made up of two elements.

The fact that brow-ridges of this form are a constant characteristic of all races of *Homo sapiens* does NOT mean that any skull which exhibits this character must automatically be classed as *Homo sapiens.* Consideration must also be given to the presence or absence of other essential characters of *Homo sapiens.* The famous Piltdown skull agrees with *Homo sapiens* in this one respect, but differs markedly in others, and so is ruled out from the species.

When we examine the brow-ridges of gorillas and chimpanzees —at the other end of the scale—we find that the form of the brow-ridge is quite unlike that in *Homo sapiens* (see the two lower photographs in Plate VII), while Neanderthal man, Peking man, and Java man, all of which are outside the range of *Homo sapiens,* are different again, and in some ways more like the apes than like ourselves.

In the past, many if not all anatomists regarded the massive brow-ridges of the ape type as a 'primitive' character, and, in consequence, when somewhat similar ridges were found to be characteristic of Neanderthal man and of Peking man, this was regarded as evidence of the 'primitiveness' of these human types. Nowadays, however, it is becoming increasingly realized that massive brow-ridges are not a 'primitive' but a very specialized character, and that their presence suggests not an ancestral stage in human evolution but a side branch that has become more specialized, in this respect, than any *Homo sapiens* type.

Next, if we look at the facial region of different types of *Homo sapiens* we find that (again with the exception of pathologically affected specimens) there is always present a depression or hollow in the bone beneath each eye, which is called the 'canine fossa' (see Plate VIII). In the region of this canine fossa there are one or more small openings in the bone for nerve canals, and these have really nothing to do with the presence or absence of the canine fossa itself, which is merely a concavity. This can be clearly seen in photographs *a* and *b* of Plate VIII.

A well-defined canine fossa is a characteristic of *all Homo sapiens* (except for pathological specimens). In the great apes and in the skulls of human species other than *Homo sapiens* it is only very rarely seen and is more commonly replaced by a convexity or puffing out of the bone in that region.

The presence or absence of a canine fossa is not by itself a criterion to use in assessing the nature of a skull, but it is one which must be taken into consideration with other characters.

Another important area of the skull of which the morphology has to be studied is the region round the ear-hole. The bony plate known as the tympanic plate (see fig. 33) is of essentially the same fundamental form and has the same position in all skulls of *Homo sapiens* type, whilst many other forms of tympanic plate occur in apes and in skulls of human types that do not belong to the species *Homo sapiens*.

As our knowledge increases so we can alter and modify our views, and we know now that the very exceptional form of tympanic plate seen in fig. 33e, in one of the Peking skulls, is not really characteristic of Peking man, and that in some of the other skulls from the Peking site a form more like fig. 33c is to be seen.

But I have yet to see a skull which, by other criteria, is not of *Homo sapiens* type, that has the *Homo sapiens* type of tympanic plate. Nevertheless, it would be most dangerous to use this criterion alone in deciding whether or not a skull belonged to the species *Homo sapiens*.

Needless to say, there are other morphological characters, too, which help to distinguish *Homo sapiens* from his extinct cousins and to distinguish one extinct genus from another, but in a short chapter such as this all that can be done is to indicate some of them: a detailed study of the mastoid process is valuable and also of the region where the lower jaw articulates with the skull; the shape and angle of the foramen magnum and many other things have to be taken into account. What must be remembered is that the classification of fossil skulls into the group *Homo sapiens* or otherwise, if done properly, is based, not on guesswork, but on the assessment of a whole mass of morphological detail.

When we come to the lower jaw or mandible we find that here, too, there are certain characters which, taken in combination and even sometimes alone, help to distinguish *Homo sapiens* from other types of man. From the point of view of the prehistorian this is important, for it sometimes happens that a jaw or a fragment of a jaw is found without any associated skull, and, if there were no distinctive characters in the jaw itself, it would be difficult to identify such specimens.

In Plate X, photographs *a*, *b*, and *c*, you can see three variations of the form of jaw found in *Homo sapiens*. Not only is the amount of projection of the chin very different in the three specimens, but so too is the shape and general proportion of the jaws. It would be

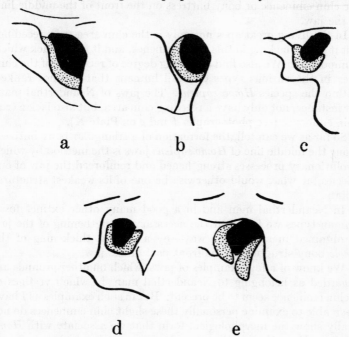

a   b   c

d   e

Fig. 33. Diagrammatic representation of variations of the tympanic plate (reduced to $\frac{7}{8}$)

easy to find examples showing a still greater variation within the species *Homo sapiens*, but all these widely differing jaws would be found on detailed examination to have certain characters in common.

First of all, there is what is called the 'chin eminence', a localized thickening of the bone on the front or outer side of the jaw, on either side of the middle line, forming a sort of raised triangle. This can be clearly seen in photograph *c*, which is a front view of a jaw of *Homo sapiens*.

In some races of *Homo sapiens* (as well as in some individuals of races which normally have a marked 'chin eminence') this character is only slightly developed, but so far as we know, it is always present in *Homo sapiens*. We often speak loosely of a person being 'chinless', by which we mean that his chin is somewhat receding instead of projecting forwards. But in the species of mankind to which we belong, even an individual with a receding chin still has the chin eminence or bony buttress on the front of the middle line of the jaw.

In the living great apes not only is the chin area very receding, but it is also lacking in this chin eminence, and it is this lack which is important. We also find a varying degree of recession of the chin area in the various types of fossil humans that are not ranked within the species *Homo sapiens*. The jaws of Neanderthal man, for instance, not only have a receding chin area, but also lack a true chin eminence (see photographs *d* and *g* on Plate X).

So far as we can tell, the formation of a triangular bony buttress along the middle line of *Homo sapiens* jaws is the method by which evolutionary processes strengthened and reinforced the jaw of our species, at what would otherwise be one of its weakest structural points.

In Neanderthal man and in a good many other extinct fossil human types we find that the necessary strengthening of the jaw is obtained in a different way—by a general thickening of the *whole* bony structure in the front part of the jaw.

We know of a few examples of jaws, which on other grounds are regarded as belonging to Neanderthal man, in which vestiges of a chin eminence seem to be present. But in such examples as I have been able to examine personally these slight chin eminences do not really show the morphological form that we associate with *Homo sapiens*. Nevertheless, there may be specimens in which an incipient true chin eminence does occur in specimens that do not belong to *Homo sapiens*, so that we must not regard this character by itself as completely diagnostic.

In the living great apes as well as in some, at least, of the fossil apes, we find that the method which Nature has used to reinforce the front of the jaw by evolutionary processes is quite distinct: instead of there being a chin eminence in front, there is a ledge of bone at the back, behind the middle line, linking the two halves of the jaw, and so giving it added strength. This ledge of bone is known as the 'simian shelf', and for a very long time it has been regarded by anatomists as a 'primitive' character of the ape-human stock and therefore one which we should expect to find in early

Plate XI

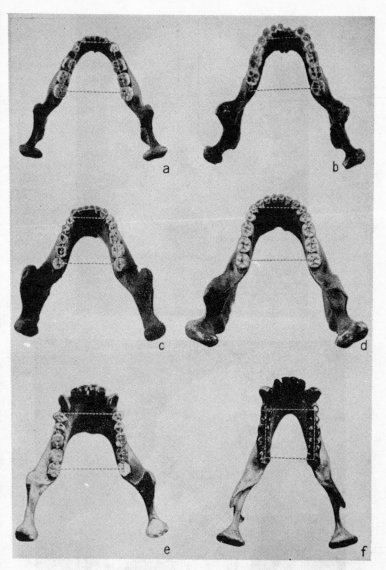

Various mandibles viewed from above to show the different types of teeth arrangement. (*a*) Negro; (*b*) Predmost; (*c*) Mauer; (*d*) Neanderthal man; (*e*) Piltdown; (*f*) Gorilla

Plate XII

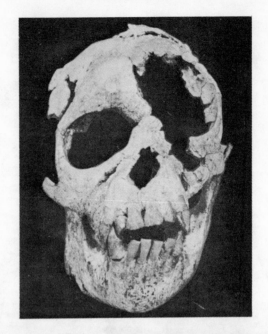

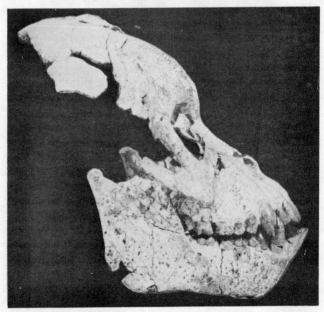

The skull of *Proconsul africanus*, full face and profile

fossils ancestral to man; a character, in fact, which has been lost in the process of evolution to the status of *Homo sapiens* and replaced by the chin eminence. But this view is no longer tenable, for, as we shall see in the next chapter, the evidence from the study of the early fossil apes reveals a different picture. In other words, it is now necessary to regard the development of the simian shelf in the living great apes as just as much a highly specialized character in one direction, as the development of the chin eminence in *Homo sapiens* is a specialization in another direction.

There is only one fossil human jaw so far known that has a real simian shelf, the jaw that is associated with the Piltdown skull, and we will discuss this anomaly in another chapter, but we may say at once that if the jaw is truly associated with the skull, then it is not evidence that Piltdown man was very primitive but instead very over-specialized.

The teeth are a matter of very great importance to us, as is the way they are arranged in the jaw.

Normally, man and the apes have four incisor teeth (two on each side), two canines (one on each side), four premolars (two on each side), and six molars (three on each side) in the upper and lower jaws respectively.

In some present-day and also fossil humans we find that the last or third molars are never formed, and this decrease in the number of molars seems to represent an evolutionary trend in man today. The teeth of *Homo sapiens* vary considerably in size, and the teeth of some races, such as those of the Australian aborigine, are noticeably larger on the average than those of most Europeans. But size alone is not very significant and is not a specific character. The actual morphology of the teeth is much more important and so is the relative size of the canines, molars, and premolars.

In man, both in *Homo sapiens* and in the extinct types of man, we do not find that the canine teeth are large or markedly protruding above the level of the other teeth, although, here again, the strange Piltdown jaw provides an exception. In the living apes, on the other hand, we always find a marked development of the canine teeth.

It has been commonly supposed that the type of reinforcement of the lower jaw that we call the simian shelf was intimately linked with the presence of large canine teeth, and the presence of these two characters in the Piltdown jaw seemed to strengthen this view, but we now have evidence of fossil ape jaws from the remote past in which there are large canine teeth but no simian shelves, so that once again, as our knowledge increases, we have to revise our ideas.

While the order in which the teeth are arranged in the jaw always remains the same, the shape of the dental arch varies considerably (see Plate XI). In the great apes, the molars and premolars on the two sides of the jaw are so arranged that lines drawn through their crowns are almost parallel, or in some cases even converge backwards very slightly, so that the width between the third molars is less than that between the first premolars. In all humans so far known—again with the exception of Piltdown man—lines drawn from the third molars to the first premolars on either side converge forward quite markedly—in *Homo sapiens* even more than in some of the extinct human types. There has been a tendency in the past to regard the type of jaw with parallel cheek-teeth as primitive, and it was thought that as man, in the course of evolution, changed from large canines to small canines, so gradually the front of his jaw narrowed and the cheek-teeth started to converge forwards. Here again we have recently had to revise our ideas, for in some types of fossil apes, as we shall see in the next chapter, large canines are present and yet the cheek-teeth converge forwards. It looks now as though it was the evolution of abnormally large incisors (which have to be fitted in between the two canines) in the modern great apes which was responsible for the change to parallel or nearly parallel cheek-teeth in these creatures. Again, we must now regard this character, not as primitive, but as highly specialized.

We cannot say that the forward converging arrangement of the cheek-teeth is diagnostic of human status in the ape-human stock, but we can say that it is a very constant character in man. We can also say that it is unlikely that the human arrangement was evolved from one similar to that found in the living great apes, but that more probably the two extreme variations were evolved from an intermediate form such as we know to have been present in the early Miocene apes (see next chapter).

So far, in this chapter, we have been dealing with skulls and jaws, but the student of human evolution must also pay a great deal of attention to other parts of the bony skeleton. Man, as represented by *Homo sapiens*, walks upright on his two feet, and in order to do so his skeletal structure has been specially modified during the course of evolution. All extinct types of fossil men also walked more or less upright, some perhaps slightly less so than others, but the upright position is regarded as an essential character of man and distinguishes him from his living ape cousins.

While monkeys are truly quadrupedal, the living great apes are neither quadrupeds nor bipeds, and they have evolved extra long arms in order to be able to move about in a semi-upright position, supporting their weight to some extent on their hands, and also to help in swinging from branch to branch in the trees. There is one school of thought which believes that man, during the course of his evolution, passed through a long-armed stage, rather like that seen in the chimpanzees and gorillas, but the evidence in support of this view is beginning to crumble. I myself, in common with many others, have a strong belief that man probably evolved direct from a true quadrupedal to a true bipedal type of progression, without ever developing extra long arms. In fact, it is possible, even likely, that in this character, as in so many others, the living great apes must be regarded as very highly specialized members of the ape-human stock, fully as specialized in their own direction as we are in ours, and that we must cease to regard them as representing a primitive form of the ape-human stock.

The study of human evolution is still in its infancy, chiefly because, up till now, the available fossil evidence upon which to base sound conclusions has been somewhat scanty. Fortunately, during the last ten years or so, a vast amount of new evidence has come to light, and there is every reason to believe that we shall continue to get more material. Inevitably, this means that we must constantly review and revise our ideas, abandoning the conceptions of human evolution held by some of our predecessors, and being prepared to alter our own ideas as new facts emerge.

While, as we have said at the beginning of this chapter, there is no doubt whatever that men and monkeys and apes and other members of the Primate family all have a common ancestor (if we go far enough back in the fossil record), we still have a great deal to learn and many more facts to unearth before we can be certain of the line followed by human evolution or of the stages through which man passed. We may also have to revise our ideas from time to time as to where the 'cradle of mankind' is to be found. This was once commonly believed to lie in Central Asia, since that region had yielded more fossil evidence that had a bearing on the subject than any other continent. Now the pendulum has swung to Africa, where we not only have very early members of the ape stock in Egypt, in Oligocene deposits (see p. 15), but also very important new discoveries in East Africa in deposits of Lower Miocene age, and in South Africa of the Pleistocene age.

As I write this chapter news comes of important new discoveries of fossil ape material in Europe, of more Pliocene ape remains, including parts of the skeleton, so that when this fresh evidence is interpreted we may have to alter our ideas once more until, at last, we hope the picture will one day be fairly complete.

CHAPTER X

Fossil Apes and 'Near-Men'

IF we wish to appreciate and understand the significance of the different characters found in the various living and extinct races of mankind and try to fathom some of the mysteries of human evolution, we must examine the available evidence relating to fossil 'apes' and to those fossil Primates from South Africa which are sometimes called 'ape-men' or 'man-apes' or 'near-men', and which are classified by scientists as *Australopithecinae*.

The usual subdivision of the higher Primates into monkeys, apes, and men will no longer serve our purpose, and at the present time there is a controversy as to whether the South African fossil Primates found by Dart and Broom should rank just within the lower limits of man or as very highly evolved apes. As we shall see later in this chapter, these fossils are much closer to man than to the true apes, as exemplified by the living great apes, and yet they fall short of the usual definition of man. To use the terms 'man-apes' or 'ape-men' begs the question, because it implies, to the ordinary person, either that these creatures were a cross between man and apes, *which they certainly were not*, or that they represent a sort of missing link between the apes and man. There are some scientists who believe this last to be the true explanation, and if they are right then 'man-apes' or 'ape-men' may be the correct terms to use, but I prefer to call them 'near-men', for it seems to express their status much more accurately.

It must be remembered throughout this chapter, however, that where the term 'ape' is used for lack of a better term in respect of early fossil members of the hominoidea, or ape-human stock, I do not mean to imply that some of these creatures have, of necessity, any direct relationship to the living great apes or any major resemblances to them. The time is approaching rapidly when another term may have to be coined for creatures which are certainly not monkeys, nor men, nor 'near-men', but which differ sufficiently from the fourth category of 'apes' to warrant a new term. It would be premature to create such a term now, as new evidence relating to the primates of the Lower Miocene is coming to light so fast that it is better to wait a few more years when we shall have much more evidence to work on.

People often ask—and will continue to ask—'Why is it that palaeontologists can give a reasonably clear picture of the stages of evolution of the horse and the elephant and of many other animals, and yet are still so far from certain about the stages of human evolution?' Let us therefore briefly try to answer this question before we consider the facts about fossil apes and 'near-men'.

The groups of fossil animals whose evolutionary history we know best are those who lived under conditions most likely to lead to a reasonably large number of them dying in circumstances under which their bones would become fossilized instead of decaying. Terrestrial animals that live on the open plains and swamp and water animals stand a far better chance of having their remains eventually fossilized than do forest and woodland animals, especially the arboreal species. Of animals that die in the open plains or in water, a proportion of the bones and sometimes whole bodies will often become buried in sand or silts or clay, or be washed by flood waters into gravel beds before the forces of decay have had time to destroy them. Generally speaking, the Primates—from the smallest members like the galagos and tarsioids to the monkeys and living apes—are forest or bush dwellers and, for this reason, the chances are very high indeed *against* their bones being washed into some formation of clay or silt before they have disintegrated. Except where some very special set of conditions have altered the situation it is very rare to find fossil remains of Primates, and the few that are found in ordinary fossil beds represent probably only a minute proportion of the population—just a few individuals who chanced to die under conditions not normal to their kind.

While the known fossil remains of horses and elephants and pigs, etc., can be numbered in tens of thousands, from sites over most parts of the world and from deposits of many different geological ages, fossil remains of Primates are rare in the extreme, with four major exceptions, namely: (1) the limestone breccias of South Africa which have yielded such quantities of remains of 'near-men' and of baboons; (2) the fossil beds in Greece with their very numerous remains of the monkey *Mesopithecus*; (3) the fossil beds in Kenya with their exceptionally numerous remains of Lower Miocene apes; (4) some of the fossil beds in Madagascar with very plentiful fossil remains of lemurs.

We are not concerned here with (2) and (4), but in respect of (1) and (3) we shall see that there probably existed special conditions, for which we must be thankful, since without the discoveries from

Kenya and South Africa our knowledge of fossil apes and 'near-men' would be even more limited than it is.

The earliest known remains that we can with assurance classify as belonging to the ape stock are those of a creature known as *Propliopithecus* from the Oligocene deposits of the Fayum in Egypt (see table on p. 15).

Propliopithecus was a little ape of about the size of a present-day gibbon, and the same deposits from which it came also yielded a primitive monkey, *Parapithecus*, showing that even at that early date the ancestral stock, from which both groups were derived, had already diverged and started along independent lines of evolution. We know all too little about *Propliopithecus*, but it seems likely that this fossil type represents the ancestors of the line that led to *Limnopithecus* in the Lower Miocene of Kenya, and eventually had one branch which evolved into the gibbons as we know them today; the European *Pliopithecus* being, probably, another offshoot of the same stock. There can be little serious doubt that in addition to *Propliopithecus* there were other branches of the ape stock already beginning to become differentiated during the Oligocene period, for it would be difficult otherwise to account for the great diversity of genera and species which are found in the next geological period, the Lower Miocene, in Kenya and elsewhere.

The main evidence for the apes of the Lower Miocene comes from Kenya Colony, from sites round the Kavirondo Gulf of Lake Victoria, like Koru and Songhor, and islands in the lake such as Rusinga. The quantity of fossil apes from these deposits is very great indeed, but before we consider what special circumstances led to the remains of so many apes being preserved as fossils in this region, we must consider the material itself.

Three genera are now recognized: *Proconsul*, *Limnopithecus*, and *Sivapithecus*. The first of these, *Proconsul*, has three species, *africanus*, *nyanzae*, and *major*, of which the first is the smallest and also best known, and the last is the largest and least known. Of *Proconsul africanus* there are not only several jaws and parts of jaws, but also the greater part of a skull with associated jaw (see Plate XII). The skull is small—for this species was smaller than a chimpanzee—but it reveals a number of features of the greatest interest. In the first place, there is no trace whatever of a ridge of bone over the eyes, separating the brain-case from the face. Instead, the forehead is smooth and rounded and curves evenly from the root of the nose, rather as in a baby. The right eye-socket is intact and undamaged and is low and rectangular instead of high and nearly round as in the living great apes. The nasal aperture is much more like that of monkeys than of apes or humans, and there are other characters in the skull which are monkey-like to some extent. The teeth are quite definitely of the form that we associate with apes and to some extent with man, but not in the least monkey-like. It could of course be argued that this single skull that we have found is that of an atypical example, but that is most unlikely. There is every reason to believe that it is quite normal and that it represents a typical *Proconsul africanus*.

The jaw is well preserved, and all the teeth are present. The canines are relatively large and the incisor teeth small but long. The first molar is the smallest and the third molar the largest. The first premolar is of a type that we associate with apes in that it is what is called 'sectorial', having a cutting edge rather than a surface adapted for chewing. The jaw has no trace whatever of a simian shelf, nor have any of the other jaws of this or the other two *Proconsul* species.

In the second and medium-sized *Proconsul*, called *nyanzae*, a creature about the size of a chimpanzee, the face is shorter than in *Proconsul africanus* and the shape of the jaw rather different. No skull has been found, but we have jaws both of adults and of juveniles. The jaw has relatively large canine teeth, small incisors, and, like *Proconsul africanus*, has a sectorial first premolar, whilst the first molar is the smallest and the third the largest. In both *Proconsul nyanzae* and *africanus* we have complete jaws, and so can be quite certain of the arrangement of the teeth. The parallel, or backward-converging arrangement of the cheek-teeth that we have seen to be typical of the living great apes is replaced by a forward convergence somewhat intermediate between the characteristic ape form and that seen in man.

The arrangement of the cheek-teeth in parallel lines, or converging backwards, as found in the living great apes, has sometimes in the past been considered to be linked with the presence of large canines, on the basis of the argument that the presence of large canines necessitates a greater width between the canines than that needed if the teeth are relatively small, as in man. But in the Kenya Miocene apes we find that the canines are large, and yet the rows of cheek-teeth still converge forwards, the width at the front of the jaw being considerably less than at the back. This, we find, is due to the fact that the incisors (which lie between the canine teeth) are relatively small and occupy far less space than in a living great ape of comparable size.

Plate XIII

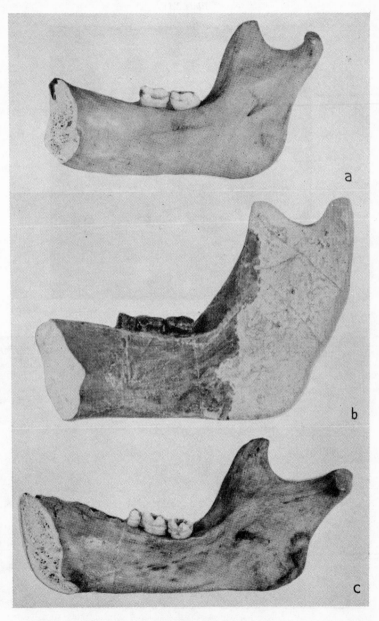

Sections through the symphysis (or middle line of the jaw) of (*a*) Man; (*b*) *Proconsul*; (*c*) Chimpanzee, to illustrate how the truly primitive form seen in *Proconsul* could evolve either into the form seen in man or into that of the living great apes

Plate XIV

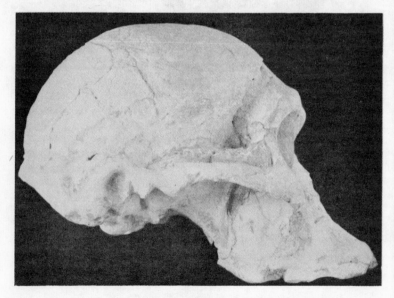

A skull of *Plesianthropus africanus*, full face and profile

There is, perhaps, rather more evidence to support the view that there is a direct correlation between the development of a simian shelf and of parallel or slightly backward convergent rows of cheek-teeth. In none of the *Proconsul* jaws—and a large number are known—is there any sign whatsoever of a simian shelf. Instead, in all the species of this genus we find a condition which is inter-mediate between the simian shelf of the great apes of today and the development of the chin eminence as found in man. In view of the remote date of the Lower Miocene we may reasonably suppose that the condition which we find in *Proconsul* is the truly primitive one (especially as we also find the same conditions in the contem-porary *Limnopithecus genus*), and that the development seen in man and in the great apes, respectively, represents evolutionary trends in divergent directions.

It seems possible that the development which led to the simian shelf, by greatly extending backwards the area where the two halves of the jaw are linked together, had the effect of drawing the sides of the jaw together, finally resulting in a more or less parallel arrangement. Following this development the space available for the incisor teeth between the canines became much increased, and in due course these teeth, having more space, became enlarged and often rather widely spaced.

As we shall see presently, in *Dryopithecus*, a European fossil ape of Middle and Upper Miocene age, a simian shelf was already developed and is associated with an arrangement of the cheek-teeth in parallel rows such as occurs in the living great apes. But the incisor teeth are still small and cannot properly occupy the space between the canines.

In Plate XIII cross-sections through the middle line or symphysis of the jaws of a chimpanzee, a man, and a *Proconsul* are shown, in order to illustrate how the truly primitive form in *Proconsul* could evolve and give rise to reinforcement of the jaw by a chin, as in man, or by a simian shelf, as in the true apes.

The limb bones of *Proconsul* are not yet known with absolute certainty, although there are some specimens from East Africa which almost certainly belong to this genus since they are without question of a Primate and are too large to be attributed to *Limnopithecus*. There are also some foot bones, including those of the heel and ankle. It is sufficient for the moment to say that these differ markedly from the corresponding bones of the modern great apes, lacking the specialized developments that go with the parti-cular method of progression adopted by the apes, and that they also differ from corresponding human bones and have a number of characters that recall those seen in monkeys. This is what we might expect to find in a truly primitive member of the ape-human stock, and again it is easy to see how evolution in divergent directions from these generalized forms could lead both to the form found in man and that seen in the great apes.

The ankle and heel bones suggest that *Proconsul* was quadrupedal, but that there may have been some tendency to stand in an upright position by balancing on the hind legs alone, as some monkeys occasionally do.

It must also be noted that in so far as the limb bones of *Proconsul* are comparable to any of the living great apes, they are rather nearer to the form seen in the gibbons than that of the gorillas or chimpanzees, and that the gibbon, of all the living apes, is the one that most often does walk on its hind legs, using its long arms for balancing.

We must now turn to the other Lower Miocene apes of Kenya. The genus *Sivapithecus* is unfortunately only known at present from small fragments. The evidence of such teeth as we have, however, most strongly suggests that the Kenya *Sivapithecus* may prove a candidate for the rôle of a direct ancestor of man in the Lower Miocene. The genus *Proconsul*, and especially the species *nyanzae*, cannot be wholly ruled out of the picture, but the *Proconsul*s have, in particular, upper molar teeth which tend to suggest specialization away from the direction taken by man, whilst *Sivapithecus* has upper molars strongly suggestive of man himself. We must wait for more *Sivapithecus* material to come to light to discover whether in other characters too this genus was tending more towards man than any of the contemporary genera.

The genus *Limnopithecus* has at present been divided into two species, one large and one small, but both are smaller than *Proconsul* and both are comparable in size to the modern gibbons. In a variety of characters, too, they strongly suggest that they may be the ancestral and generalized representatives of the stock which eventually gave rise—among other things—to the true gibbons. *Limnopithecus*, however, differs notably from the gibbons of today in the relative proportions and structure of such limb bones as we have preserved, and did not have the extreme specialization of the forearm.

When we leave the Lower Miocene for the Upper and Middle Miocene periods it is mainly to Europe that we must turn for our evidence; good fossiliferous deposits of this age are not yet known in Africa, but probably will be found in due course.

In *Pliopithecus*, which occurs both in the Middle and Upper Miocene deposits of Europe, we have a small ape of about the size of the larger species of *Limnopithecus* and possibly derived from it. *Pliopithecus* has forward-converging rows of cheek-teeth, as in *Proconsul* and *Limnopithecus*, and only the slightest suggestion of a simian shelf. It probably stands either in the direct line leading to the gibbons from *Limnopithecus*, or else it represents a side branch from that stock which has no living descendants; it is certainly not far removed from the line of evolution of the gibbon.

Dryopithecus, which occurs not only in Europe, in the Middle and Upper Miocene, but also in India and Europe in the Lower Pliocene (see later), is an extinct genus of ape which in the past has been widely regarded as perhaps representing the stock from which both man and the great apes were derived. This view was formulated in the days when many anatomists considered that a simian shelf and parallel rows of cheek-teeth—both of which occur in *Dryopithecus*—were primitive and not specialized characters of apes. Quite a number of specimens have been included in this genus, some of which will almost certainly have to be separated from it, but it seems clear that the typical *Dryopithecus* was already evolved along the branch of specializations that led eventually to the modern great apes. The simian shelf is well developed and the rows of cheek-teeth are parallel (for instance, in the specimen from the Middle Miocene of St. Gaudens in France). On the other hand, the incisors filling the space between the large canines are small, as in *Proconsul*, and not large, as in the living great apes; and they are spaced widely apart.

On the present available evidence it is most unlikely that the typical *Dryopithecus* has any ancestral relationship to man; it is already too specialized in the direction of the great apes, but it may well be near the line leading to the modern apes.

Something very akin to *Dryopithecus* may be expected in Africa also, in Middle or Upper Miocene deposits, providing the ancestral line leading to the gorilla and chimpanzee.

Dryopithecus may be one of the side branches leading off from *Proconsul*, but tending more and more in the direction taken by the living great apes in its special development.

A genus named *Paedopithex* by Pollig is now commonly regarded as being synonymous with *Dryopithecus*. This is by no means certain, and the validity of *Paedopithex* as a distinct genus may have to be reconsidered when more evidence becomes available.

Paedopithex has a femur almost identical in form to that in the femur ascribed to *Proconsul*, and if this femur really belongs to *Dryopithecus*, then this genus had evolved further towards the living great apes in its jaw structure than it had in the modification of its limb bones.

From the Middle and Upper Miocene we turn to the Pliocene, and here again it is from Europe and India that the evidence for the evolution of the ape-human stock is derived. *Dryopithecus* continues to exist (unless the identifications prove to need revision), and we have also numbers of fragmentary remains of other genera. *Sivapithecus*, whose presence in the Lower Miocene of Kenya was noted earlier in this chapter, is now present in India and is represented by a more evolved species. As in the Kenya Lower Miocene, the *Sivapithecus* material from the Pliocene of India is extremely scanty, but this ape, in its Pliocene form, has a number of characters which suggest that it may be a direct offshoot from the line leading to the several divergent branches of man.

Probably, by Pliocene times, the branch leading to *Homo* and the branches leading to some of the extinct genera of man had already separated, and better material of the Indian Pliocene species of the genus *Sivapithecus* is urgently needed to elucidate this problem.

In India there have also been found other genera of fossil apes such as *Ramapithecus*, *Sugrivapithecus*, and *Bramapithecus*, all known from relatively scanty material, as well as specimens attributed to several other genera, but it is beyond the scope of this chapter to discuss these finds, except to say that *Ramapithecus* seems to be allied to *Sivapithecus* while the others seem to stand nearer to *Dryopithecus* and the true apes of today.

From the Pliocene we come to the Pleistocene period, and once again we turn to Africa for our information. This time, however, we shall be dealing with what I have termed the 'near-men' rather than apes, even using that word in its widest sense.

I have referred at the beginning of this chapter to the fact that these South African creatures—the *Australopithecinae*—have been called by some scientists 'ape-men' and by others 'man-apes', and have given reasons why I consider these terms unsatisfactory. Just recently the term 'proto-hominids' has also been used, but that description is not satisfactory either, as the word 'proto' implies that these creatures were ancestral to man, whereas it is more likely, as we shall see, that they represent a very aberrant and specialized offshoot from the stock which gave rise to man. In very many respects, however, they certainly stand much nearer to man than they do to any of the living great apes, so that the term 'near-men' seems to fit them well.

The first specimen of the *Australopithecinae* to be described was the immature skull which was published in 1925 by Professor R. Dart as *Australopithecus africanus*. This find was correctly regarded by Dart as representing a creature which was nearer to man than to the great apes, but for a very long time few scientists outside South Africa were prepared to accept this view.

Then came a whole series of very important similar discoveries made by Dr. Robert Broom. To start with, in 1936, came the discovery of a specimen from Sterkfontein in the Transvaal which was first called *Australopithecus transvaalensis* and later given new generic rank as *Plesianthropus transvaalensis*. This was followed in 1938 by the discovery of a skull at Kromdraai which was named *Paranthropus robustus*. Following these initial discoveries many more finds were made, and soon the South African 'near-men' were known from numerous skulls and jaws as well as a certain number of limb bones, and, most important of all, fragments of the pelvis.

Still more recently, in 1947, Professor Dart described another species of *Australopithecus*, while Dr. Broom found and described a second and very large species of *Paranthropus* which he called *crassidens* and which was found at Swartzkrans.

Although there is still a great deal of discussion as to whether the subdivision of these fossils into three genera is correct, there is no doubt that they represent several distinct species of 'near-men', and it is also reasonably certain that they are not all contemporary. The two *Paranthropus* species would seem to be geologically younger than *Plesianthropus*, while there is a possibility that the original *Australopithecus* specimen is older than any of the others, and possibly belongs to the end of the Pliocene rather than to the Pleistocene.

The second *Australopithecus* species, which Dart has named *prometheus* (believing that it was a creature who knew the use of fire), is probably younger than *A. africanus* and contemporary with *Plesianthropus*.

The really important thing about all these different species of 'near-men' is that they *are* 'near-men', and reveal to us a branch of the ape-human stock of which we have so far no knowledge from elsewhere. Moreover, they provide the most important evidence against the theory that man was derived from some creature in any way resembling the great apes of today.

The most important characters of these 'near-men' (see Plate XIV) are:

(1) that they had a shape of skull and brain more similar to man than to the apes, and yet smaller than the lowest limits of true man;

(2) that the jaws have a form which is not unlike that seen in some of the extinct types of man, such as that represented by the Heidelberg jaw. They completely lack a simian shelf, and a chin eminence;

(3) that the arrangement of the teeth in the jaw is remarkably like that of man;

(4) that the teeth themselves and especially the canines are of human and not of ape type;

(5) that the milk teeth, especially the milk molars, are as in man and not as in the apes;

(6) that the pelvic bones are remarkably like those of man, although differing in certain points of detail, but they show that the *Australopithecinae* walked erect;

(7) that such fragments of limb bones as are preserved are more like those of man than of the great apes, but also exhibit a few points of resemblance to monkeys.

This combination of characters has led some scientists to conclude that the South African *Australopithecinae* should be classified at the extreme lower limit of the hominidae, and just within the range of man. If we were to confine ourselves to a rigid division between the higher members of the Primate family into men, apes, and monkeys, then certainly this would be the only reasonable answer. But that classification was worked out before the finds of fossil Primate material were available and there is no reason why it should not be enlarged to meet changing circumstances and new evidence.

The terms 'man' and 'human' have come to have a definite significance for most of us, and among other things they suggest: (1) a brain size larger than that found in any of the South African 'near-men'; (2) a tool-making creature.

There is at present no sound evidence that the *Australopithecinae* fulfil either of these conditions of 'man', although claims have been made that *Paranthropus crassidens* had a brain size that would fall just within the human range (if the estimated size is correct). But the estimate of size is based upon such a crushed specimen that it cannot be accepted as certain. Similarly, it has been claimed that some of the baboon skulls in the same deposit as *Plesianthropus* at Sterkfontein show signs of having been struck by a blow, and it is suggested that these blows were the work of the Sterkfontein 'near-men'. Even if this were the case (and I am not convinced that it is), it still would not prove that the Sterkfontein creature *made* tools or weapons, only that he *used* some kind of weapon, and until actual tools are found with Sterkfontein types of skull and under conditions showing that these creatures definitely *made* the tools, we cannot accept them as tool-makers.

But since the *Australopithecinae* are certainly not apes or monkeys, they must either—as some would have it—range within the lower limits of man and be given a separate classification to denote how close they stand to man *without being human or directly ancestral to man*, or else we must provide a new category, as I have done, and call them by some such name as 'near-men'. It has been claimed by Broom that some at least of the *Australopithecinae* represent a direct link in the chain leading to man, but he claims an age for these fossils that is not Pleistocene but Pliocene, a claim which is not supported by the evidence of the associated fossils. It is true that among the contemporary fauna there are some species which occur in the Pliocene of Europe, but an examination of the total fauna reveals that there are also forms which are typically Pleistocene; we must therefore regard these Pliocene forms as survivals and certainly not use them for dating purposes.

We have an exactly similar state of affairs at Olduvai in Tanganyika Territory, where the fauna that is associated with the Hand-axe culture includes such survivals from the Pliocene as *Hipparion, Dinotherium,* and a chalicothere. This does not justify our regarding the Hand-axe culture at Olduvai as of Pliocene age; similarly, the Pliocene forms that are associated with the *Australopithecinae* can only be regarded as survivals, since there are other animals present which did not evolve until the Pleistocene period.

Were it true that *Plesianthropus* and *Australopithecus* belonged to the Pliocene, then certainly many anatomists would incline to the view that these creatures were in the direct line leading to man. but we must reject this interpretation because we know that true man already existed at the beginning of the Pleistocene.

To many, the *Australopithecinae* represent the persistence, as a side branch, of a stage through which man did actually pass. In other words, they envisage a time, probably in the Early or Middle Pliocene, when the stock from which man eventually came was represented by an Australopithecene such as *Plesianthropus*, and

that the stock then divided, with the main stem evolving further
into man, while a side branch went off and remained more or less
unchanged (but continued to survive) until it became contemporary
with man.

It is to be doubted, however, whether such an interpretation does
not take too little account of the fact that the *Australopithecinae*
or 'near-men' show a number of characters which very strongly
suggest over-specialization in directions which did not lead towards
man. The very peculiar flattening of the face, the raising of the
eye-sockets high above the level of the root of the nose, and the
shape of the external orbital angles are among such specializations,
as is also the forward position of the root of the cheek-bone process.
In general, it seems better to regard the 'near-men' as close cousins
of man and not as ancestors or even representatives of a direct
ancestral stage.

In an earlier part of this chapter we referred to the fact that
remains of fossil Primates are usually rare compared with the
remains of many other mammalian groups, except under special
conditions. We have since seen that the remains of the Lower
Miocene apes of Kenya and of the 'near-men' of South Africa are
unusually plentiful, and before closing this chapter we must briefly
consider what were the special conditions leading to their
preservation.

So far as the Kenya Miocene deposits are concerned, some 500
specimens have now been found, ranging from single isolated teeth
to the skull of *Proconsul*, and these 500 specimens, judged by their
distribution in the deposits, represent not less than 450 individuals.

The extent of the Miocene deposits is very great, and the fossils
that have so far been found have come from a few limited areas
where natural erosion has made investigation possible. Since it
cannot be assumed that Nature has selectively eroded just those
areas which are most rich in fossils of Miocene apes, we must
believe that the fossils we have found so far represent a very small
proportion of those that are still buried in the inaccessible parts of
the Miocene deposits. This fact alone postulates an immense
ape population in Lower Miocene times, but if we were to assume
further that the Miocene apes of the period were living under
conditions which but rarely allowed their remains to become
fossilized, we should have to multiply the figure by a large amount.

It seems more probable that the Lower Miocene apes of Kenya—
whose remains are not much less plentiful than those of contemporary pigs, antelopes, and hyracoids—were not real forest dwellers

but, like these other creatures, were more or less terrestrial and lived in relatively open country. In other words, it seems likely that they were not really arboreal apes at all, but lived somewhat in the manner of baboons today, largely on the ground, but capable of climbing trees when required.

In the case of the 'near-men' of South Africa, the evidence of their limb bones points clearly to the fact that they were two-legged animals which walked and ran erect. The associated fauna here, too, also suggests open country as their habitat, and they would therefore be as liable to have their remains fossilized as any of the other animals. Their skulls and bones occur in breccias, consisting of cemented stone fragments and sand, in limestone caves and fissures, along with the skulls and bones of numerous other animals. There does not seem to be any justification for regarding these caves as their dwelling-places, and their bones, as well as those of the other fauna, were probably dragged into these caves by hyaenas and other carnivora. The relatively large numbers of 'near-men' represented in these bone breccias is probably due to the fact that they fell a fairly easy prey to the carnivora of the period.

To conclude this chapter it must be stressed that there is far more evidence concerning apes and 'near-men' from the African continent than from any other area: in the Oligocene deposits of Egypt; in the Lower Miocene beds of Kenya; and in the Pleistocene limestone breccias of South Africa. This fact, taken in conjunction with the existence in Africa today of the two most man-like of the living great apes, the gorilla and the chimpanzee, and a very wide variety of other Primates such as monkeys and galagos, strongly suggests that the African continent was the main evolutionary centre for the higher Primates and the birth-place of man himself.

CHAPTER XI

Our Stone Age Cousins

FROM the apes and 'near-men' we have next to turn to man him-self, and in this chapter we will deal with the extinct types of man; specialized side branches from the stock which gave rise to *Homo sapiens*, which have no descendants living in the world today.

In my original edition of *Adam's Ancestors* I regarded the majority of these extinct types as members of a distinct sub-family, the *Palaeoanthropidae*, which broke away from the stock which gave rise to *Homo* possibly as far back as the Miocene. I treated Peking man, Java man, and the Neanderthaloids as all belonging to this sub-family, more closely related to each other than to man as we know him today. In this I believe that I was wrong. I think that the more likely interpretation in the light of present-day knowledge is that all of these extinct types, as well as some others, are really nothing but various aberrant and over-specialized branches that broke away *at different times* from the main stock leading to *Homo*. I am not prepared, however, to go as far as a few modern anatomists and place all of them merely as distinct species of the genus *Homo*.

Taxonomically, and from the zoological point of view, I believe that the differences between the types to be described in this chapter and *Homo* are fully as great as the differences between the gorilla and the chimpanzee, and that several distinct genera can be recognized.

It has been customary, for so long, for physical anthropologists to use the term 'primitive' when referring to extinct human types in order to denote characters that show some resemblance to ones found in the living great apes, that I must reiterate, once more, that since we can no longer regard many of the characters which we find in the great apes as 'primitive', but rather as 'over-specialization', we similarly cannot regard the presence of such characters in extinct human forms as being primitive. I myself, as I have already said, was guilty of misusing the word 'primitive' in my early editions of *Adam's Ancestors*. I confess, too, that I still find it difficult not to think loosely of such things as the simian shelf and

Plate XV

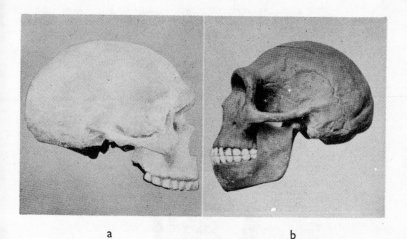

a   b

c   d

Profile views of (*a*) the Steinheim skull (reconstructed), an early species of the Neanderthal genus (*Palaeoanthropus steinheimensis*); (*b*) the Eyasie skull (*Pithecanthropus njarasensis*) reconstructed; (*c*) a reconstruction of one of the skulls from Solo (*Pithecanthropus soloensis*), the end-product of the *Pithecanthropus* line; (*d*) one of the Neanderthal skulls of the Palestine race of this species of *Palaeoanthropus*

Plate XVI

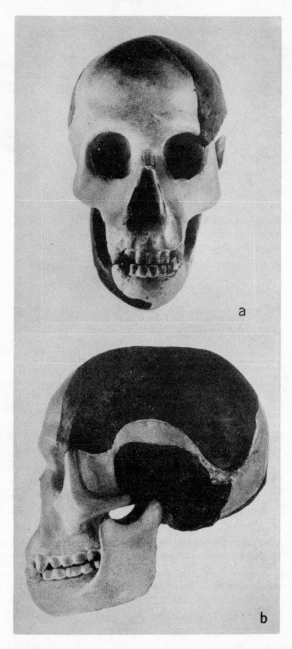

Reconstruction of the skull of Piltdown man (*Eoanthropus dawsoni*)

a massive brow-ridge as 'primitive', although I am fully convinced that they are not.

The number of fossil remains of extinct types of man that have now been found is so great that it will be better to consider them region by region in this chapter and then discuss general matters concerning their significance at the end of the chapter.

Taking Europe and the Near East first of all, we find that there are the Mauer jaw, the Steinheim skull, the Piltdown skull and mandible, and various remains that are grouped together as Neanderthal man, to be discussed.

The Mauer jaw (see Plate XI), from a sandpit near Heidelberg, in Germany, was found in 1907. Although no Stone Age tools were found with it, nor any other parts of the skeleton, the geological evidence and that of the fossil animals found in the same deposit leave little doubt that it represents the earliest known human from Europe and that it belongs to the Mindel-Riss interglacial. The jaw is massive and has no trace either of a simian shelf or of a chin eminence and indeed the whole bone of the jaw in the front region is unusually thick and massively constructed. The teeth are essentially human in structure, and the canine teeth are very small in proportion to the general massiveness of the jaw. This jaw reminds us more of the jaws of Neanderthal man than of any others, and it may well represent a creature that was directly ancestral to Neanderthal man. While frequently referred to as *Homo heidelbergensis* it seems better to treat it as generically distinct from *Homo*, and I regard it as of the same genus as Neanderthal man, *Palaeoanthropus*.

The Steinheim skull, also from Germany, is of very considerable importance, for it is grouped by most scientists within the same species as Neanderthal man. It is, however, geologically somewhat older than the typical remains of Neanderthal man (which belong to the period of the Würm glaciation). Most authorities today ascribe the Steinheim skull to the Riss-Würm interglacial, but others would put it back as far as the Mindel-Riss interglacial and so make it contemporary with the Mauer jaw.

The very great interest of the Steinheim skull (see Plate XV*a*) lies in the fact that, in spite of many similarities to more typical Neanderthal skulls, it is markedly less specialized, both in respect of the face and of the skull itself. In other words, it confirms our belief that the typical Neanderthal type is the product of progressive over-specialization, away from the common stem that gave rise to *Homo sapiens*.

In respect of the characters in which the Steinheim skull differs from Neanderthal man it approaches more to *Homo sapiens*. There is a distinct canine fossa below the cheek-bones, the massive brow-ridges have not quite the distinctive form of Neanderthal man, and the contour of the skull is also more domed.

An alternative to the suggestion that the Steinheim skull represents an earlier and less specialized stage in the evolution of Neanderthal man is that it may represent a cross between a typical Neanderthaloid and a *Homo sapiens*. While this possibility cannot be wholly ruled out, it seems less likely than the first explanation.

The Piltdown skull (Plate XVI) from Sussex in England is still an enigma. In my earlier editions of *Adam's Ancestors* I gave the age as early Pleistocene, and I described it not in the chapter dealing with our Stone Age cousins but in the chapter dealing with our Stone Age ancestors. The age then given has since had to be greatly modified.

The gravel beds in which the skull was found contained two different types of fossil fauna; there were some remains that were of Lower Pleistocene animals and others which belonged to the late Middle Pleistocene or even the Upper Pleistocene. The skull was usually regarded as being contemporary with the earlier fauna.

Recent intensive studies by Oakley and his colleagues, in analysing the fluorine content of fossil bones, have shown fairly conclusively that the skull and jaw belong with the younger fauna, while new geological investigations have also placed the age of the Piltdown gravel bed at the very end of the Middle Pleistocene or beginning of the Upper Pleistocene.

The Piltdown remains consist of parts of a very thick skull, which, however, has no trace of a big and massive brow-ridge, but instead is markedly like *Homo sapiens*. Undoubtedly, had the skull been found without the lower jaw it would have been regarded as a form of *Homo sapiens*. The lower jaw, however, has a well-developed simian shelf, and there is also a large canine tooth which is attributed to the skull. It is these two things that make the Piltdown find such an enigma.

If the jaw really belongs to the same individual as the skull, then Piltdown man was unique in all humanity, for no other known human of any living or extinct type has either of these characters. It must be admitted that it is tempting to argue that the skull on the one hand and the jaw and canine tooth on the other do not belong to the same creature, and to regard the skull as comparable to the Fontéchevade and Swanscombe human remains (see next chapter). Indeed, there are a number of anatomists who do maintain that the skull and jaw cannot belong to the same individual, and who see in the jaw and canine tooth evidence of a contemporary anthropoid ape.

Some of us had hoped that when Dr. Oakley carried out his fluorine tests he would find that the skull was of a different age from the jaw and tooth, and so solve the problem. His results, however, leave no doubt that not only the skull, but also the jaw and canine tooth are of the same age and belong with the younger fossil fauna of the Piltdown gravels.

On the evidence at present available it seems best for the time being to regard the jaw, skull, and canine tooth as parts of the same individual, but if we do this, we can only treat Piltdown man as an extinct and very *abnormal* cousin, a most peculiar side branch from the human stem, in which a simian shelf was evolved although no such shelf occurs in any other human or even 'near-man' form. However, the door cannot be completely closed to the possibility that the jaw and canine tooth do NOT belong with the skull, and for some of us it will be easier to believe in the million-to-one chance of the only known ape jaw from the Pleistocene of Europe being found in association with the Piltdown skull, rather than to believe that Piltdown man, alone of all known human or near-human types, independently evolved such modern ape-like characters as the simian shelf and a large canine.*

Turning next to Neanderthal man (see Plate XVII*a*), we find that this species of man, which is commonly described in most books as a species of the genus *Homo*, although I prefer to regard it rather as belonging to *Palaeoanthropus*, is represented by a very large number of important finds, both in Europe and in the Near East.

The skull which gives its name to the species was found in 1856, near Düsseldorf, in Germany, in the Neander Gorge, and it was the first skull of an extinct type of human to be described scientifically. This was done by Professor Schaaffhausen, to whom Dr. Fahlroth handed it after he had obtained the skull from some workmen.

The discovery of this skull raised a great controversy, and there were many who refused to regard it as anything but a freak.

The next skull of the same species to be brought to the notice of the scientific world was the skull which had been found in Gibraltar in 1848, six years before the discovery of the Neanderthal skull, but which was not described until 1868.

Next came the discovery by Marcel de Puydt and Maximin

* *For addendum see page 226*

Lohest at a rock-shelter at Spy, near Namur. Two reasonably well-preserved skeletons were found here, and they were associated with remains of extinct animals and with Stone Age tools, giving the first definite evidence of the geological age of this Neanderthal type of man and of the culture with which he was associated. The culture was originally described as Mousterian, but, from the illustrations, it seems likely that it is what we should now term Levalloisio-Mousterian rather than classical Mousterian.

The two Spy skulls were accompanied by mandibles which have been claimed by some to have traces of a chin. Examination shows, however, that although the body of the jaw projects more forwards in front than in some Neanderthal jaws, there is no *chin eminence* in the sense in which we have defined it, such as is seen in *Homo sapiens*.

Isolated jaws attributable to Neanderthal man were found in 1887 at Bañolas in Spain, and in 1889, at Malarnaud in France, but the next major discovery was at Krapina in Croatia, during the period 1895–1905, and described by Professor Gorjanovic-Kramberger. The Krapina remains are very important in many respects, for, unlike the Spy skulls, they were associated with a warm-climate fauna instead of a glacial fauna, and with a culture which, although described as Mousterian, seems to have greater affinities with a very developed Clactonian. The Krapina remains indicate that Neanderthal man at this site was a cannibal and most of the remains were very fragmentary, owing to the fact that they represent remains of cannibal feasts and not of burials.

From the available published evidence there seems no doubt that the Krapina fossils belong to *Palaeoanthropus neanderthalensis*, but in some respects they are less specialized than the typical remains of this species, as we know it from rather later deposits belonging to the Würm glaciation. This is in keeping with our belief that the Neanderthal type became more and more specialized as it approached extinction.

A discovery of great importance was that made by a German named Hauser, in France at Le Moustier, in the Dordogne, during 1908. This specimen is that of an immature male, and there was clear evidence that the body had been buried with great care—as also at Spy. The associated culture was what is known as classical Mousterian, although the Le Moustier site, as shown by later excavations, also has levels with other variants of the Mousterian, including Levalloisio-Mousterian and Acheuleo-Mousterian.

Plate XVII

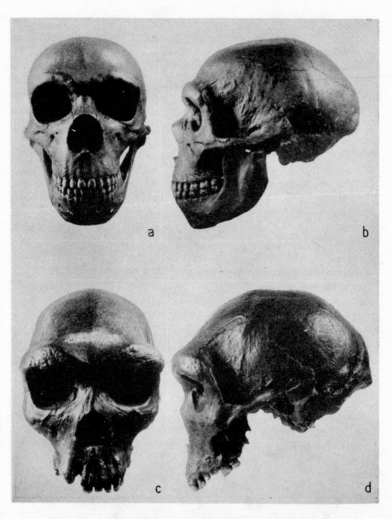

A typical Neanderthal skull. (*a, b*) *Palaeoanthropus neanderthalensis*, from La Chapelle, France; (*c, d*) the skull of Rhodesian man (*Palaeoanthropus rhodesiensis*)

Plate XVIII

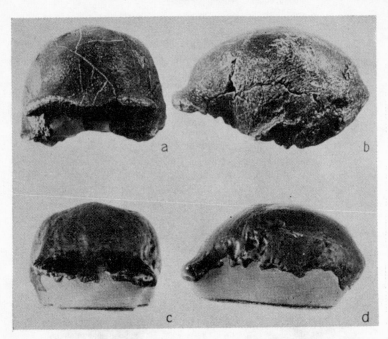

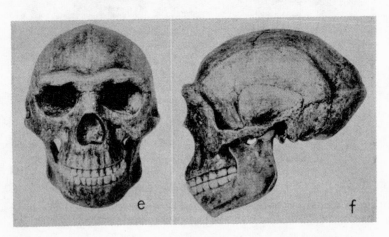

Skulls of (*a, b*) *Pithecanthropus pekinensis* (Peking); (*c, d*) *Pithecanthropus erectus* (Java); (*e, f*) reconstruction of Peking man

Also in 1908, came the discovery of the La Chapelle skull and skeleton, which is often regarded as a sort of 'type specimen' of Neanderthal man, because it has been so fully described by the late Professor Boule. The culture associated with the La Chapelle skull is what we should now call Levalloisio-Mousterian, while the fauna is typical of the Würm glaciation. The body had been carefully placed in a shallow grave. The La Chapelle skull is illustrated in Plate XVIIa. It cannot really be described as a typical Neanderthal skull, for there seems to be such variability in points of detail among the many known Neanderthal-type skulls that there is none that we can call 'typical'. In fact, there is little doubt that the species had already divided up into a number of racial variants before it became extinct, comparable with the variants that we find in the races of living man today.

The La Chapelle skull will, however, serve well to emphasize the essential characteristics of *Palaeoanthropus neanderthalensis*, namely:

(1) Massive brow-ridges over the eyes, with the ridge over each eye consisting of one solid bar, instead of the two components above each eye which characterize *Homo sapiens*.

(2) A puffing-out of the bone below the orbits so that instead of a 'canine fossa' we have a convexity.

(3) A low dome to the top of the skull.

(4) A jaw which has neither a chin eminence nor a simian shelf, but which is massively built and thick from front to back in the chin region. (The chin does not always slope backwards as much as the La Chapelle skull.)

It is impossible, within the scope of this chapter, to give details of the long list of discoveries of human remains of Neanderthal man that have been made since 1900. They include the skeleton found by M. Peyrony at La Ferrassie; the skeletons at La Quina found by Dr. Henri-Martin—including that of a child; the discoveries in the Ehringsdorf region of Germany, which are probably contemporary with Krapina rather than with Le Moustier, La Chapelle, or Spy, as they were accompanied by a warm fauna and a culture which seems to be a local variant of the Levalloisian rather than the Mousterian.

Of special interest is the fact that a jaw from Ehringsdorf, which in all other characteristics is typically of the Neanderthal type, has just the slightest trace of a chin eminence. The Ehringsdorf skull found in 1925 also has a more domed skull than that found in most

Neanderthal specimens, in this respect resembling the Steinheim skull. Discoveries of importance have also been made at Gibraltar and in Italy, and in Palestine by Professor Garrod and Dr. McCown. The infant skull from Gilbraltar is of special importance, for, with the La Quina child of greater age, and the youth of Le Moustier, it makes it possible to study growth changes in the Neanderthal species. From these studies we can see that the essential characters were present even in youth, although of course the brow-ridges were only indicated in youth, to develop gradually as maturity was approached. But the formation of the bone structure over the eyes makes it clear that the difference between the *Homo sapiens* type and the *Palaeoanthropus neanderthalensis* type is a character which was present even in infancy.

The discoveries in Italy include the skulls from Saccopastore and Monte Circeo, both of which are important because they exhibit a mutilation of the bones of the skull believed to have been made directly after death in order to remove the brain. We cannot tell whether this removal of the brain was part of some ritual belief or whether it was done in connexion with cannibalism, or possibly a combination of both. The skulls from Italy, while definitely of the Neanderthal species, probably represent a race nearer to that of Gibraltar than to any other of the variants known to us, and I group them all as the South European race of Neanderthal man.

The Palestine skulls (see Plate XV*d*) and skeletons are of the greatest interest, for while some of them are in every way characteristic of Neanderthal man, one or two show characters which are much closer to *Homo sapiens*. Some authorities have quoted this fact as indicating that Neanderthal man was evolving towards the *Homo sapiens* type and was ancestral to him. The weight of evidence is against this, however, for we should have to postulate a reversal of evolution and the discarding of specialized characteristics, with a return to more generalized ones. While *not* completely impossible, it is unlikely, especially as we know from other evidence that in Neanderthal man specialization was increasing as time went on. It seems more likely that some of the Palestine skulls represent the result of crossing between Neanderthal man and *Homo sapiens*—a cross which should be possible, although perhaps sterile.

There is still a very marked tendency to regard 'Neanderthal man' and 'Mousterian man' as synonymous terms, because so many of the discoveries were made at a time when no distinction was made between pure Mousterian, Levalloisio-Mousterian, Acheuleo-Mousterian, and developed Clactonian, and therefore all the culture associated with the early finds was labelled Mousterian. But the time has now come when someone should re-examine all the remains of Neanderthal man that have been found in association with any Stone Age culture, as well as the associated stone tools, to discover to what extent—if at all—the distinct *racial* variations of the Neanderthal species are linked with distinctive cultural elements. For someone who is looking for a field for post-graduate research I can very strongly recommend this as a subject which would be of the highest value to the science of Prehistory.

From this brief survey of our cousins in Europe and the Near East we must turn next to Africa and see what light this continent can throw on extinct types of man.

On 17 June, 1921 an interesting and in many ways an important discovery was made at the Broken Hill Mine in Northern Rhodesia. A practically complete fossil human skull (see Plate XVII*b*) was found which has a number of resemblances to Neanderthal man, but which also differs from this type in several significant respects. According to the ideas of the time it ranked as a very 'primitive' skull, but in fact it is a very highly specialized one.

The skull was found by a miner called Zwieglar when mining a mass of deposits comprising the filling of an ancient cave in the Broken Hill kopje. These ancient cave deposits which were full, not only of Stone Age cultural material but also of fossil animal bones, were—most unfortunately for prehistorians—very much impregnated with the same minerals which were contained in the rock forming the hill, zinc and lead, and, in consequence, the cave deposits were in process of being dug out and sent to the smelting furnaces together with the adjacent rock.

Seventeen years before, Dr. F. P. Mennel had visited the mine and had reported that the mining operations were exposing a cave deposit containing human artifacts and fossils, and it was when the deeper levels of this cave were being exploited for their mineral content that the skull came to light. The medical officer of the mine saw the skull a day or two after Zwieglar had found it, and he took steps to have it sent to England, to the British Museum for study. At the same time he sent some of the fossil bones of animals from the deposit to London. There has been a good deal of controversy as to whether the skull came from the same level as the animal bones, and also the very striking human leg-bone that was sent to England at the same time, for it was known that parts of the deposits in the cave were impregnated with zinc and others with lead, with the lead levels lower and older than the zinc levels. This question has been solved by tests that have been made recently on the skull, leg-bone, and animal bones by Dr. Oakley, and there is no doubt that the skull and other remains all come from the upper or zinc levels. This is important, for the fossil animals and the culture of the upper or zinc levels show clearly that they are geologically of recent age, probably Upper Pleistocene. This makes the age of Rhodesian man (sometimes called *Homo rhodesiensis*, but according to our classification *Palaeoanthropus rhodesiensis*) more or less of the same period as the more recent members of the Neanderthal species. In other words, the same tendency for branches to break away from the main human stem and become over-specialized and then extinct was present in this part of Africa as in Europe. Or it may even be that the Rhodesian skull represents a local divergence from the Neanderthal stock, after it had broken away from the parent stock. At any rate, the main interest of the discovery lies in two things:

(1) The survival into Upper Pleistocene times, in Rhodesia, of a type of man that later became extinct and which shows specialization comparable with that of Neanderthal man, in respect of brow-ridges and absence of a canine fossa.

(2) That this type of man was associated in Africa with a culture which has very distinct affinities with the Levalloisian, one of the cultures associated with the Neanderthal type elsewhere.

Another important find of an extinct type of man in Africa was that made by Dr. Kohl-Larsen in September 1935, on the eastern shores of Lake Eyasie, in Tanganyika Territory, East Africa. These remains, while much less complete than the Rhodesian skull, are sufficient to give a good idea of the type of man represented. It resembles the *Sinanthropus* and *Pithecanthropus* skulls from China and Java more than either Neanderthal or Rhodesian man, and I believe that, from the zoological point of view, it should be classed as of the same genus but a distinct species and called *Pithecanthropus njarasensis* (see Plate XVb). Dr. Weinert, the German scientist who has described it, has called it *Africanthropus njarasensis*, but this name, anyhow, cannot stand in science, for the term *Africanthropus* was used years earlier in South Africa for a skull which eventually turned out to be of *Homo sapiens* type, and the term *Africanthropus* is therefore pre-occupied and cannot be used again for something quite different.

The Eyasie skull, like the Rhodesian skull, is geologically of recent age—Upper Pleistocene—although Dr. Weinert has attempted to attribute to it a greater age, on the grounds that it is a 'primitive type of man'. It is *not* primitive, but very highly specialized. Like Rhodesian man and some Neanderthal types, it was associated with a form of Levalloisian culture.

In North Africa fragmentary human remains which have been provisionally attributed to the Neanderthal type have been found at Rabat.

All the other fossil human skulls from Africa, so far known, belong to the next chapter, since they are closer to *Homo sapiens* or are actual *Homo sapiens*.

The third region of the world to yield remains of our extinct cousins is the Far East, in China and Java.

In 1887 Dr. Dubois, a young Dutch anatomist who had become greatly interested in the controversy that was just starting in Europe about the Neanderthal, Gibraltar, and Spy skulls, made up his mind that the East Indies was a likely place to find early fossil remains and he succeeded in getting an appointment as a health officer in the Dutch Colonial Service with the express object of being able to test the truth of his convictions. At first he was stationed in Sumatra, but later was transferred to Java, and in 1891, at Trinil, he discovered a series of deposits which were unusually rich in fossils. He set to work to study these deposits and collect fossils from them and accumulated a large collection of other mammalian remains before he found first a human tooth and then a human skull-cap (see Plate XVIII *c* and *d*), and a month later a human leg-bone. Dubois formed the opinion (which, in the light of the evidence then available, was not unreasonable) that the age of these fossil beds, as indicated by the fauna, was Pliocene, but more detailed studies by von Koenigswald and others have shown that the Trinil beds are much later, and of Middle Pleistocene age.

Dr. Dubois described these human remains under the name of *Pithecanthropus erectus*, choosing the name to indicate that on the one hand the skull showed many simian traces, while the leg-bone indicated that the creature to whom it belonged walked fully erect as *Homo sapiens* does today.

Dubois's discovery started an extensive and prolonged controversy, some maintaining that the remains were not human at all, but represented a gigantic, extinct gibbon. The size of the brain was small and only just within human limits and the dome of the skull exceedingly flat, while other unusual characters included a bar of bone across the forehead above the eyes that was even more like that of some of the great apes than of Neanderthal man.

Since, as we have pointed out several times in this book, such resemblances to the great apes were regarded as evidence of a 'primitive' condition, the skull came to be regarded as 'the most primitive human skull-cap that has been found'. These, I regret to say, are the words which I used in my first edition of this book. In reality the Java skull is not a very primitive, but a very highly specialized, human form—an offshoot that developed certain characters which are reminiscent of the living great apes. On the other hand, the leg-bone shows that the breakaway from the human stock did not take place until the human stem had already achieved an erect posture, and in respect of his limbs *Pithecanthropus* retained the essentially human form.

From 1931 to 1941 Professor von Koenigswald carried out extensive explorations of the Java fossil beds in the hope of discovering more fossil human remains. He was more than successful and found remains of what he regarded as three distinct types of human in the Djetis deposits, which are geologically older than the Trinil beds and belong to the Lower Pleistocene.

Of the three human species which he recognizes, he places two into the genus *Pithecanthropus*, but ascribes them to species distinct from *erectus* of Dubois. He calls them *Pithecanthropus modjokertensis* and *Pithecanthropus dubius*.

The former is represented by the skull of a child, by parts of the skull and face of an adult, and by a mandible and a number of teeth. Only time will tell if the separation of this material into a species distinct from *erectus* is justified, or whether the observed differences are not due to individual or at least racial variations. The fact that they are somewhat older than *erectus* may well agree with their being a distinct and ancestral species of the genus.

The second species, *dubius*, is based upon a fragment of jaw found in 1939 and one other tooth. It is by no means certain that it should not be regarded simply as an aberrant form of *Pithecanthropus modjokertensis*. More material is needed to clear up this point.

The third type of human found in the Djetis or Lower Pleistocene beds of Java is *Meganthropus palaeojavanicus*. This seems to be a gigantic and quite distinct creature, at least as far as its jaw and teeth are concerned; but it may not have been a giant in respect of skull and limb bones for the jaws of the 'near-man', *Paranthropus crassidens* from South Africa, are not dissimilar in size. According

to von Koenigswald this jaw 'shows so many "primitive" characteristics that it cannot be regarded as a mere side branch of
mankind, but must be placed within the line leading to modern
man'. With this view I cannot agree. The jaw shows a number of
essentially human characters, such as the relatively small size of
the canines, but it also exhibits specializations which suggest to me
that it belongs to a side branch which broke away from that
leading to modern man, and eventually became extinct, just as
Pithecanthropus did.

Another series of discoveries of the greatest importance, also
from Java, are the skulls from Ngandong on the Solo River. No
less than eleven skulls were found there, in excavations carried out
by the Geological Survey of Java from 1931 to 1933. They have
recently been described in considerable detail in a paper which
Professor Weidenreich left unfinished at his death.   Fortunately
the paper describes most of the material adequately though we
have no means of knowing what conclusions he had formed as to
the position these skulls should take in the human story.

The Solo deposits, from which all these skulls came, are younger
than the Trinil fossil beds, being of Upper Pleistocene age—an age
comparable with that of most of the later specimens of Neanderthal
man in Europe and of the Rhodesian and Eyasie skulls of Africa.
The Solo skulls seem to exhibit very marked resemblances to the
Trinil skull in certain respects, while differing from them in others
(see Plate XV*c*). They have been referred to the genus *Homo* and
named *Homo soloensis*, but I believe it would be more correct to
regard them as a special late-surviving species of *Pithecanthropus*,
comparable in this respect with the Eyasie skull. I consider they
should be called *Pithecanthropus soloensis*.

Von Koenigswald considers that 'The Ngandong finds fill the
gap between the *Sinanthropus-Pithecanthropus* and the Neanderthal groups'. This is believed also to have been the view of
Weidenreich, who, however, went further and believed that they
ultimately developed into *Homo sapiens*.

It is hard to see how the Solo skulls can fill the gap between
Pithecanthropus and the Neanderthal types since they are of the
same geological age as the latter, and it is better to regard them
as different end-products of independent branches that originally
broke away at about the same time from the common human
stock, with Rhodesian man and Eyasie man as end-products of
yet other similar divergent branches.

In 1918.Dr. S. G. Andersen, a Swedish geologist, was studying some limestone deposits near Peking when he noticed some fossil-bearing deposits in caverns and crevices of the limestone. He returned to the site in 1921 with two other scientists, and on that occasion found a still larger and richer pocket of fossil breccia. While examining this he noticed that caught up in the matrix were fragments of quartz, which he knew from his geological studies did not occur in this area and must have been brought in by man from elsewhere, and he made the following prophetic remark to his two companions: 'Here is primitive man; now all we have to do is to find him.'

Later that year, one of his companions, Dr. Otto Zadansky, began excavations at the site and returned to continue the work in 1923. His work resulted in the acquisition of a large number of mammalian fossils which were taken to Upsala in Sweden for study. Among these fossils were two teeth which were clearly either human or very closely allied to man, and this fact was announced in 1926 at a meeting in Peking. As a result of the interest which was aroused, the Geological Survey of China, in conjunction with the Peiping Union Medical College, started a detailed study of the sites with the late Dr. Davidson Black in charge of operations. As a result of this work by Black, and, following Black's untimely death, by the late Professor Weidenreich with many of the original team, a most remarkable series of skulls and jaws and teeth of Peking man have been made known to science. This work was brought to an end by the Sino-Japanese war, and it is believed that most of the specimens were lost or destroyed during the war. Fortunately detailed descriptions had already been published and casts made, so that the loss, though serious, is not so great as it might have been.

The Peking humans (see Plate XVIII*a*) differ most markedly from *Homo sapiens* and in many obvious ways resemble the *Pithecanthropus* group from Java. Davidson Black named the fossil types *Sinanthropus pekinensis*, and Weidenreich has followed this lead, but most anatomists now consider that Peking man is only a distinct species of *Pithecanthropus* and that it ought to be called *Pithecanthropus pekinensis*.

Peking man, as we know now from many specimens, had neither a simian shelf nor a true *chin eminence*; had a very massive brow-ridge, rather low-vaulted skull, small canine teeth, and a human arrangement of the two rows of cheek-teeth. Peking man was certainly human, and, by the *old terminology*, primitive. Today, however, we would say that, far from being primitive, Peking man was an over-specialized offshoot of the human stem. The late Professor Weidenreich, however, maintained that Peking man was ancestral to *Homo sapiens*, and some scientists still hold this view. It cannot, however, be accepted, for the skulls show many marked specializations and also have now been proved to be of Middle Pleistocene age, a date which is far too recent for them to be regarded as ancestral to *Homo sapiens*.

The deposits from which all these fossils come are at Choukoutien, but the skulls and other remains were obtained from several different levels and are *not* all of the same age. Some are early Middle Pleistocene and some late Middle Pleistocene.

We may summarize this chapter as follows:

Remains of fossil humans of extinct types are now known from Europe, Asia, and Africa. They range in time from the Lower Pleistocene in Java (*Meganthropus, Pithecanthropus modjokertensis*), through the Middle Pleistocene in Europe, China, and Java, to the Upper Pleistocene in Europe, the Near East, Africa, China, and Java.

None of the types described in this chapter was, on the available evidence, in any way ancestral to *Homo sapiens* (in spite of some opinions to the contrary), for all show specializations which are away from the *Homo sapiens* type; specializations which were once thought of as 'primitive' characters, and which led to the belief that these types represented 'primitive' stages of man, not highly specialized offshoots of the human stock.

CHAPTER XII

Our Stone Age Ancestors

IF we review the facts set out in the preceding chapter we find that the vast majority of the human fossils representing extinct types of man belong to the Upper Pleistocene period, while only a limited number of specimens from a very small number of sites represent fossils from the Middle and Lower Pleistocene periods.

Nearly all the Neanderthal remains, as well as the Eyasie skull, the Rhodesian skull, the Piltdown skull, and all the Solo skulls belong to the Upper Pleistocene, and the only fossils that we could with certainty assign to the Middle Pleistocene among our known extinct forms were the *Pithecanthropus* remains from Trinil, the Peking skulls from China, the Mauer jaw, and the Steinheim skull. The position in respect of the Lower Pleistocene was still more limited, with *Meganthropus* and the earlier *Pithecanthropus* remains from the Djetis beds as the sole examples.

It is most important to remember these facts when we turn to a consideration of the fossil remains of our ancestors—forerunners of present-day *Homo sapiens*—because a number of false arguments have been put forward as a result of an inadequate grasp of these facts.

Those who would have us believe that *Homo sapiens* is a descendant of Neanderthal man or Peking man or any of the other specialized types of extinct man, argue that if ancestral forms of *Homo sapiens* were in fact present in Lower and Middle Pleistocene times their remains should be not less common than the remains of their contemporary cousins. They go on to suggest that this is the case and that therefore such fossils as have been found should be regarded as doubtful. The facts of the case, as I see it, are as follows:

In Lower Pleistocene deposits we only know of human fossils from two sites so far—the Djetis beds in Java which have yielded *Meganthropus*, and the earlier form of *Pithecanthropus*, and the Kanam beds in Kenya which yielded the Kanam jaw fragment, which, as we shall see presently, has affinities to *Homo sapiens*.

In Middle Pleistocene deposits we know of four sites which have yielded remains of our extinct cousins: Choukoutien near Peking,

Plate XIX

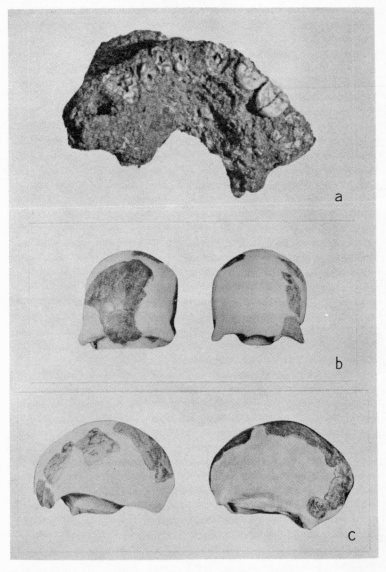

(a) The Kanam mandible (*Homo kanamensis*); (b, c) The Kanjera skulls (of *Homo sapiens* type)

Plate XX

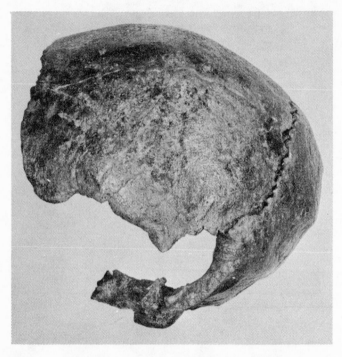

The Swanscombe skull (of *Homo sapiens* type)

Trinil in Java, and Mauer and Steinheim in Germany. On the other side of the picture we find that there are three Middle Pleistocene sites that have yielded remains which suggest *Homo sapiens* affinities: Swanscombe in England; Fontéchevade in France; and Kanjera in Kenya.

It is, of course, true that from the point of view of numbers of individuals our extinct cousins have a stronger position, this being chiefly due to the fact that one site, Choukoutien, yielded such a quantity of human remains, but that should not be allowed to dim the fact that *so far* only seven Middle Pleistocene sites have yielded human remains that can be placed in one or the other category (ancestors or specialized cousins), and that of these sites, three of the seven have yielded forms which suggest that they are in the direct line leading to *Homo sapiens*.

While Upper Pleistocene deposits have yielded vast numbers of specimens representing our extinct cousins, they have yielded fully as many that represent our ancestors, as we shall see presently, and we must therefore consider briefly why human remains of both groups are so much more commonly found in deposits of Upper Pleistocene age than in earlier deposits. The major reason is probably to be found in the fact that by Upper Pleistocene times man, including both *Homo sapiens* and his cousins Neanderthal man, Solo man, etc., had reached a stage where he held certain definite beliefs which proved a major contributory factor in the preservation of his remains as fossils. In the first place, we have the custom of ceremonial burial, practised by many Neanderthal tribes and by many *Homo sapiens* Upper Palaeolithic people. Once the idea of burial was conceived the chances of preservation were greatly increased, and the majority of our fossil human finds of the Upper Pleistocene owe their preservation to deliberate burial in deposits which were rich in lime and other minerals which brought about fossilization. In Upper Pleistocene times there was also a custom in certain groups of what was probably 'ceremonial cannibalism'. In other words, the body, or parts of the body, were consumed, not necessarily simply as food, but as a ritual, in order to pass on to the living some of the powers of the deceased.

The Solo skulls (see Chapter XI) were found in midden deposits along with stone tools and the remains of other mammals, and every skull had been broken open at the base to extract the brain. The same is true of a number of Neanderthal skulls—more particularly those from Saccopastore and Monte Circeo in Italy—while the Krapina human remains also showed evidence of cannibalism.

Ritual cannibalism is known among some present-day races, and we need not be any more surprised at its appearance in the Upper Pleistocene than at the appearance of ritual burial. Both these customs are certainly responsible for the great number of fossil human remains that we find in the Upper Pleistocene.

In the Middle Pleistocene we have only a suggestion of a comparable practice at two sites: Choukoutien, the site of Peking man, and Fontéchevade in France (see later). The fossils from the other sites of Middle Pleistocene age are casual fossils that owe their preservation to chance—the washing of fragments of a human skeleton into a geological deposit in process of formation, before they had decomposed and turned to dust.

Sooner or later other Middle Pleistocene human remains will be found, but it is doubtful if we shall ever have very abundant evidence of man of this period, except for isolated sites like Choukoutien, where ritual or possibly ordinary cannibalism was responsible.

From this general introduction let us turn to a brief examination of the actual specimens that seem to represent our direct ancestors.

First of all, we have the solitary find of the Kanam mandible (see Plate XIX*a*) in Lower Pleistocene deposits in Kenya. Doubt has been cast on this specimen by Professor Boswell, and there are some who, with him, still prefer to regard this as a 'doubtful' specimen. An ever-increasing number, however, agree with me that it is a genuine example of Lower Pleistocene man. The Kanam mandible was found in 1932 by Juma Gitau, a native member of my 1931–2 expedition, and he was only a few yards away from me when he found it. He had earlier found a tooth of the Pleistocene extinct elephant *Dinotherium* and had been told to dig farther into a cliff to see if he could get more teeth. He detached a block of hard matrix with his pick, and saw projecting from it a tooth. He passed the block to Dr. MacInnes, another member of the party, who saw that the tooth was human, and called me over. It was only after hours of laborious developing that the fragmentary human jaw was revealed.

There is no doubt whatsoever as to the age of the deposits in which the jaw was found—the fossil evidence is clear and undisputed: they are Lower Pleistocene beds. Professor Boswell, however, has suggested that the human jaw fragment found its way down to the place where it was finally imbedded in Lower Pleistocene deposits by slipping down a crack at some much later date. I cannot accept this interpretation, for which there is no evidence. The state of preservation of the fossil is in every respect identical to that of the Lower Pleistocene fossils found with it. Had the Kanam mandible been a specimen representing some specialized extinct type of man (such as used to be called 'primitive') no one would have suggested that it was not contemporary with the other fossils of the same horizon. At the time of the discovery, however, most people thought of the 'chin eminence' of *Homo sapiens* type as a character only acquired by man in very recent times, and the fact that the Kanam mandible has a distinct chin eminence certainly influenced some people against accepting its authenticity.

In certain respects the Kanam mandible differs from modern *Homo sapiens*—in the large size of the premolars, for example, and in general massiveness, and I have named it *Homo kanamensis* to emphasize these differences. But the Kanam mandible shows such resemblances to *Homo sapiens* that it must be regarded as an ancestor and not a cousin.

In the Middle Pleistocene the most important find that can be regarded as ancestral to *Homo sapiens* is the Swanscombe skull (see Plate XX) from the 100-ft. terrace gravels of the Thames, found by Dr. Marston in 1935–6. This skull is represented only by the occipital bone (the hind part of the skull) and a part of one side, and most unfortunately the front of the skull and face and teeth are missing. Nevertheless, those who have studied it closely consider that it stands far closer to *Homo sapiens* than to the Neanderthal skulls. It can be regarded with some degree of certainty as an ancestor of *Homo sapiens*. It is very thick and bears some resemblance to the Piltdown skull, and for this reason some scientists prefer to regard it as a second and older member of the Piltdown group. On the balance of evidence, however, it seems closer to true *Homo sapiens*, and I am satisfied that it represents one of the Middle Pleistocene direct ancestors of *Homo sapiens*.

Also from Middle Pleistocene deposits are the fragments of three human skulls from Kanjera (see Plate XIX*b* and *c*) in Kenya. Parts of one only of these were found *in situ* in geologically datable deposits, while the other fragments were found lying on the surface of the deposits from which they had been washed by erosion. The Kanjera skulls are notable, like the Swanscombe skull, for great thickness. The front part of the skull is preserved, in a damaged condition, in two of the specimens, and from this we can see that there was no trace of a bony brow-ridge above the eyes. Instead we find a very small and simple form much as in a child, but certainly of *Homo sapiens* type.

Professor Boswell has also thrown doubts upon the Kanjera

skulls, but I found part of No. 3 specimen *in situ* myself, and I have no doubt whatever about its genuineness. Most other scientists now also accept the age of the Kanjera skull fragments and regard them as representing an early stage of *Homo sapiens*. The age of the Kanjera beds is not in doubt; they represent the later stages of the Middle Pleistocene and are roughly contemporary with the Swanscombe beds. Both at Kanjera and Swanscombe we find also tools of the Acheulean stage of the Hand-axe culture. The Swanscombe skull and the Kanjera skulls are the only human remains which so far have been found in association with the Acheulean culture, and both thus point to the fact that this great culture was the product of *Homo sapiens*.

The third site to have yielded human remains of *Homo sapiens* type are the rock-shelters at Fontéchevade in France. In 1947 Mademoiselle Henri-Martin, daughter of the discoverer of the La Quina Neanderthaloid skulls, found charred fragments of two human skulls in a hearth in a level which had yielded tools of the Tayacian culture. These fragments of human skull represent individuals of *Homo sapiens* type, so far as can be judged by the nature of the frontal area.

We have already seen that the other two finds of human remains of Middle Pleistocene age with affinities to the *Homo sapiens* form were found in deposits which contained hand-axes—the Kanjera and the Swanscombe finds. We also know that wherever remains of extinct non-*Homo sapiens* types of humans have been found in association with Stone Age tools the culture has been one of the group which includes Levalloisian, Clactonian, and Mousterian, or else with some very crude and poorly made culture such as the Choukoutienian. I, and others, have postulated that *Homo sapiens*, with his superior brain, was the maker of the Hand-axe culture, and that it was our extinct cousins who made the Levalloisian, Clactonian, Mousterian, and allied cultures. The discovery of remains recalling *Homo sapiens* in deposits which yielded hand-axes, at Swanscombe and Kanjera, gave added strength to this theory. When the fragmentary charred remains of two skulls of true *Homo sapiens* type were found at Fontéchevade by Mademoiselle Henri-Martin several prehistorians expressed the view that this find, once and for all, disposed of the theory that *Homo sapiens* was associated with the Hand-axe culture and that the Neanderthaloids and their cousins were responsible for the Mousterian, Levalloisian, and Clactonian cultures. It is essential, therefore, to consider briefly whether this line of argument is valid or not.

The Fontéchevade skull fragments are reported: (1) to be charred; (2) to be very broken up; and (3) to show, on one skull at least, signs of death having been caused by a blow on the head with 'a blunt instrument'. We know from our study of the cultures of Europe that the Tayacian culture, with which the Fontéchevade skull fragments were found, is related to the Clactonian and Mousterian and was also contemporary with the closing stage of the Acheulean Hand-axe culture. In the circumstances it seems just as reasonable to consider that the Fontéchevade skulls represent two makers of the Acheulean culture who were victims of an attack by the makers of the Tayacian, and who were cooked and eaten (just as other animals killed in the chase), as it is to believe that they represent the actual makers of the Tayacian culture.

The whole question is, of course, still open, and more reliable finds are needed to give a final answer, but certainly the balance of the available evidence, viewed impartially, does strongly suggest that *Homo sapiens* or his direct ancestors made the Hand-axe culture, while our extinct cousins made the Mousterian, Levalloisian, Clactonian, and comparable cultures.

We must now leave the discussion of Lower and Middle Pleistocene ancestors of present-day man and turn to the Upper Pleistocene period.

The number of fossil remains of *Homo sapiens* in the Upper Pleistocene is so great that it will only be possible to review the more important finds, and it will be more convenient to do so regionally, by continents, rather than by cultures.

EUROPE

In Europe, during the earlier part of the Upper Pleistocene, climatic conditions were very far from favourable to man. Large parts of northern Europe were uninhabitable, and those parts that were habitable were very cold. Neanderthal man seems to have reigned supreme at that time over the habitable parts of Europe, and we find associated with his remains—as we have already seen —Levalloisian, Mousterian, and Levalloisio-Mousterian cultures. It was only during the later stages of the Upper Pleistocene that Europe was overrun by *Homo sapiens* tribes coming from the Near East, bringing with them the Aurignacian and Chatelperronian cultures. The evidence suggests that, with their superior weapons, they soon exterminated Neanderthal man, although there must have been some overlapping. The struggle for food, however, was probably such that there was little room for real overlapping in any given hunting area.

Following the Chatelperronian and the Aurignacian came the Solutrean and the Magdalenian cultures, and fossil remains of all the *Homo sapiens* races of Europe responsible for these cultures are relatively well known.

The earliest authenticated find of Upper Palaeolithic *Homo sapiens* in Europe was made in 1863, only a few years after the Neanderthal skull was found. Two human mandibles with parts of the skulls were found at Bruniquel in France, in association with a culture which we should now class as Magdalenian. Shortly after this a fragmentary *Homo sapiens* skull was found at La Madeleine, in the Dordogne, also with a Magdalenian culture, at what is, in fact, the type site of this culture. Then came the famous discovery of human remains at Cromagnon, with a true Aurignacian culture. Here, thanks to careful excavation, was the first evidence of *Homo sapiens* remains of both man and woman carefully buried. These skulls have become the type specimens of what we now call the Cromagnon race. The males had relatively large brow-ridges, but of the same form as we know in *Homo sapiens* and quite unlike Neanderthal man. Similar skulls come from Predmost (see Plate XXI*c* and *d*) and many other European sites.

Between 1868 and 1900 remains of more than eighty individuals of *Homo sapiens* type were found in France alone, with the Aurignacian, Solutrean, and Magdalenian cultures, and since 1900 finds in Europe have increased until now more than two hundred are known. It is impossible, in the scope of this book, to discuss all of these in detail, and it must suffice to refer to a few finds which are of special interest.

The Cromagnon type of man is represented by many finds, not only in France, but also in other parts of Europe, such as Predmost in Moravia. The skulls are long and rather narrow, the faces short and wide, and the noses very prominent, while the males have rather rugged brow-ridges. The Cromagnon race is, in fact, still represented among the European population of today, and people can still be found whose skulls differ in no marked way from Cromagnon man.

Another racial type of this period from Europe is what we call the Combe Capelle race (see Plate XXI*a* and *b*)—using a skull found by Hauser in 1909 at Combe Capelle, in the Perigord district of France —as the type for this race. The Combe Capelle race had a longer and narrower skull than the Cromagnon race, less massive brow-ridges, differently shaped jaw, and rather lower vault to the head. It does not differ very markedly from some of the skulls of what we call the Mediterranean race today.

There are still a good many prehistorians who refer to the two skulls and skeletons found near Mentone, at the Grimaldi cave, as the 'Negroid skulls of Grimaldi', and these two skulls have been used to build up a theory of a negroid migration into Europe from Africa in Upper Palaeolithic times. We owe the suggestion that these skulls are negroid to Dr. Verneau who first described them, and to the published photographs of the reconstructed skulls. It is quite clear from the original description that these specimens were badly damaged during excavation and removal to a laboratory and that much reconstruction was necessary. Examination of the original specimens most strongly suggests that the particularly negroid features of both specimens are due to faulty reconstruction and that both specimens belong to the Combe Capelle race. There is certainly nothing upon which to base the suggestion of a negro invasion of Europe, and in fact we can find no evidence that the negro was in Africa, at all, at that particular time.

The famous and much discussed Chancelade skull, found in 1888 at Raymonden in the Chancelade district of France, was in association with an industry which we now class as Magdalenian. The skull has repeatedly been compared with modern Eskimo skulls, and it certainly has a number of characters which link it with the Eskimo of today. There are also not a few cultural links between the Magdalenian culture and that of the Eskimos. On the other hand, it has to be remembered that many of the other skulls found with the Magdalenian culture do *not* show these Eskimo traits, and it would be wrong to think of the makers of the Magdalenian culture as fundamentally of the same race as the modern Eskimo. It is probable, however, that the Chancelade skull represents one of the several Magdalenian tribal types and that the Eskimos are descended from this stock, with some other admixtures.

Another Upper Palaeolithic racial type in Europe is that represented by the human remains at Obercassel, found mainly in association with a Magdalenian, and representing another tribal variation of the makers of this culture. The race represented by the Obercassel skull and others approximates to an ancestral form of the Nordic type.

We also find evidence of one or more broad-headed or brachycephalic types in Upper Palaeolithic times in Europe. The first finds in the Aurignacian—as distinct from the Solutrean—levels at

Solutré (the type site of the Solutrean culture) were regarded with doubt because they were broad-headed and it had come to be regarded as axiomatic that Upper Palaeolithic man was always long-headed. Further excavations at Solutré in 1921, however, yielded some more brachycephalic human skulls in the Aurignacian level under conditions which left no doubt as to their authenticity. We may accept as a fact that there was a brachycephalic racial element in Europe at that time. It has been suggested that an ultra-brachycephalic type was also present with the Chatelperronian culture at Chatelperron itself, but the evidence that the skull belongs with the industry is not very satisfactory.

What can be said with certainty is that, so far as Europe is concerned, a number of very distinct racial variants of *Homo sapiens* were present in Upper Palaeolithic times (foreshadowing some of the major racial elements in present-day Europe), a fact which makes it certain that *Homo sapiens* goes back a very long way in the time-scale, even though his remains are so scarce in earlier deposits.

AFRICA

Turning from Europe to Africa, we find that in the Upper Pleistocene in North Africa *Homo sapiens* is represented in late Upper Palaeolithic times by a number of finds, some of which recall the Cromagnon racial type, as, for example, the skulls from Metcha el Arbi and Beni Segoual. These finds both seem to represent the same race, although the first was associated with a Capsian culture and the second with Oranian. Special note should be made of the fact that the Beni Segoual skulls show evidence that the upper central incisors were deliberately extracted early in life, a condition which is widespread in Africa at the present time. Similar dental mutilation is also found in the Asselar skull, which was discovered some 220 miles north of Timbuktu, but without any cultural associations. Its late Upper Pleistocene age is suggested by the accompanying fauna.

Boule and Vallois consider that the Asselar skull (see Plate XXII) shows certain negroid characters, although some dispute this; if so, the skull represents the earliest suggestion of a negroid type so far found in Africa.

In East Africa the skulls from Gamble's Cave, Elementeita, found in association with an Upper Kenya Capsian culture, strongly recall the Combe Capelle type of skull from France. These skulls are dolichocephalic and not prognathous.

Plate XXI

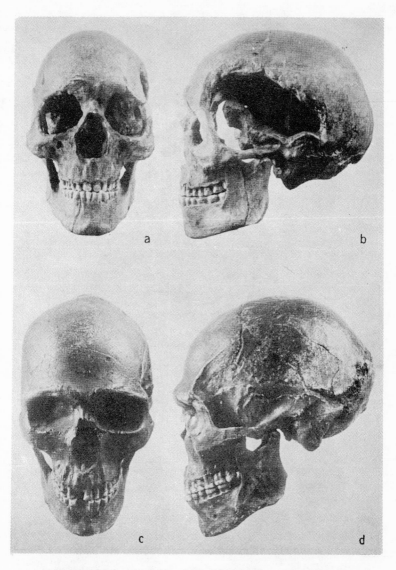

(*a, b*) The Combe Capelle skull, which has given its name to this race of *Homo sapiens*; (*c, d*) one of the Predmost skulls allied to the Cromagnon race

Plate XXII

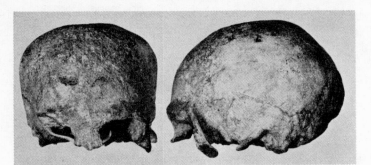

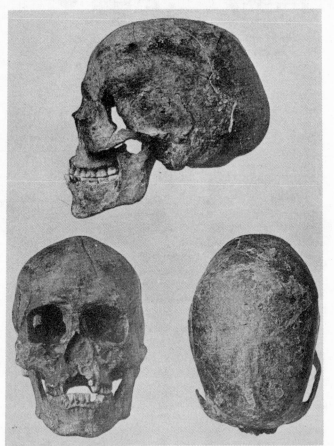

(a) The Singa skull from the Sudan, an ancestral Bushman;
(b) The Asselar skull from N. Africa, possibly an ancestral negroid

The Olduvai skull, which was originally claimed by Professor Reck to be of Middle Pleistocene age, has now been shown to be of Upper Pleistocene age, contemporary with the Gamble's Cave skulls. It is somewhat crushed, but probably represents the same racial type. The skull from Naivasha rock-shelter is also of the same age, and again resembles the Combe Capelle type more than any other.

From the Sudan we have the very interesting fossil skull from Singa (see Plate XXII). This, though found many years ago, has only recently been described in detail. It is regarded by Wells as being similar to the Boskop skull from South Africa and to represent a large and ancestral representative of the Bushman race. It is certainly of Upper Pleistocene date and was found in association with a culture which has been described as Levalloisian, but which seems to me, from the illustrations, to savour more of the Stillbay.

In South Africa the Fishhoek skull, also of proto-Bushman type, probably belongs to the late Upper Pleistocene, as does the Boskop skull-cap, but most of the other skulls, including those from Cape Flats and Springbok Flats, are more probably of what we would call Mesolithic age, and, like the Elementeita race of Kenya, do not concern us in this book.

There is one South African skull, however, in addition to those from Fishhoek and Boskop, which is of Upper Pleistocene age and which needs special comment. This is the Florisbad skull. It has been regarded by some as representing a non-*Homo sapiens* type, but this does not seem to be the case. The Florisbad skull should be regarded rather as a specialized offshoot of *Homo sapiens*, or just possibly the result of a cross between *Homo sapiens* and the non-*Homo sapiens* type from Broken Hill in Rhodesia.

ASIA

When we turn to Asia we find that at present we have relatively little good evidence of *Homo sapiens* in the Upper Pleistocene, though there can be no doubt at all that he was present and that material will be forthcoming, when more work has been done in this continent.

There are a certain number of important finds in association with Upper Palaeolithic cultures in Soviet territories, but the literature on them is hard to obtain. There are also some fragmentary human remains from Aurignacian levels in Palestine.

The upper levels at Choukoutien, near Peking, yielded a *Homo sapiens* skull in association with a late Upper Palaeolithic culture, and there are a few other finds of fragments belonging to *Homo sapiens* from China.

To summarize this chapter, we find first of all that, so far, fossil remains of *Homo sapiens* type that can be dated with any degree of certainty as Middle and Lower Pleistocene are very scarce indeed. The reason for this seems to lie in the fact that the practice of burial had not yet appeared, and man, as a roving creature, only occasionally died under conditions which led to his remains becoming fossilized, instead of being either consumed by carrion feeders or rotting to dust. There is, however, no longer any doubt that the *Homo sapiens* type goes back to an early date in the Pleistocene and was contemporary with the more specialized extinct types of man. There is also some reason for believing that the early types of *Homo sapiens* were mainly linked with the great Hand-axe culture, while his extinct cousins were in the main, if not wholly, linked with the Clactonian-Levalloisian-Mousterian complex and kindred cultures outside Europe.

By the Upper Pleistocene a very wide range of racial variants of *Homo sapiens* had been evolved, a condition which itself shows that the common ancestral form must go back at least to the beginning of the Pleistocene.

Having briefly reviewed, in the last three chapters, the fossil apes and 'near-men', the extinct human types, and fossil types related to *Homo sapiens*, we have reached the point where we may endeavour to draw up a family tree. It should be clearly understood that this can only be regarded as speculative, since many of the specimens at present available are too incomplete to give us much of the information we need.

It seems very nearly certain now that the human stem separated from the one which led to the living great apes—the gorilla, the chimpanzee, and the orang-outan—as well as to many of the Upper Pleistocene and Pliocene apes, at least as far back as the Lower Miocene and possibly even in the Oligocene. For the moment I prefer to place the division at the base of the Lower Miocene. The gibbons, however, seem to have broken away from the stem in the Oligocene, and it may well be that the separation of the stocks leading to men and to the great apes also took place in the Oligocene. *Parapithecus* and *Propliopithecus* from the Oligocene of Egypt seem to start in the line which leads to *Limnopithecus* in the Lower Miocene of Kenya and thence to *Pliopithecus* in the Middle and Upper Miocene of Europe.

While it is impossible to say that there is a direct line of evolution from *Propliopithecus* through *Limnopithecus* to *Pliopithecus* and thence to the modern gibbons, it is possible to suggest that all of these creatures represent the hylobatine or gibbon stock, with the earlier forms not yet showing the specializations found in the gibbons of today.

It is most unfortunate that we still know so little about the creature that has provisionally been called *Sivapithecus africanus* from the Kenya Lower Miocene beds, for this creature may well prove to be a true representative of the stock from which man came. On the other hand, the intermediate-sized *Proconsul*—the species called *nyanzae*—may also be said to have some claim to this position. For the moment I think it best to place the genera *Proconsul* and *Sivapithecus*, as represented by the species *africanus*, both at a point just before the separation of the human from the ape stems.

The Dryopithecenes, as represented by the species *fontaini* and '*pilgrim*', etc., are, in my opinion, an offshoot stem parallel to that leading to the great apes. They exhibit features such as the simian shelf, which show that they had already developed the specializations which are so characteristic of the true great apes, but not of man.

Sugrivapithecus too, from India, shows a simian shelf and must go with this branch of the family tree, and so probably does *Bramapithecus*.

The Indian *Sivapithecus* group is not easy to place, owing to lack of adequate specimens, just as this genus is so far also represented by inadequate specimens in the Lower Miocene of Kenya.

We have no direct evidence as to the presence or absence of a simian shelf in this genus, but the conformation of the anterior part of a jaw from India (which is unfortunately broken off before the symphysial area) suggests to me that a simian shelf must have been present. Should that prove to be the case, then the Indian species would, in my opinion, have to go into a branch of the ape stem rather than into the human one; but a branch in which the pattern of the cusps of the upper molars approximates more to that seen in man than to the living great apes.

Of *Ramapithecus* we have little material, but I suspect it of being a branch of the *Sivapithecinae*.

The Australopithecenes from South Africa are, as we have seen, too late in geological time to be regarded as direct ancestors,

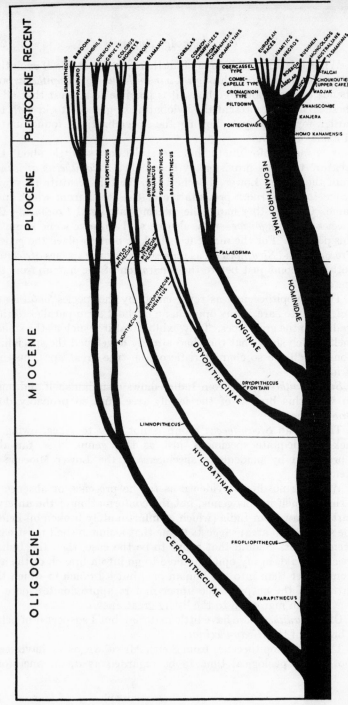

Fig. 34

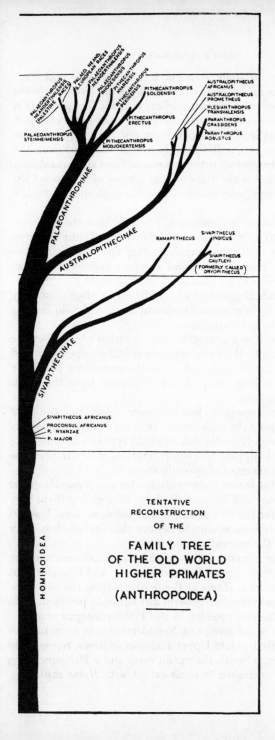

PALAEOANTHROPUS NEANDERTHALENSIS (PALESTINE)

PALAEO NE AND. & EUROPEAN RACES

PALAEOANTHROPUS RHODESIENSIS

PALAEOANTHROPUS HEIDELBERGENSIS

PITHECANTHROPUS MAURENSIS

PITHECANTHROPUS PEKINENSIS

PITHECANTHROPUS SOLOENSIS

AUSTRALOPITHECUS AFRICANUS

AUSTRALOPITHECUS PROMETHEUS

PLESIANTHROPUS TRANSVALENSIS

PARANTHROPUS CRASSIDENS

PARANTHROPUS ROBUSTUS

PALAEOANTHROPUS STEINHEIMENSIS

PITHECANTHROPUS ERECTUS

PITHECANTHROPUS MODJOKERTENSIS

PALAEOANTHROPINAE

AUSTRALOPITHECINAE

RAMAPITHECUS

SIVAPITHECUS INDICUS

SIVAPITHECUS CAUTLEYI (FORMERLY CALLED) ORYOPITHECUS

SIVAPITHECINAE

SIVAPITHECUS AFRICANUS

PROCONSUL AFRICANUS

P. NYANZAE

P. MAJOR

TENTATIVE
RECONSTRUCTION
OF THE

FAMILY TREE
OF THE OLD WORLD
HIGHER PRIMATES
(ANTHROPOIDEA)

HOMINOIDEA

while they are also in some respects too specialized, and they must be regarded as an offshoot which broke away from the main human stem in Pliocene (or even earlier) times. This gives us a reasonable degree of certainty that the Pliocene ancestors of man differed a great deal from the stock represented by *Dryopithecus* and *Sugrivapithecus*, etc., and was only a little different from the later Australopithecenes, but without some of their specializations.

It may well be that while some of the species of *Proconsul* led towards the ape stem, one species may have given rise to the human stem.

So far as man himself is concerned, I believe that the evidence suggests a major division at least as early as the Middle Pliocene and perhaps earlier, with one branch leading up to *Homo sapiens* races of today via Kanam man, and Kanjera and Swanscombe, etc., with the other leading to the stock represented by Java man, the Mauer jaw, and *Meganthropus*, in the early stages, and by Neanderthal man, Eyasie man, Rhodesian man, and Solo man as end-products just before extinction.

The Piltdown skull is a problem. The question of whether the jaw and skull belong to the same creature is still an open one, and personally I feel that they do not. For the moment I place the Piltdown skull as a direct but aberrant offshoot from the stock leading to *Homo sapiens*.

It must again be repeated that there are those who still hold that Peking man and Java man should be listed as direct ancestors of *Homo sapiens*, with Neanderthal and Solo types as intermediate forms, but I cannot support this interpretation, which implies too great a measure of reversal of specialization.

I have changed the terms *Palaeoanthropidae* and *Neoanthropidae* to Palaeoanthropinae and Neoanthropinae, thus giving them only sub-family status for the two stems, but at the same time I would point out that there is no reason to believe that one stock is older than the other, as the names seem to imply.

I believe that the Neanderthal type and also Rhodesian man are only species of a single genus *Palaeoanthropus*, and consider that they are as distinct from *Homo* as the gorilla is from the chimpanzee, and believe that therefore generic distinction is justified. Solo man I regard as the end-product of the *Pithecanthropus* stock.

Several distinct racial groups of Neanderthal man seem to have become differentiated in late Upper Pleistocene times, represented by a northern race, a South European race, and a Palestine race; the latter may have crossed to some extent with *Homo sapiens*.

CHAPTER XIII

What of the Future?

ON the final page of the first edition of this book I wrote: '*The last ten years have seen great advances in our knowledge of the past . . . the next ten years should see a still greater increase.*' It is not ten but nineteen years since I wrote those words, and the discoveries that have been made have been far more numerous than I had expected.

The picture as we know it today of Stone Age man's cultures during the Pleistocene period is a complex one—so complex that only a condensed summary has been possible in this book, but we may be absolutely certain that what we know at present is only the barest outline of the facts. There are still vast gaps in our knowledge of the Stone Age cultures and of the interaction of one culture upon another, where two or more are contemporary. There are, as we have seen, still greater gaps in our knowledge of the stages of evolution by which man reached his present status.

We have seen that the evidence that is available today points very strongly to the African continent as the place where man and the great apes were evolved. But Africa is still only very partially explored from the point of view of Prehistory, and there are immense areas where no prehistorian has worked at all. Although we must now look more and more to Africa for the evidence of the earlier stages of human evolution, we must not let ourselves forget that Asia may well have played a very important part in the story too. It was the discoveries in the Siwalik Hills of India that first led scientists to think of Asia as the possible birthplace of humanity, and although we now know that the Siwalik deposits are much younger, geologically, than the Lower Miocene beds of Kenya, nevertheless we cannot ignore the possibility that during the Upper Miocene and Pliocene periods the Siwalik area may have been a major, even though secondary, centre of evolution of the higher Primates.

We have at present no means of knowing at which stage the human stock divided into the branches leading on the one hand to *Homo sapiens* and on the other to the extinct groups like *Pithecanthropus* of Java. Comparisons between the remains of many other groups of fossil animals from Africa and the Siwaliks suggest that there are very close links, and it may well be that we should not think in terms of the continents as we know them today when we talk about the place of origin and evolution of the higher Primates, but rather of a zone which could include the region from North India in the east to Kenya in the west.

Whatever the final verdict may be, it is certain that we shall need to do a very great deal more research before we can begin to say that the story of human evolution is even half as clear as that, shall we say, of the horse.

Probably one of the most urgent needs today is for fresh and very thorough investigations to be made of the Oligocene and Lower Miocene deposits in Egypt. In the days when *Parapithecus* and *Propliopithecus* were discovered there, more attention was being given to the fossil remains of the large animals that occur in these deposits than to the small ones, and the discovery of Primate material was, in a sense, incidental to the search for early ancestors of the elephants and the anthrecotheres, etc. Fossil remains of the smaller animals require a much more careful search, and often prolonged work, not day after day but year after year.

The discoveries in Kenya in the Lower Miocene suggest that *Limnopithecus* must be a descendant of *Propliopithecus* of Egypt, but they also leave little doubt that the Egyptian Oligocene deposits should contain forms ancestral to *Proconsul* as well as *Sivapithecus*.

Research work in the Oligocene deposits in Egypt, directed especially towards the search for fossil Primate material, is a most urgent need today if we are to throw more light on the early stages of the evolution of man and the great apes. It will be costly and difficult work, and whoever undertakes it may have to expect months or even years of hard work before the prize is found, but I feel sure the prize is there.

In very much the same way there is an urgent need for fresh work in the Siwalik Hills of India, directed *mainly* towards a search for more complete remains of the fossil apes of that area, which we know only from fragmentary remains. Better specimens must be there, and though they may, perhaps, be found by some brief and hasty expedition, it is more likely that they will only be found by prolonged search over a period of years by some person who is determined 'to search until he finds'; someone prepared to devote a lifetime, if necessary, to the discovery of this part of the missing chain of evidence in ape and human evolution.

Much, too, remains to be done in the Lower Miocene deposits of

Kenya, which have already yielded such good results since 1930, and it may be hoped that the next ten years will see the discovery there of more complete remains of *Proconsul, Sivapithecus,* and *Limnopithecus,* as well, probably, as other new genera.

It must be remembered that in South-west Africa there are Lower Miocene beds which years ago yielded a fossil fauna not dissimilar to that from the Kenya beds. These deposits would certainly be worth re-examining with a special view to finding fossil Primate material.

The recent (and as yet undescribed) discovery of parts of a skeleton of *Pliopithecus* in Austria serve to remind us, too, that the deposits of the Middle and Upper Miocene and Pliocene of Europe, which have yielded a small amount of *Pliopithecus* and *Dryopithecus* material, might well repay further extensive study.

Since the various discoveries of human remains in the Pleistocene leave no room for doubt that man's direct ancestors were present (even if not tool-makers) in the Pliocene, much more careful attention is now needed for the known Pliocene fossil beds that contain land mammals. Somewhere in them, even if only as very rare fossils, the remains of Pliocene creatures directly ancestral to man must, in due course, be found.

In particular the vast continent of Africa, so little explored from this point of view, must somewhere hold fossiliferous deposits of truly Pliocene age, and when they are found, very interesting light on human evolution is almost certain to come from them. The vast fossiliferous deposits of the Lower Pleistocene in the Omo Valley of southern Abyssinia should also be further explored. Apart from the original expedition there in 1903 by Bourg de Boaz, the brief expedition by Professor Arambourg in 1935 and some spasmodic collecting by one of my men during the war years, this field is still untouched. Such work as has been done has been mainly directed to the larger mammals because they are easier to find and more spectacular, but the Omo fossil beds must, I feel sure, somewhere conceal the remains of contemporary early Pleistocene man.

The fossil-rich fissure fillings and limestone caves of South Africa are already yielding a mass of new evidence of the 'near-man' or *Australopithecus* and allied forms. Much more work remains to be done here, and similar deposits are known to occur in Angola, the Congo, and Northern Rhodesia. These need intensive exploration.

Turning from the search for man's pre-human ancestors and the evidence of the evolution of the human stock to man himself and his Palaeolithic cultures, the gaps in our knowledge are also vast. There is a most urgent need, for example, to explore vast regions in Africa and Asia where no prehistorian has ever set foot. India is perhaps one of the biggest gaps of all. We know that vast numbers of stone tools of many different cultural stages can be found—and have been found—in different parts of India, but we still lack any comprehensive scientific account of the Stone Age cultures of India and their relation to climatic changes, except in the extreme north.

Apart from Palestine and Syria, the Palaeolithic of the Near East is still, also, a large blank in our knowledge.

In Africa the vast Sahara zone, most of Abyssinia, and the Congo, large parts of the Sudan, all of Nyasaland, and many parts of West Africa have still yielded little evidence concerning the Palaeolithic, though the evidence must be there.

Even in Europe, the home of prehistoric studies, we have a great deal still to learn; much of the early work needs checking and re-checking in the light of more scientific methods of excavation and interpretation. Quite apart from field studies there is an urgent need in Europe for a re-examination of many collections originally described in general terms as 'Mousterian' (and often found in association with Neanderthaloid remains) to see whether they are true Mousterian, Levalloisian, late Clactonian, or some result of culture contact.

One of the most urgently needed field studies in Europe is in connexion with the great Hand-axe culture in this area. Much has been done, it is true, but in all too many cases the records of Hand-axe culture in river gravel and other deposits in Europe have been based upon material collected from commercial workings and often by untrained workmen without adequate reference to the stratigraphy of the deposits, so that prolonged scientifically conducted excavations are needed to check the earlier interpretations. Then, too, there still remains the opportunity of finding further remains of the men who made the Hand-axe culture in these geological deposits.

Dr. Marston's famous discovery of the Swanscombe skull is an example of how patient and continuous search of the gravel deposits of Europe which contain the Hand-axe culture does, in the end, yield worth-while results. Any interested reader of this book who is prepared to take time and trouble and make accurate observations in the old gravels of the higher terraces in the south of England, for example, may well be rewarded, one day, by the discovery of another skull or a jaw of the men who made the Hand-axe culture. Should such a discovery be made, the important thing would be to report the find at once to some competent authority, so that the evidence could be checked and studied at once.

This book has only summarized the story of our Stone Age ancestors roughly up to 10,000 B.C. and the end of the Upper Palaeolithic period. The story, of course, goes on, and we come first to what is called the Mesolithic period, which was really a sort of transitional stage from the Upper Palaeolithic to the Neolithic, where settled community life and the domestication of animals and plants laid the foundations for the dawn of the metal age and of historical times.

One of the interesting things that emerges from our study of man's past is that the evolution of material culture proceeds at an ever-increasing rate; we might almost say in reversed geometric progression rather than by steady and even advances, or arithmetical progression. The period of time that was needed for the evolution of the simple pebble cultures into the first true stage of the Hand-axe culture was immensely long—literally hundreds of thousands of years—and far longer than was needed for the evolution of the Hand-axe culture from its most primitive to its most advanced stages. Similarly, the evolution of cultures in the Upper Palaeolithic, though proceeding at a much faster rate than in hand-axe times, was much slower than the evolution from the end of the Upper Palaeolithic to the dawn of the metal age. We know, too, from history that so-called progress, progress of material culture, gets faster and faster. Developments of material culture (in terms of aeroplanes and cars and atom bombs and wireless) have been infinitely faster in the last fifty years than the developments of material culture of the previous five hundred years.

But, on the other side of the picture, we find that the evidence points to a very, very much slower rate of physical evolution of the human stock. The physical differences between Kanjera man and Swanscombe man and the men who made the Aurignacian and the late Upper Palaeolithic cultures are small, while, as we have seen, in physical characters the Aurignacians can be paralleled in the living populations of the present day. In other words, the evolution of material culture is far outstripping the physical evolution of man himself except in one thing—in the complexity and development of his brain power.

Brain complexity and the ability to use the brain must not be confused with size of brain. There is, in fact, no close correlation between brain size and brain ability. The Neanderthal race had, on the average, bigger brains than we have today, but they were not more clever. The complexity of their brain convolutions was much less.

We know from the study of evolution that, again and again, various branches of different animal stock have become over-specialized, and that over-specialization has led to their extinction. Present-day *Homo sapiens* is in many physical respects still very unspecialized—less specialized, for example, than either his extinct cousins Java man and Peking man or his much more recent living cousins, the great apes. But in one thing man, as we know him today, is over-specialized. His brain power is very over-specialized compared with the rest of his physical make-up, and it may well be that this over-specialization will lead, just as surely, to his extinction as other forms of over-specialization have done, in the past, for other groups.

Not only has the over-specialization of our brain power made us capable of inventing the means of the destruction of our species by atom bombs, but it has also resulted in our creating for ourselves such a highly specialized material culture that we are far more— not less—at the mercy of Nature than man ever was before. We know that in the past, since man first became man, there have been very great changes both of climate and geography. Violent earthquakes such as those that must have accompanied much of the Rift Valley faulting in Africa at the end of the hand-axe times would have disturbed man of those times very little, except for the few in the immediate vicinity, but today similar earthquakes would cause more havoc and a higher death-rate than any atom bomb.

Theoretically, the fact that *Homo sapiens* has specialized in his brain, rather than in any other way, should make him more capable of survival, because he should be more capable of finding ways and means of meeting Nature's vagaries. But, if we are to control our future, we must first understand the past better. History only gives us a picture of a minute fraction of the total time that man has been man; Prehistory can tell us the rest of the story, as well as the story of the major changes of climate and geography that have happened in the past, and that will certainly happen again. It is only by the study and understanding of the past that we can hope to foretell, and perhaps control, the future.

Bibliography

SHORT LIST OF USEFUL BOOKS AND PAPERS TO READ

CHAPTER II

Climate Through the Ages, by C. E. P. Brooks. London, 1950.
Dating the Past, by F. Zeuner. London, 1946.
'The Climate During the Pleistocene Period', by C. G. Simpson, *Proceedings of the Royal Society of Edinburgh*. 1929–30.
'The Plio-Pleistocene Boundary'. Various authors in *Proceedings of Section H of the 18th International Geological Congress*. London, 1950.
'Radio-Carbon Dating of Late Pleistocene Events', by R. F. Flint and Edward S. Deevey in *American Journal of Science*. April 1951.
The Fluorine Dating Method, by K. P. Oakley. New York, 1951.

CHAPTERS II & III

Man the Toolmaker, by K. P. Oakley, Brit. Mus. Nat. Hist. London, 1951.
'Primitive Methods of Working Stone', by Alonzo W. Pond, *Logan Museum Bulletin*, vol. II, No. 1. 1930.

CHAPTERS V, VI, & VII

The Prehistory of Uganda Protectorate, by T. P. O'Brien. Cambridge, 1939.
The Stone Age Cultures of N. Rhodesia, by J. D. Clark. Claremont, Capetown, 1951.
The Prehistory of S. Rhodesia, by Neville Jones. Cambridge, 1949.
The Stone Age of Mount Carmel, by D. A. E. Garrod and D. M. A. Bate. Oxford, 1937.
The Geology and Archaeology of the Vaal River Basin, by P. G. Songhe and C. van Riet Lowe. Pretoria, 1937.
'The Lower Palaeolithic Cultures of Southern and Eastern Asia', by Hallam L. Movius, *Transactions of the American Philosophical Society*. 1948.

Die Höhlenfunde von Jabrud (Syrie), by A. Rust. Neumunster,1950.

Studies on the Ice Age in India, and Associated Human Cultures, by H. de Terra and T. T. Paterson. Washington, 1939.

'The Levalloisian Industries of Egypt', by G. Caton-Thompson. *Proceedings of the Prehistoric Society.* 1946.

'The Aterian Industry: its Place and Significance in the Palaeolithic World', by G. Caton-Thompson, *Journal of the Royal Anthropological Institute.* 1947.

Le Capsien de l'Abri 402, by E. G. Gobert and R. Vaufrey. Paris, 1950.

Stone Age Africa, by L. S. B. Leakey. Oxford, 1936.

Tentative Study of Pleistocene Climatic Changes and Stone Age Culture Sequence in N.E. Angola, by L. S. B. Leakey. Lisbon, 1949.

Olduvai Gorge, by L. S. B. Leakey. Cambridge, 1951.

Proceedings of the First Pan-African Congress on Prehistory. Oxford, 1952.

'Report on Excavations at Jaywick Sands, Essex', by K. P. Oakley and M. D. Leakey, *Proceedings of the Prehistoric Society.* 1937.

Stone Age Cultures of Kenya Colony, by L. S. B. Leakey. Cambridge, 1931.

Also various scientific articles which have appeared in the following publications since 1938:

Proceedings of the Prehistoric Society; l'Anthropologie; Transactions of the Royal Society of S. Africa; South African Journal of Science; Man; South African Archaeological Bulletin; Journal of the Royal Anthropological Institute.

CHAPTER VIII

The Lascaux Cave Paintings, by F. Windels. London, 1949.

L'Arte Rupestre della Libia, by P. Graziosi. Naples, 1942.

Forty . . . of Prehistoric Art, by H. Breuil. 1952.

Stone Age Africa, by L. S. B. Leakey. Oxford, 1936.

Also papers in the periodicals listed above for Chapters V, VI, and VII.

CHAPTER IX

Up from the Ape, by E. A. Hooton. London, 1931.

An Introduction to Physical Anthropology, by M. F. Ashley Montague. Illinois, 1951.

'The Riddle of Man's Ancestry', by W. L. Strauss. *Quarterly Review of Biology.* 1949.

CHAPTER X

The Miocene Hominoidae of E. Africa, by W. E. Le Gros Clark and L. S. B. Leakey, Brit. Mus. Nat. Hist. London, 1951.

Fossil Anthropoids of the Yale-Cambridge India Expedition, by W. K. Gregory, M. Hellman, and G. E. Lewis. Carnegie Inst. Washington, 1938.

Associated Jaws and Limb Bones of Limnopithecus Macinnesi, by W. E. Le Gros Clark and D. P. Thomas, Brit. Mus. Nat. Hist. London, 1951.

'Hominoid Characters of the Australopithecene Dentition', by W. E. Le Gros Clark, *Journal of the Royal Anthropological Institute*.

The South African Fossil Ape Men, by R. Broom and G. W. H. Schaepers. Pretoria, 1946.

The Sterkfontein Ape Men, by R. Broom and J. T. Robinson. Pretoria.

History of the Primates, by W. E. Le Gros Clark, Brit. Mus. Nat. Hist. London, 1950.

Also various papers in the Year Book of Physical Anthropology from 1945 onwards, published by the Viking Fund Inc., New York.

Articles and Notes in *Nature*; *The South African Journal of Science*; publications of the Royal Society of South Africa; *The American Journal of Physical Anthropology* from 1946 onwards, on the Australopithecenes, *Proconsul*, etc.

CHAPTER XI

Numerous reports on *Sinanthropus pekinensis* in *Palaeontologia Sinica*, by D. Black, F. Weidenreich, etc.

The Stone Age of Mount Carmel, vol. II, by T. D. McCown and A. Keith. Oxford, 1939.

Early Man in the East, by various authors. Philadelphia, 1949.

'Morphology of Solo Man', by F. Weidenreich. *Anthropological Papers of the American Museum of Natural History*. New York, 1951.

'Fossil Hominids from the Lower Pleistocene of Java', by G. H. R. von Koenigswald, in *Report of the 18th Session of the International Geological Congress*. London, 1950.

Les Hommes Fossiles, by Marcellin Boule, revised edition by H. V. Vallois. Paris, 1946.

History of the Primates, by W. E. Le Gros Clark, Brit. Mus. Nat. Hist. London, 1950.

'Pithecanthropus in Peking', by W. E. Le Gros Clark, *Antiquity*. 1945.

CHAPTER XII

'New Evidence on the Antiquity of Piltdown Man', by K. P. Oakley and C. R. Hosking. *Nature*, pp. 379–82. 1950.

'The Fontéchevade Fossil Men', by H. V. Vallois in *American Journal of Physical Anthropology*. 1949.

'Report on the Swanscombe Skull', by the Swanscombe Committee. *Journal of the Royal Anthropological Institute*. 1938.

The Stone Age Races of Kenya, by L. S. B. Leakey. Oxford, 1933.

'Studies on Palaeolithic Man', by various authors in *Annals of Eugenics*. 1926–8 and 1930.

Hommes Fossiles, by Marcellin Boule, revised edition by H. V. Vallois. Paris, 1946.

History of the Primates, by W. E. Le Gros Clark, Brit. Mus. Nat. Hist. London, 1950.

APPENDIX I

IN view of the fact that the 'Middle Stone Age Complex' in South Africa is dealt with so briefly in this book, which was partly due to the fact that the picture which I obtained from an exhaustive study of the literature was so blurred and inconsistent, I am very happy to be able to include the following note prepared by Dr. Basil Cooke and accepted by Professor C. Van Riet Lowe, Mr. B. D. Malan and Mr. A. J. H. Goodwin as giving a correct summary of their knowledge of the culture complex in July 1952.

The Middle Stone Age Complex in South Africa

The cultures which comprise the Middle Stone Age Complex in South Africa all depend primarily on the faceted platform technique, which produced several different types of prepared cores. The commonest tool types are unifaced points, points with convergent longitudinal flake scars on one side, unifaced points with a faceted butt, points with reduced bulbs, various types of scrapers, gravers, bolas stones and, finally, backed blades. The line of demarcation between the Earlier and Middle Stone Ages is somewhat blurred owing to a mastery of the faceted platform technique in the upper divisions of the former, so that some tool types occur in both Ages. Hand-axes are absent in the Middle Stone Age and lance-heads do not occur in the Earlier Stone Age.

Within the Middle Stone Age (often abbreviated to M.S.A.) there are recognized a number of distinct cultures and *variations* whose interrelation is rendered uncertain by lack of stratigraphical evidence. It is known that several different races of man inhabited the region in Middle Stone Age times and it may be expected that there were cultural differences related to different ethnic groups. It is probable that the various cultures now distinguished overlap each other and are partly different and contemporaneous facies of the same complex. The term Middle Stone Age Complex is thus becoming recognized as the most convenient and elastic term.

The Pietersburg Culture, now widely known in the Transvaal and adjoining areas, shows a long development through several stages from the final tool types of the Earlier Stone Age to refined products comparable with the South African Magosian stage typified at Modderpoort in the Orange Free State. The Pietersburg Culture, together with its later developments in the same region, may well represent the whole of the period of the M.S.A. Complex, but it does not include all the elements found in the other regional developments.

Of importance equal to the Transvaal cultural stages is the development of the Still Bay Culture in the southern mountain region of the Cape of Good Hope. Within this region there are local variations, such as the Mossel Bay industry in which remarkably simplified unifaced points and blades of Table Mountain Sandstone displace the normally characteristic bifaced lance-heads. A stage equivalent to the Magosian is attained in this region, possibly independently of the corresponding development in the interior plateau.

In the belt between the southern mountain region of the Cape and the high plateau of the Transvaal, there occur several cultures whose relationships are still undetermined and whose characteristics may be influenced by the distribution of indurated shale. The belt runs broadly from Natal, through the Orange Free State of Griqualand West (west of Kimberley in the northern Cape of Good Hope). The cultures include the Natal Still Bay, the Mazelspoort-Vlakkraal Culture, and the Alexandersfontein Complex. The South African Magosian is well developed in this belt.

HBSC July 1952: approved CVRL, BDM and AJHG.

APPENDIX II

A Note on the Capsian-Oranian Complex in North Africa

AS a result of my recent visit to North Africa, after the text of Adam's Ancestors had gone to press, I have formed the very definite opinion that the differences between the Capsian culture and the Oranian are much less real than has previously been supposed, and that the apparent differences are in the main due to ecological reasons.

It seems to me probable, now, that the Capsian culture arrived in Algeria from the south and that, having reached the open high plateau there, three things may have happened. Part of the population of the high plateau—which is bitterly cold in winter—began to make a habit of moving down to the warmer coastal plain during the winter months, returning again to the open plains on the plateau in summer. The differing needs for the hunting life on the open plains and for the winter life (mainly in rock-shelters) on the coastal belt, is quite capable of explaining the main differences in the tool assemblages of the two 'cultures', while it also, of course, explains the differences in mode of life. In the summer the Capsians lived in open camps, on a diet which included vast numbers of snails which resulted in the building up of the characteristic 'escargatoires' of the Capsian culture; in winter they lived in rock-shelter homes and had a somewhat different diet.

Subsequently (and perhaps very soon after the first experiments in moving to the coastal zone for winter and returning to the plateau in summer) some of the people seem to have decided to remain always in the coastal belt and gradually moved westwards, right along this zone to Morocco. As they did so they naturally made full use of the snail as an article of diet in summer, so that as one moves to the west one finds that the deposits in caves and rock-shelters which are associated with the so-called Oranian culture include huge snail-shell levels, while the tool types are those adopted to the ecology of the coastal zone, while in the main falling within the range of the Capsian culture types.

225

IN November, 1953, after the publication of this book, a special issue of the Bulletin of the British Museum (Natural History) vol. 2, no. 3, was issued, entitled 'The Solution of the Piltdown Problem'. This consists of a report by J. S. Weiner, K. P. Oakley, and W. E. Le Gros Clark, announcing the discovery of the fact that the Piltdown mandible is not a genuine fossil at all, but is the jaw of a modern ape that was 'faked' and artificially coloured to make it appear to belong with the original main parts of the Piltdown skull, the genuine character of which is not in question.

The doubts expressed on page 189 of this book, and my personal conviction that the jaw does not belong with the skull stated on page 212, are therefore justified. Without the jaw the Piltdown skull falls into its proper place as *Homo sapiens*, and need no longer be placed among our extinct cousins.

The revelations made in the Bulletin leave little doubt that the 'hoax' was a carefully planned one, and go a long way to exonerate those who fell into the trap and accepted the mandible as genuinely belonging with the skull. There are some further points, however—in this connexion—which should be stressed and which become very significant, now that the 'hoax' has been unmasked.

On the Piltdown mandible—now shown to be that of a modern ape—the condyle of the jaw was missing, as was that part of the mandible which would normally carry the first premolar tooth. No amount of faking of the condyle could ever have made it fit the entirely human 'socket' on the skull itself, with which the condyle should articulate. Obviously it was for this reason that the condyle of the jaw had to be destroyed during the faking.

Similarly the first premolar of an ape, both in its crown and also in its root structure, differs so completely from a human first premolar, that this part of the jaw had also to be destroyed if the 'hoax' was not to be detected at the outset.

Finally, the nature of the genuine socket for the condyle of the jaw on the skull itself was of such a nature that the teeth of the jaw that belonged to it must have exhibited the human type of wear and not the ape pattern of attrition. Consequently the perpetrator of the 'hoax' had to rub down the crowns of the teeth to simulate this human wear.

All these points, as well as others enumerated in the Bulletin, indicate that whoever was responsible for the 'hoax', knew enough about ape and human anatomy to be fully aware which features might perhaps pass muster, and which, on the other hand, would give him away immediately.

Index

ABBEVILLE, discoveries at, 8
ABBEVILLIAN, 73, 82
ABERDARE, the range, 101
ABYSSINIA, 104; Stillbay in, 132, 216
ACHEULEAN, the flaking technique, 42; Upper, in Near East, 106; derivatives of, 109, 113
ACHEULEO-LEVALLOISIAN, the, 115
ACHEULEO-MOUSTERIAN, the, 115, 139
ACHEULEO-TAYACIAN, the, 98
ADMIRALTY ISLANDS, 61
AFRICA, the Chelleo-Acheul culture in, 55; need for exploration in, 216
AFRICANTHROPUS NJARA-SENSIS, 194
AMERICA, climatic changes in, 22
AMIENS, discoveries at, 8
ANDERSEN, DR. S. G., 197
ANGOLA, 124, 144, 215; North Sangoan culture in, 100; Upper Palaeolithic, 136
ANTLER, use of by prehistoric man, 50
ANVIL TECHNIQUE, 41
ANYATHIAN, the, 87, 109, 143
APES, fossil, concentration of remains, 184, 185; fossil, discussion of, Chapter X; fossil, limb proportions of, 159 et. seq.; the great, 158
ARABIA, 130
ARAMBOURG, Professor, 215
ART, PALAEOLITHIC, Chapter VIII, classification, 148; Magdalenian, 148; in South Africa, 148–154; pigments used, 148, 149; techniques of 149 et seq.; evidence of age, 151; sites, 151; superpositions, 152, 153; styles, 153; cultures associated with, 154; in East Africa, 154; in Rhodesia, 154; in North Africa, 154; reasons for, 154, 155, 156
ASIA, climatic changes in, 22; Chelleo-Acheul culture in, 81; cultures of, 87, 88; Upper Palaeolithic cultures of, 139 et seq.; need for exploration in, 216

ASIA MINOR, cultures of, 106, et seq.
ASSELAR, skull from, 208
ASSEMBLAGES OF SPECIMENS, importance of, 7
ATERIAN, the, 60, 105, 113; development of, 144; discussion of, 123 et seq.; late, in Egypt, 128
ATLITIAN, the, 142, 144
AUDI POINTS, 60, 83, 116
AURIGNACIAN, the, 99, 143; origin of, 109; Lower, 116, 140; Upper, 118, 142; discussion of, 118, 205, 206; the Kenya, 128; Middle, 116, 140
AUSTRALIA, climatic changes in, 22
AUSTRALIAN ABORIGINES, 160, 165
AUSTRALOPITHECINAE, the, 173, 180, 182; age of, 183; status of, 183
AUSTRALOPITHECUS, 215; *africanus*, 181, *prometheus*, 181; *transvaalensis*, see *Plesianthropus transvaalensis*
AWLS, uses of, 62

BACKED BLADES, uses of, 61
BAÑOLAS, sites at, 190
BARNFIELD PIT, Swanscombe, 82
BECHUANALAND, the Sangoan in, 139
BEMBESI CULTURE, the, 134
BENI SEGOUAL, skulls from, 208
BIZE, site at, 8
BLACK, DR. DAVIDSON, 198
BLADE & BURIN CULTURE, tool types of, 61; distribution of, 61; evolution of, 114, 116
BOAZ, BOURG de, 215
BOLAS, uses of, 58, 59; making of, 58, 59; in the hand axe culture, 81; in the Fauresmith, 102
BONE, use of by prehistoric man, 50
BOSKOP, skull from, 209
BOSWELL, PROFESSOR, 202
BOUCHER DE PERTHES, discoveries by, 8
BOULE, PROFESSOR, 191, 208

227

hARPER ✦ ϹORϹhBOOKS

HUMANITIES AND SOCIAL SCIENCES

American Studies: General

LOUIS D. BRANDEIS: Other People's Money, and How the Bankers Use It. ‡ Ed. with an Intro. by Richard M. Abrams   TB/3081
THOMAS C. COCHRAN: The Inner Revolution. Essays on the Social Sciences in History   TB/1140
HENRY STEELE COMMAGER, Ed.: The Struggle for Racial Equality   TB/1300
EDWARD S. CORWIN: American Constitutional History. Essays edited by Alpheus T. Mason and Gerald Garvey △   TB/1136
CARL N. DEGLER, Ed.: Pivotal Interpretations of American History   Vol. I TB/1240; Vol. II TB/1241
A. HUNTER DUPREE: Science in the Federal Government: A History of Policies and Activities to 1940   TB/573
A. S. EISENSTADT, Ed.: The Craft of American History: Recent Essays in American Historical Writing
Vol. I TB/1255; Vol. II TB/1256
CHARLOTTE P. GILMAN: Women and Economics: A Study of the Economic Relation between Men and Women as a Factor in Social Evolution. ‡ Ed. with an Introduction by Carl N. Degler   TB/3073
OSCAR HANDLIN, Ed.: This Was America: As Recorded by European Travelers in the Eighteenth, Nineteenth and Twentieth Centuries. Illus.   TB/1119
MARCUS LEE HANSEN: The Atlantic Migration: 1607-1860. Edited by Arthur M. Schlesinger   TB/1052
MARCUS LEE HANSEN: The Immigrant in American History.   TB/1120
JOHN HIGHAM, Ed.: The Reconstruction of American History △   TB/1068
ROBERT H. JACKSON: The Supreme Court in the American System of Government   TB/1106
JOHN F. KENNEDY: A Nation of Immigrants. △ Illus.
TB/1118
LEONARD W. LEVY, Ed.: American Constitutional Law: Historical Essays   TB/1285
LEONARD W. LEVY, Ed.: Judicial Review and the Supreme Court   TB/1296
LEONARD W. LEVY: The Law of the Commonwealth and Chief Justice Shaw   TB/1309
HENRY F. MAY: Protestant Churches and Industrial America. New Intro. by the Author   TB/1334
RALPH BARTON PERRY: Puritanism and Democracy
TB/1138
ARNOLD ROSE: The Negro in America   TB/3048
MAURICE R. STEIN: The Eclipse of Community. An Interpretation of American Studies   TB/1128
W. LLOYD WARNER and Associates: Democracy in Jonesville: A Study in Quality and Inequality ¶ TB/1129
W. LLOYD WARNER: Social Class in America: The Evaluation of Status   TB/1013

American Studies: Colonial

BERNARD BAILYN, Ed.: Apologia of Robert Keayne: Self-Portrait of a Puritan Merchant   TB/1201
BERNARD BAILYN: The New England Merchants in the Seventeenth Century   TB/1149
JOSEPH CHARLES: The Origins of the American Party System   TB/1049
HENRY STEELE COMMAGER & ELMO GIORDANETTI, Eds.: Was America a Mistake? An Eighteenth Century Controversy   TB/1329
CHARLES GIBSON: Spain in America †   TB/3077
LAWRENCE HENRY GIPSON: The Coming of the Revolution: 1763-1775. † Illus.   TB/3007
LEONARD W. LEVY: Freedom of Speech and Press in Early American History: Legacy of Suppression TB/1109
PERRY MILLER: Errand Into the Wilderness   TB/1139
PERRY MILLER & T. H. JOHNSON, Eds.: The Puritans: A Sourcebook of Their Writings
Vol. I TB/1093; Vol. II TB/1094
EDMUND S. MORGAN, Ed.: The Diary of Michael Wigglesworth, 1653-1657: The Conscience of a Puritan
TB/1228
EDMUND S. MORGAN: The Puritan Family: Religion and Domestic Relations in Seventeenth-Century New England   TB/1227
RICHARD B. MORRIS: Government and Labor in Early America   TB/1244
KENNETH B. MURDOCK: Literature and Theology in Colonial New England   TB/99
WALLACE NOTESTEIN: The English People on the Eve of Colonization: 1603-1630. † Illus.   TB/3006
JOHN P. ROCHE: Origins of American Political Thought: Selected Readings   TB/1301
JOHN SMITH: Captain John Smith's America: Selections from His Writings. Ed. with Intro. by John Lankford
TB/3078
LOUIS B. WRIGHT: The Cultural Life of the American Colonies: 1607-1763. † Illus.   TB/3005

American Studies: From the Revolution to 1860

JOHN R. ALDEN: The American Revolution: 1775-1783. † Illus.   TB/3011
MAX BELOFF, Ed.: The Debate on the American Revolution, 1761-1783: A Sourcebook △   TB/1225
RAY A. BILLINGTON: The Far Western Frontier: 1830-1860. † Illus.   TB/3012
EDMUND BURKE: On the American Revolution: Selected Speeches and Letters. ‡ Edited by Elliott Robert Barkan   TB/3068
WHITNEY R. CROSS: The Burned-Over District: The Social and Intellectual History of Enthusiastic Religion in Western New York, 1800-1850 △   TB/1242
GEORGE DANGERFIELD: The Awakening of American Nationalism: 1815-1828. † Illus.   TB/3061

---

† The New American Nation Series, edited by Henry Steele Commager and Richard B. Morris.
‡ American Perspectives series, edited by Bernard Wishy and William E. Leuchtenburg.
* The Rise of Modern Europe series, edited by William L. Langer.
** History of Europe series, edited by J. H. Plumb.
¶ Researches in the Social, Cultural and Behavioral Sciences, edited by Benjamin Nelson.
§ The Library of Religion and Culture, edited by Benjamin Nelson.
Σ Harper Modern Science Series, edited by James R. Newman.
º Not for sale in Canada.
△ Not for sale in the U. K.

1

3

G. G. COULTON: Medieval Village, Manor, and Monastery
TB/1022

CHRISTOPHER DAWSON, Ed.: Mission to Asia: *Narratives and Letters of the Franciscan Missionaries in Mongolia and China in the 13th and 14th Centuries* △
TB/315

HEINRICH FICHTENAU: The Carolingian Empire: *The Age of Charlemagne* △
TB/1142

GALBERT OF BRUGES: The Murder of Charles the Good. *Trans. with Intro. by James Bruce Ross*
TB/1311

F. L. GANSHOF: Feudalism △
TB/1058

DENO GEANAKOPLOS: Byzantine East and Latin West: *Two Worlds of Christendom in the Middle Ages and Renaissance*
TB/1265

EDWARD GIBBON: The Triumph of Christendom in the Roman Empire *(Chaps. XV-XX of "Decline and Fall," J. B. Bury edition).* § △ *Illus.*
TB/46

W. O. HASSALL, Ed.: Medieval England: *As Viewed by Contemporaries* △
TB/1205

DENYS HAY: Europe: The Emergence of an Idea TB/1275

DENYS HAY: The Medieval Centuries ○ △
TB/1192

J. M. HUSSEY: The Byzantine World △
TB/1057

ROBERT LATOUCHE: The Birth of Western Economy: *Economic Aspects of the Dark Ages.* ○ △ *Intro. by Philip Grierson*
TB/1290

FERDINAND LOT: The End of the Ancient World and the Beginnings of the Middle Ages. *Introduction by Glanville Downey*
TB/1044

ACHILLE LUCHAIRE: Social France at the Time of Philip Augustus. *New Intro. by John W. Baldwin*
TB/1314

MARSILIUS OF PADUA: The Defender of the Peace. *Trans. with Intro. by Alan Gewirth*
TB/1310

G. MOLLAT: The Popes at Avignon: 1305-1378 △ TB/308

CHARLES PETIT-DUTAILLIS: The Feudal Monarchy in France and England: *From the Tenth to the Thirteenth Century* ○ △
TB/1165

HENRI PIRENNE: Early Democracies in the Low Countries: *Urban Society and Political Conflict in the Middle Ages and the Renaissance. Introduction by John H. Mundy*
TB/1110

STEVEN RUNCIMAN: A History of the Crusades. △
Volume I: *The First Crusade and the Foundation of the Kingdom of Jerusalem. Illus.*
TB/1143
Volume II: *The Kingdom of Jerusalem and the Frankish East, 1100-1187. Illus.*
TB/1243
Volume III: *The Kingdom of Acre and the Later Crusades*
TB/1298

SULPICIUS SEVERUS et al.: The Western Fathers: *Being the Lives of Martin of Tours, Ambrose, Augustine of Hippo, Honoratus of Arles and Germanus of Auxerre.* △ *Edited and trans. by F. O. Hoare*
TB/309

J. M. WALLACE-HADRILL: The Barbarian West: *The Early Middle Ages, A.D. 400-1000* △
TB/1061

History: Renaissance & Reformation

JACOB BURCKHARDT: The Civilization of the Renaissance in Italy. △ *Intro. by Benjamin Nelson & Charles Trinkaus. Illus.*
Vol. I TB/40; Vol. II TB/41

JOHN CALVIN & JACOPO SADOLETO: A Reformation Debate. *Edited by John C. Olin*
TB/1239

ERNST CASSIRER: The Individual and the Cosmos in Renaissance Philosophy. △ *Translated with an Introduction by Mario Domandi*
TB/1097

FEDERICO CHABOD: Machiavelli and the Renaissance △
TB/1193

EDWARD P. CHEYNEY: The Dawn of a New Era, 1250-1453. * *Illus.*
TB/3002

G. CONSTANT: The Reformation in England: *The English Schism, Henry VIII, 1509-1547* △
TB/314

R. TREVOR DAVIES: The Golden Century of Spain, 1501-1621 ○ △
TB/1194

G. R. ELTON: Reformation Europe, 1517-1559 ** ○ △
TB/1270

DESIDERIUS ERASMUS: Christian Humanism and the Reformation: *Selected Writings. Edited and translated by John C. Olin*
TB/1166

WALLACE K. FERGUSON et al.: Facets of the Renaissance
TB/1098

WALLACE K. FERGUSON et al.: The Renaissance: *Six Essays. Illus.*
TB/1084

JOHN NEVILLE FIGGIS: The Divine Right of Kings. *Introduction by G. R. Elton*
TB/1191

JOHN NEVILLE FIGGIS: Political Thought from Gerson to Grotius: 1414-1625: *Seven Studies. Introduction by Garrett Mattingly*
TB/1032

MYRON P. GILMORE: The World of Humanism, 1453-1517. * *Illus.*
TB/3003

FRANCESCO GUICCIARDINI: Maxims and Reflections of a Renaissance Statesman *(Ricordi). Trans. by Mario Domandi. Intro. by Nicolai Rubinstein*
TB/1160

J. H. HEXTER: More's Utopia: *The Biography of an Idea. New Epilogue by the Author*
TB/1195

HAJO HOLBORN: Ulrich von Hutten and the German Reformation
TB/1238

JOHAN HUIZINGA: Erasmus and the Age of Reformation. △ *Illus.*
TB/19

JOEL HURSTFIELD: The Elizabethan Nation △
TB/1312

JOEL HURSTFIELD, Ed.: The Reformation Crisis △ TB/1267

ULRICH VON HUTTEN et al.: On the Eve of the Reformation: *"Letters of Obscure Men." Introduction by Hajo Holborn*
TB/1124

PAUL O. KRISTELLER: Renaissance Thought: *The Classic, Scholastic, and Humanist Strains*
TB/1048

PAUL O. KRISTELLER: Renaissance Thought II: *Papers on Humanism and the Arts*
TB/1163

NICCOLÒ MACHIAVELLI: History of Florence and of the Affairs of Italy: *from the earliest times to the death of Lorenzo the Magnificent.* △ *Introduction by Felix Gilbert*
TB/1027

ALFRED VON MARTIN: Sociology of the Renaissance. *Introduction by Wallace K. Ferguson*
TB/1099

GARRETT MATTINGLY et al.: Renaissance Profiles. △ *Edited by J. H. Plumb*
TB/1162

MILLARD MEISS: Painting in Florence and Siena after the Black Death: *The Arts, Religion and Society in the Mid-Fourteenth Century.* △ *169 illus.*
TB/1148

J. E. NEALE: The Age of Catherine de Medici ○ △ TB/1085

ERWIN PANOFSKY: Studies in Iconology: *Humanistic Themes in the Art of the Renaissance.* △ *180 illustrations*
TB/1077

J. H. PARRY: The Establishment of the European Hegemony: 1415-1715: *Trade and Exploration in the Age of the Renaissance* △
TB/1045

BUONACCORSO PITTI & GREGORIO DATI: Two Memoirs of Renaissance Florence: *The Diaries of Buonaccorso Pitti and Gregorio Dati. Ed. with an Intro. by Gene Brucker. Trans. by Julia Martines*
TB/1333

J. H. PLUMB: The Italian Renaissance: *A Concise Survey of Its History and Culture* △
TB/1161

A. F. POLLARD: Henry VIII. ○ △ *Introduction by A. G. Dickens*
TB/1249

A. F. POLLARD: Wolsey. ○ △ *Introduction by A. G. Dickens*
TB/1248

CECIL ROTH: The Jews in the Renaissance. *Illus.* TB/834

A. L. ROWSE: The Expansion of Elizabethan England. ○ △ *Illus.*
TB/1220

GORDON RUPP: Luther's Progress to the Diet of Worms ○ △
TB/120

FERDINAND SCHEVILL: The Medici. *Illus.*
TB/1010

FERDINAND SCHEVILL: Medieval and Renaissance Florence. *Illus.*
Volume I: *Medieval Florence* TB/1090
Volume II: *The Coming of Humanism and the Age of the Medici*
TB/1091

R. H. TAWNEY: The Agrarian Problem in the Sixteenth Century. *New Intro. by Lawrence Stone* TB/1315

G. M. TREVELYAN: England in the Age of Wycliffe, 1368-1520 ○ △
TB/1112

VESPASIANO: Renaissance Princes, Popes, and Prelates: *The Vespasiano Memoirs: Lives of Illustrious Men of the XVth Century. Intro. by Myron P. Gilmore* TB/1111

History: Modern European

FREDERICK B. ARTZ: Reaction and Revolution, 1815-1832. * *Illus.* TB/3034

MAX BELOFF: The Age of Absolutism, 1660-1815 △ TB/1062

ROBERT C. BINKLEY: Realism and Nationalism, 1852-1871. * *Illus.* TB/3038

EUGENE C. BLACK, Ed.: European Political History, 1815-1870: *Aspects of Liberalism* TB/1331

ASA BRIGGS: The Making of Modern England, 1784-1867: *The Age of Improvement* ○ △ TB/1203

CRANE BRINTON: A Decade of Revolution, 1789-1799. * *Illus.* TB/3018

D. W. BROGAN: The Development of Modern France. ○ △ Volume I: *From the Fall of the Empire to the Dreyfus Affair* TB/1184
Volume II: *The Shadow of War, World War I, Between the Two Wars. New Introduction by the Author* TB/1185

J. BRONOWSKI & BRUCE MAZLISH: The Western Intellectual Tradition: *From Leonardo to Hegel* △ TB/3001

GEOFFREY BRUUN: Europe and the French Imperium, 1799-1814. * Illus. TB/3033

ALAN BULLOCK: Hitler, A Study in Tyranny. ○ △ *Illus.* TB/1123

E. H. CARR: German-Soviet Relations Between the Two World Wars, 1919-1939 TB/1278

E. H. CARR: International Relations Between the Two World Wars, 1919-1939 ○ △ TB/1279

E. H. CARR: The Twenty Years' Crisis, 1919-1939: *An Introduction to the Study of International Relations* ○ △ TB/1122

GORDON A. CRAIG: From Bismarck to Adenauer: *Aspects of German Statecraft. Revised Edition* TB/1171

DENIS DIDEROT: The Encyclopedia: *Selections. Ed. and trans. by Stephen Gendzier* TB/1299

WALTER L. DORN: Competition for Empire, 1740-1763. * *Illus.* TB/3032

FRANKLIN L. FORD: Robe and Sword: *The Regrouping of the French Aristocracy after Louis XIV* TB/1217

CARL J. FRIEDRICH: The Age of the Baroque, 1610-1660. * *Illus.* TB/3004

RENÉ FUELOEP-MILLER: The Mind and Face of Bolshevism: *An Examination of Cultural Life in Soviet Russia. New Epilogue by the Author* TB/1188

M. DOROTHY GEORGE: London Life in the Eighteenth Century △ TB/1182

LEO GERSHOY: From Despotism to Revolution, 1763-1789. * *Illus.* TB/3017

C. C. GILLISPIE: Genesis and Geology: *The Decades before Darwin* § TB/51

ALBERT GOODWIN, Ed.: The European Nobility in the Eighteenth Century △ TB/1313

ALBERT GOODWIN: The French Revolution △ TB/1064

ALBERT GUÉRARD: France in the Classical Age: *The Life and Death of an Ideal* △ TB/1183

CARLTON J. H. HAYES: A Generation of Materialism, 1871-1900. * *Illus.* TB/3039

J. H. HEXTER: Reappraisals in History: *New Views on History and Society in Early Modern Europe* △ TB/1100

STANLEY HOFFMANN et al.: In Search of France: *The Economy, Society and Political System in the Twentieth Century* TB/1219

A. R. HUMPHREYS: The Augustan World: *Society, Thought, & Letters in 18th Century England* ○ △ TB/1105

DAN N. JACOBS, Ed.: The New Communist Manifesto *and Related Documents. Third edition, revised* TB/1078

LIONEL KOCHAN: The Struggle for Germany: *1914-45* TB/1304

HANS KOHN: The Mind of Germany: *The Education of a Nation* △ TB/1204

HANS KOHN, Ed.: The Mind of Modern Russia: *Historical and Political Thought of Russia's Great Age* TB/1065

WALTER LAQUEUR & GEORGE L. MOSSE, Eds.: Education and Social Structure in the 20th Century. ○ △ *Vol. 6 of the* Journal of Contemporary History TB/1339

WALTER LAQUEUR & GEORGE L. MOSSE, Eds.: International Fascism, 1920-1945. ○ *Volume 1 of* Journal of Contemporary History TB/1276

WALTER LAQUEUR & GEORGE L. MOSSE, Eds.: The Left-Wing Intellectuals between the Wars 1919-1939. ○ △ *Volume 2 of* Journal of Contemporary History TB/1286

WALTER LAQUEUR & GEORGE L. MOSSE, Eds.: Literature and Politics in the 20th Century. ○ △ *Vol. 5 of the* Journal of Contemporary History TB/1328

WALTER LAQUEUR & GEORGE L. MOSSE, Eds.: The New History: *Trends in Historical Research and Writing since World War II.* ○ △ *Vol. 4 of the* Journal of Contemporary History TB/1327

WALTER LAQUEUR & GEORGE L. MOSSE, Eds.: 1914: *The Coming of the First World War.* ○ △ *Volume 3 of* Journal of Contemporary History TB/1306

FRANK E. MANUEL: The Prophets of Paris: *Turgot, Condorcet, Saint-Simon, Fourier, and Comte* TB/1218

KINGSLEY MARTIN: French Liberal Thought in the Eighteenth Century: *A Study of Political Ideas from Bayle to Condorcet* TB/1114

ROBERT K. MERTON: Science, Technology and Society in Seventeenth Century England ¶ *New Intro. by the Author* TB/1324

L. B. NAMIER: Facing East: *Essays on Germany, the Balkans, and Russia in the 20th Century* △ TB/1280

L. B. NAMIER: Personalities and Pow_rs: *Selected Essays* △ TB/1186

L. B. NAMIER: Vanished Supremacies: *Essays on European History, 1812-1918* ○ TB/1088

NAPOLEON III: Napoleonic Ideas: *Des Idées Napoléoniennes, par le Prince Napoléon-Louis Bonaparte. Ed. by Brison D. Gooch* TB/1336

FRANZ NEUMANN: Behemoth: *The Structure and Practice of National Socialism, 1933-1944* TB/1289

FREDERICK L. NUSSBAUM: The Triumph of Science and Reason, 1660-1685. * *Illus.* TB/3009

DAVID OGG: Europe of the Ancien Régime, 1715-1783 ** ○ △ TB/1271

JOHN PLAMENATZ: German Marxism and Russian Communism. ○ △ *New Preface by the Author* TB/1189

RAYMOND W. POSTGATE, Ed.: Revolution from 1789 to 1906: *Selected Documents* TB/1063

PENFIELD ROBERTS: The Quest for Security, 1715-1740. * *Illus.* TB/3016

PRISCILLA ROBERTSON: Revolutions of 1848: *A Social History* TB/1025

GEORGE RUDÉ: Revolutionary Europe, 1783-1815 ** ○ △ TB/1272

LOUIS, DUC DE SAINT-SIMON: Versailles, The Court, and Louis XIV. ○ △ *Introductory Note by Peter Gay* TB/1250

HUGH SETON-WATSON: Eastern Europe Between the Wars, 1918-1941 TB/1330

ALBERT SOREL: Europe Under the Old Regime. *Translated by Francis H. Herrick* TB/1121

N. N. SUKHANOV: The Russian Revolution, 1917: *Eyewitness Account.* △ *Edited by Joel Carmichael*
Vol. I TB/1066; Vol. II TB/1067

A. J. P. TAYLOR: From Napoleon to Lenin: *Historical Essays* ○ △ TB/1268

A. J. P. TAYLOR: The Habsburg Monarchy, 1809-1918: *A History of the Austrian Empire and Austria-Hungary* ○ △ TB/1187

G. M. TREVELYAN: British History in the Nineteenth Century and After: 1782-1919. ○ △ *Second Edition* TB/1251

6

9

Christianity: The Middle Ages and The Reformation

Christianity: The Protestant Tradition

Christianity: The Roman and Eastern Traditions